QUICK & EASY CROSSWORDS

QUICK & EASY CROSSWORDS

Abbeydale Press

This edition published in 2006 by
ABBEYDALE PRESS
An Imprint of Bookmart Ltd
Registered Number 2372865
Trading as Bookmart Ltd
Blaby Road
Wigston
Leicester LE18 4SE

3 5 7 9 10 8 6 4 2

ISBN 10: 1-86147-176-9
ISBN 13: 978-1-86147-176-5

Compiled by Omnipress
Produced by Omnipress, Eastbourne
Printed in England

CONTENTS

SECTION ONE

CROSSWORDS

1

ACROSS

1 Render senseless (8)
5 Posterior portion (4)
8 Possessive form of we (3)
9 Shortened (8)
11 An open space (4)
13 Dispersed (6)
15 Learned (7)
16 Considerable height (6)
19 A school of whales (3)
21 Occupy a position (3)
22 Small tower (6)
25 Small natural indentations (7)
26 Prove to be false (6)
30 Periods of time (4)
31 A pigment (8)
32 Frozen water (3)
33 Sediment formed during fermentation (4)
34 By this means (8)

DOWN

2 Short heavy cape (6)
3 Blocks of metal (6)
4 Moves about restlessly (4)
5 Wild swine (4)
6 A halo (7)
7 Team of rowers (4)
10 Not outside (6)
12 Irate (5)
14 Small freshwater duck (4)
17 Marine gastropod mollusc (6)
18 To put away (5)
19 Preliminary statement (7)
20 A depression (4)
23 Full-course meal (6)
24 A weasel-like mammal (6)
27 Lake in northern Ontario (4)
28 Puts into service (4)
29 Imprint clearly (4)

2

ACROSS

1 Outcry (11)
8 Command (5)
10 Norwegian (5)
12 Permit (3)
14 Flexible (7)
16 Leap (Scot.) (4)
18 Resinous deposit (3)
20 Large African antelope (4)
21 Catch sight of (4)
22 Ballet step (3)
24 Paste tense of do (3)
25 Flat circular plate (4)
26 Travel from place to place (4)
27 Cutting tool (3)
28 River in central Europe (4)
29 Access hole with cover to sewer, drain etc. (7)
33 Become firm (3)
35 Fragrant resin (5)
36 Instruct (5)
37 Person with a healthy appetite (11)

DOWN

1 12th month of the Jewish calendar (4)
2 Semi-solid mass (4)
3 Helper (4)
4 Distinctive quality (4)
5 Contraction of is not (4)
6 Condition of deep stupor (8)
7 Drowsy (6)
9 Unearthly or eerie (8)
11 Greased (5)
13 Venomous snake (6)
15 Sexpartite (8)
17 Bring up to date (6)
19 Casing or covering (8)
23 Go away (5)
25 University lecturer (6)
30 Pleasing (4)
31 Auricular (4)
32 Overhanging lower edge of a roof (4)
33 Fraud (4)
34 Web-footed aquatic bird (4)

ACROSS

1 Parody (4)
3 Development (8)
6 Kitchen implement (7)
9 Herbaceus desert plant (5)
12 Remaining (4)
14 21st letter of Greek alphabet (3)
15 Mistaken (9)
17 Portico (4)
18 Hog (3)
19 Slow, easy stroll (5)
21 Put down (3)
22 To the inside of (4)
23 Without one's knowledge (9)
27 Influenza (inf.) (3)
29 Close (4)
30 Japanese dish (5)
31 Gaunt (7)
33 Last (8)
34 Tibetan oxen (4)

DOWN

1 Foam (5)
2 Large cask (3)
3 Useful (5)
4 Rhizome (9)
5 Technician (abbrev.) (4)
7 Flagrant (9)
8 The Lion (3)
10 Breed of riding horse (9)
11 Full of hills (5)
13 Melt together (4)
16 A silvery, metallic, radioactive element (9)
18 Breathes fast and hard (5)
20 First-class (1-3)
24 Exclamation of contempt (3)
25 Efface (5)
26 Nest (5)
28 Soothe (4)
32 Fellow (3)

4

ACROSS

2 Ropelike hairstyle (10)
7 Rectangular pier (4)
8 Free from obligation (6)
10 Pistol (3)
11 Monetary unit of Lesotho (5)
13 Strike lightly (3)
15 Mythical bird (3)
16 Part of skeleton (4)
17 Drive back (5)
20 Canal boat (5)
21 Lifeless (9)
22 Full of ruts (5)
24 In front (5)
26 Skills (4)
27 Belonging to us (3)
29 Highest mountain in Crete (3)
30 Overturn (5)
31 To prohibit (3)
32 Founder of the Red Cross (6)
34 Ultimate (4)
35 Tending to use bombast (10)

DOWN

1 A huntsman (6)
2 Barrier to hold back water (3)
3 Go into (5)
4 Elegance (4)
5 An assembly of Boy Scouts (8)
6 Seat for two or more persons (6)
8 And so on (abbrev.) (3)
9 Sharp pain (4)
12 Corrupting (7)
14 Leases (5)
16 Wash (5)
18 Scanty wage (8)
19 Put down (3)
20 Bleat of a sheep (3)
22 Commando (6)
23 Official language of Pakistan (4)
25 Indicate (6)
27 Choose (3)
28 Pear-shaped, medieval fiddle (5)
30 Remarkable (4)
33 A right-angled bend (3)

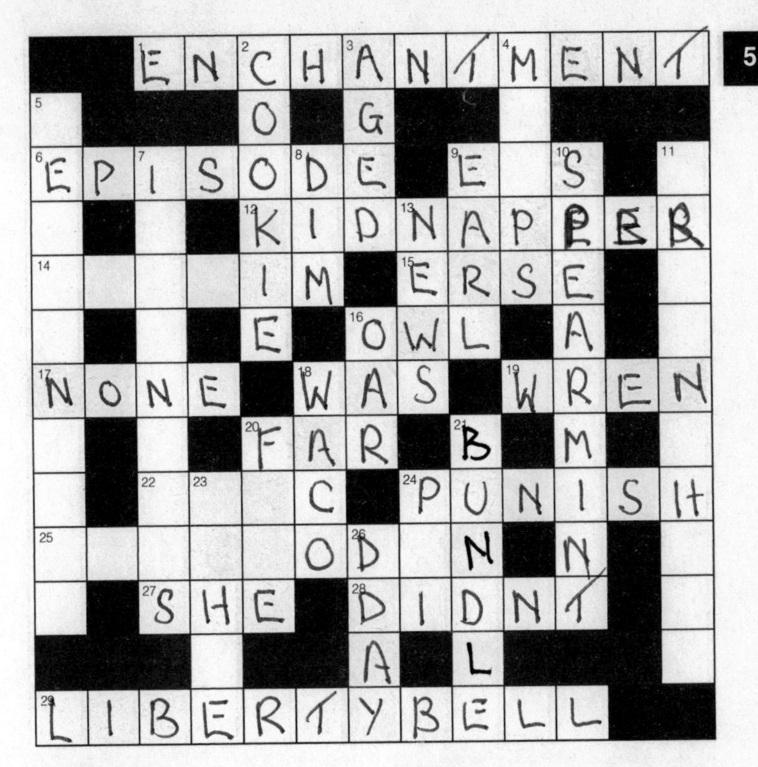

5

ACROSS

1 Captivation (11)
6 Incident (7)
9 Printer's measures (3)
12 Abductor (9)
14 A caprice or fancy (6)
15 Scottish Gaelic (4)
16 Nocturnal bird (3)
17 Not any (4)
18 Used to be (3)
19 Tiny songbird (4)
20 At a great distance (3)
22 Pertaining to the ear (4)
24 Subject to a penalty (6)
25 Dinosaur (9)
27 Fem. pronoun (3)
28 Contraction of did not (5)
29 Bell of Indepence (7-4)

DOWN

2 American biscuit (6)
3 Old (4)
4 Parotitis (5)
5 Art of handwriting (10)
7 Resourceful (9)
8 Lacking in brightness (3)
9 British nobleman (4)
10 A garden herb (9)
11 Invention (10)
13 Information (4)
16 Lever for rowing (3)
18 City in central Texas (4)
20 Of high grade (4)
21 Package (6)
23 Lake in the Sierra Nevada (5)
24 Hawaiian dish of taro root (3)
26 6 June, 1944 (4)

6

ACROSS
1 Worshipped (6)
4 Skilled (6)
7 Memory improvement (9)
10 Secondhand (4)
11 In favour of (3)
12 African antelope (4)
13 Edible roots (4)
15 Seaport in SE Scotland (5)
18 Walk (5)
20 Bedouin (4)
21 Entrance (4)
22 Lascivious man (5)
24 Freedom from war (5)
26 Morse element (4)
29 Prepare for publication (4)
31 Fifth sign of the Zodiac (3)
32 Having wings (4)
33 Environment requiring little water (9)
34 Cedes (6)
35 Walk nonchalantly (6)

DOWN
1 Yearly (6)
2 Outer covering (4)
3 Short and stout (5)
4 Poisonous fluid (5)
5 Large stone (4)
6 Withdraw financial support from (6)
7 Woman who mediates (9)
8 Towards the mouth (4)
9 Surmountable (9)
14 Cease (4)
16 Attempt (3)
17 Solid (4)
19 Fish eggs (3)
22 Passionate (6)
23 Employs (4)
25 Consisting of earth (6)
27 Assumed name (5)
28 Hoax (5)
30 Narrate (4)
32 Monkeys (4)

7

ACROSS
1 Hotel (8)
5 A chicken pen (4)
8 Chafe (3)
9 Pertaining to the shore (8)
11 Smallest component (4)
13 A blemish (6)
15 Fortunately (7)
16 Gum-yielding leguminous shrub (6)
19 Triangular sail (3)
21 Malt beverage (3)
22 French fashion designer (6)
25 Fluctuant (7)
26 Crevice (6)
30 Unit of mass (Abbrev.) (4)
31 Repair (8)
32 Automobile (3)
33 Glide on surface (4)
34 Capital of Nepal (8)

DOWN
2 Detestable (6)
3 Arrogant (6)
4 Quick, sharp bark (4)
5 Stuff (4)
6 Go faster than (7)
7 Ancient Greek coin (4)
10 Deceive (4-2)
12 Decoration (5)
14 South American Indian (4)
17 Immigration of Jews to Israel (6)
18 In a cocked position (5)
19 Spanish ball game (3-4)
20 Capital of Switzerland (4)
23 Hidden (6)
24 Followed (6)
27 Hay stack (4)
28 Standard (4)
29 Yellow of an egg (4)

8

ACROSS
1 Pertaining to horology (11)
8 External (5)
10 Dolt (5)
12 Total (3)
14 Brother or sister (7)
16 Ooze (4)
18 Woman's leg (inf.) (3)
20 Is not (4)
21 Weapons (4)
22 Annoy by persistent fault-finding (3)
24 Bark sharply (3)
25 Prefix for small (4)
26 British nobleman (4)
27 Snakelike fish (3)
28 Performs (4)
29 Originate (7)
33 Gymnasium (Abbrev.) (3)
35 Criminal (5)
36 Nocturnal tropical lizard (5)
37 Displace (11)

DOWN
1 Possessive pronoun (4)
2 Chamber (4)
3 A great deal (4)
4 Clothes (4)
5 Basic monetary unit of Ghana (4)
6 Underwear (8)
7 Pyramid at Giza (6)
9 German physicist (8)
11 Retract (5)
13 Containing uranium (6)
15 Able to read and write (8)
17 Sovereignty (6)
19 Short mantle (8)
23 Gadget (5)
25 Slender insect with delicate membranous wings (6)
30 Old Indian coin (4)
31 Matures (4)
32 Reflected sound (4)
33 Spanish painter (4)
34 Small particle (4)

ACROSS

1 To fail utterly (4)
3 Given to diligent study (8)
6 Unlit (7)
9 Suggest (5)
12 Related by blood (4)
14 Handwoven Scandinavian rug (3)
15 An area of uncultivated land (9)
17 Horse's hoof sound (4)
18 Sister (abbrev.) (3)
19 Religion founded in Iran (5)
21 Long dashes used in punctuation (3)
22 Roofing item (4)
23 Lacking symmetry (9)
27 Resin used to make varnish (3)
29 Moderately cold (4)
30 Large Nepalese knife used by the Gurkhas (5)
31 Ardently (7)
33 Surprised (8)
34 Delineate (4)

DOWN

1 Eating implements (5)
2 Friend (3)
3 Agave fibre (5)
4 Flagging (9)
5 Displeasing to the eye (4)
7 A measuring stick that is three feet long (9)
8 Jamaican popular music (3)
10 Power-driven shaft with radiating blades (9)
11 Fenced areas (5)
13 A member of the Quechuan people (4)
16 Biblical scholar (9)
18 Slink (5)
20 Air (prefix) (4)
24 Eurasian deer (3)
25 Antelope (5)
26 Semi-synthetic textile (5)
28 Wife of one's uncle (4)
32 Former measure of length (3)

10

1			2		3			4		5		6

ACROSS

2 Difficult to bear (10)
7 Beat up (4)
8 Commotion (6)
10 Cardinal number (3)
11 Be silent (5)
13 Cut off (3)
15 Unit of illumination (3)
16 Desert in E. Asia (4)
17 Vends (5)
20 Having ears (5)
21 Capable of being adapated (9)
22 Grew less (5)
24 Emblem (5)
26 Blessing (4)
27 Sesame plant (3)
29 Ingot (3)
30 Country residence (5)
31 Hasten (3)
32 Containing iridium (6)
34 Your uncle's wife (4)
35 Sociable (10)

DOWN

1 Fortification of tree branches (6)
2 Unit of electrical resistance (3)
3 Pertaining to the pope (5)
4 Native of Scotland (4)
5 Beseeched (8)
6 Venomous fanged snake (6)
8 Jinx (3)
9 Roundish projection (4)
12 Cut short (7)
14 Ancient (5)
16 Australian cockatoo (5)
18 Supporter of the Labour Party (8)
19 Sorrowful (3)
20 Flow back (3)
22 Refluent (6)
23 Male swine (4)
25 Happenings (6)
27 Involuntary muscular contraction (3)
28 Grassy plain (5)
30 A stringed instrument of India (4)
33 Possesses (3)

ACROSS

1 Liberality in bestowing gifts (11)
6 Spicy (7)
9 Highest mountain in Crete (3)
12 Polygon having 12 sides (9)
14 Part of the foot (6)
15 Delicatessen (abbrev.) (4)
16 Gave food (3)
17 Increased in size (4)
18 Vase (3)
19 Sharp pain (4)
20 Some (3)
22 Hawaiian honeycreeper (4)
24 Rare-earth element (6)
25 Profitable (9)
27 Speak (3)
28 Long (5)
29 Unnecessary use of lengthy words (11)

DOWN

2 Male goose (6)
3 In bed (4)
4 Commemorative disc (5)
5 Chinese side dish (6-4)
7 Makeup (9)
8 Summit (3)
9 Chilled (4)
10 Commotion (9)
11 Betrothal (10)
13 Paradise (4)
16 Small, recently-hatched fish (3)
18 Single entity (4)
20 Apart (4)
21 Visions (6)
23 Inhabitant of Iraq (5)
24 Evening (3)
26 8th month of the Jewish calendar (4)

12

ACROSS

1 Cared for (6)
4 Person who signs (6)
7 Blown by the wind (9)
10 Aromatic plant (4)
11 Speck (3)
12 Seaweed (4)
13 Spool-like toy (4)
15 Plant fibre used for making rope (5)
18 Second king of Israel (5)
20 Streetcar (4)
21 Illustrious warrior (4)
22 Sums owing (5)
24 Set again (5)
26 Poor actors (4)
29 Sea eagle (4)
31 Pinch (3)
32 Smallest unit of matter (4)
33 Remove nitrogen from (9)
34 Person to whom a lease is granted (6)
35 Revolve (6)

DOWN

1 Infectious disease (6)
2 A negligible amount (4)
3 Father (5)
4 Saline (5)
5 Simpleton (4)
6 Ran away (6)
7 Cuff (9)
8 Derrick (4)
9 Nervousness (9)
14 European river (4)
16 Illustrative craft (3)
17 Whip (4)
19 Part of verb to be (3)
22 Fuel oil (6)
23 Send forth (4)
25 Topple (6)
27 Aniseed (5)
28 Mine prop (5)
30 Long fish (4)
32 From a distance (4)

13

ACROSS

1 Made by hand (8)
5 Aggregate of fibres (4)
8 Japanese sash (3)
9 Bilateral (8)
11 Amusement (4)
13 Gave a speech (6)
15 Amount that can be carried in one arm or both arms (7)
16 Take vengeance for (6)
19 Chatter (3)
21 Ovum (3)
22 Checked (6)
25 Seasoned pork sausage (7)
26 Animated (6)
30 High fidelity (Abbrev.) (2-2)
31 Of mixed European and Asian parentage (8)
32 Newt (3)
33 Woody plant (4)
34 Owner of a hotel (8)

DOWN

2 Teeming (6)
3 Aural (6)
4 Root of the taro (4)
5 Indian exercise method (4)
6 Subsiding (7)
7 Hoar (4)
10 Woody (6)
12 Gardening tool (5)
14 Split apart (4)
17 Exit (6)
18 Tactless (5)
19 Long-necked ruminant (7)
20 Summon (4)
23 Edible taproot (6)
24 Mental condition (6)
27 Pillar (4)
28 Religious practice (4)
29 Yes (Inf.) (4)

14

ACROSS

1 Reliable (11)
8 Leers (5)
10 Quick, sharp sound (5)
12 Tavern (3)
14 Culinary department (7)
16 On sheltered side (4)
18 Curve (3)
20 Seaward (4)
21 Resembling vines (4)
22 Organ of hearing (3)
24 Conclusion (3)
25 Middle Eastern bread (4)
26 TV award (4)
27 Alcoholic liquor (3)
28 First man (4)
29 Food canning factory (7)
33 Exclamation of disgust (3)
35 Money (slang) (5)
36 Crews (5)
37 French national holiday (8-3)

DOWN

1 Pith helmet (4)
2 Atop (4)
3 Confer (4)
4 Kiln for drying hops (4)
5 British technical college (abbrev.) (4)
6 Lamb or kid (8)
7 Annie ------, sharpshooter (6)
9 Physicist famous for his theory of relativity (8)
11 Depart (5)
13 Sea nymph (6)
15 Scottish broadsword (8)
17 Termination (6)
19 Underground cemetery (8)
23 Pertaining to a ramus (5)
25 Located on the palm of the hand (6)
30 Seizes (4)
31 Small case for needles (4)
32 Ship's small boat (4)
33 Secondhand (4)
34 Consecrated (4)

15

ACROSS

1 Floating ice (4)
3 Dwarf (3-5)
6 Six-legged creature (7)
9 Bantu language (5)
12 Pipe (4)
14 North American nation (Abbrev.) (3)
15 So much the better (Fr.) (9)
17 Bring forth young (4)
18 Sink or bend downwards (3)
19 Abyss (5)
21 Vase (3)
22 Musical instrument (4)
23 Edible plant (9)
27 Monetary unit of Romania (3)
29 Image of a deity (4)
30 Deride (5)
31 Mark given for offence (7)
33 Cut into two equal parts (8)
34 Feathers (4)

DOWN

1 Lacking brightness (5)
2 Supplement (3)
3 All (mus.) (5)
4 Not subject to taxation (3-6)
5 Untidy condition (4)
7 Jewish house of worship (9)
8 Bring civil action against (3)
10 Exceed in number (9)
11 Brother of Moses (5)
13 Purchases (4)
16 Fungus-infecting virus (9)
18 Ledge (5)
20 Have regard (4)
24 Deity (3)
25 Choose (5)
26 Consumed (5)
28 Otherwise (4)
32 An outcome (3)

16

ACROSS

2 Large city (10)
7 At the bow of a vessel (4)
8 South American cowboy (6)
10 Powdery residue (3)
11 Spur (5)
13 Manipulate (3)
15 Comrade (3)
16 Beancurd (4)
17 Convocation of witches (5)
20 A washbowl (5)
21 Mistaken (9)
22 Imagination (5)
24 Concerning (5)
26 Crescent-shaped figure (4)
27 Opposite of flow (3)
29 Metal-bearing mineral (3)
30 Navy (5)
31 Adult male (3)
32 Island in Western Samoa (6)
34 Wheel shaft (4)
35 During the recent past (10)

DOWN

1 Erase (6)
2 Encountered (3)
3 Band (5)
4 Resound (4)
5 Ball game (8)
6 Military commander of Japan (6)
8 Jelly (3)
9 Equipment for the reproduction of sound (2-2)
12 One who aspires (7)
14 Sham (5)
16 Mock (5)
18 Highest peak in Gt. Britain (3-5)
19 Attempt (3)
20 Fur scarf (3)
22 Downy (6)
23 Presence (4)
25 Flammable material (6)
27 Biblical high priest (3)
28 Light greyish brown (5)
30 Flute (4)
33 Armed conflict (3)

17

ACROSS

1 Surgical removal of a kidney (11)
6 More than two (7)
9 Pinch (3)
12 Ignorant (9)
14 Self-centred person (6)
15 Veinlike deposit (4)
16 Possesses (3)
17 Prejudice (4)
18 Devoted follower (3)
19 Portent (4)
20 Long period of time (3)
22 The villain in Othello (4)
24 Combines (6)
25 Make worldwide (9)
27 Incline head (3)
28 Municipal (5)
29 Precedence (11)

DOWN

2 Read with care (6)
3 Trundle (4)
4 Next after the second (5)
5 Large gathering (10)
7 Infringement (9)
8 Insect (3)
9 Temple (4)
10 Pertaining to air (9)
11 Direct (10)
13 Dash (4)
16 A dynasty in China (3)
18 Stupid person (4)
20 Mild oath (4)
21 Not uniform (6)
23 Residence (5)
24 Compact Israeli submachine gun (3)
26 Chilled (4)

18

ACROSS

1 Ill will (6)
4 A cabinet or enclosed recess (6)
7 The pouch of a marsupial (9)
10 On the top (4)
11 Abstract being (3)
12 Germinated grain used in brewing (4)
13 Monetary unit of Cambodia (4)
15 Go into (5)
18 Pertaining to the ileum (5)
20 Republic in SW Asia (4)
21 Rode a river (anag.) (4)
22 Decaffeinated (Abbrev.) (5)
24 Unit of weight (5)
26 Horse's gait (4)
29 Burn slightly (4)
31 Malt beverage (3)
32 Egyptian deity (4)
33 American state (3-6)
34 Jerk rapidly (6)
35 Thespians (6)

DOWN

1 Revolve (6)
2 Fellow (4)
3 Vertical face of a stair (5)
4 Thicket (5)
5 Egg cell (4)
6 Plan (6)
7 Funeral director (9)
8 Single entity (4)
9 Motherhood (9)
14 Public swimming pool (4)
16 Period of history (3)
17 Floating platform (4)
19 Romanian money (3)
22 Duplicity (6)
23 Flat-fish (4)
25 Morals (6)
27 Indian prince (5)
28 Earth (5)
30 Hire (4)
32 Heating fuel (4)

19

ACROSS

1 Affording remedy (8)
5 Blunt (4)
8 North American nation (3)
9 Near sea level (8)
11 Small piece of wood (4)
13 Diners (6)
15 Base (7)
16 Severe experience (6)
19 Used for resting (3)
21 Musical instrument (3)
22 Bloc (6)
25 Person who drives a wagon (7)
26 Reside in (6)
30 Tides that attain the least height (4)
31 Person who eulogizes (8)
32 Revised form of Esperanto (3)
33 Small secluded valley (4)
34 Anticlimax (8)

DOWN

2 Adequate (6)
3 Tapering mass of ice (6)
4 Sled (4)
5 Conduit (4)
6 Conducted (7)
7 Den (4)
10 Young lion (6)
12 Sacred song (5)
14 Atmosphere (prefix) (4)
17 Plant-eating aquatic mammal (6)
18 Offspring (5)
19 Elaborate fabric (7)
20 Low in pitch (4)
23 Large saltwater game fish (6)
24 Reduce (6)
27 Overlay with wood (4)
28 Atop (4)
29 To lamb (4)

20

ACROSS
1 Assenting (11)
8 Sweetheart (5)
10 Willow (5)
12 Honey (3)
14 No longer in existence (7)
16 Very small quantity (4)
18 Taxi (3)
20 Potpourri (4)
21 Augury (4)
22 Fastener (3)
24 Negative (3)
25 Son of Isaac and Rebekah (4)
26 Shrewd (4)
27 To pay court or woo (3)
28 Repudiate (4)
29 Mimic (7)
33 Label (3)
35 Non-human creature (5)
36 Sun-dried brick (5)
37 Divisor (11)

DOWN
1 Starch resembling sago (4)
2 Cut down (4)
3 Frost (4)
4 Female relative (4)
5 Image (4)
6 Concise summaries (8)
7 Inhabitant of Germany (6)
9 Related, or located in an axil (8)
11 Offspring (5)
13 Pass by (6)
15 Unbreakable (8)
17 Flat roofing tile (6)
19 Tofu (8)
23 Flat-topped seamount (5)
25 Fit to be eaten (6)
30 Unskilled labourer (4)
31 Still (4)
32 Ripped (4)
33 Nipple (4)
34 Endure (4)

ACROSS
1 Call (4)
3 N. American larch (8)
6 Altar boy (7)
9 Unbolt (5)
12 Minerals (4)
14 A single entity (3)
15 Ornate (9)
17 Leave out (4)
18 Purse (3)
19 Silly (5)
21 Central body of the solar system (3)
22 Fencing sword (4)
23 Negotiator (9)
27 Mineral spring (3)
29 Not conforming to Kosher laws (4)
30 Traditional portion of Muslim law (5)
31 Endless (7)
33 Armed soldier (8)
34 High-pitched tone (4)

DOWN
1 Rob (5)
2 Girl or woman (3)
3 Teacher (5)
4 Entertainment (9)
5 Group of people related by blood (4)
7 Protestant of N. Ireland (9)
8 Period of history (3)
10 Warrant officer on a warship (9)
11 Prevail (5)
13 English public school (4)
16 Turn towards the east (9)
18 Consecrate (5)
20 Never (4)
24 Command to a horse (3)
25 Many times (5)
26 Bell-shaped flower (5)
28 Hungarian sheepdog (4)
32 Chafe (3)

22

ACROSS

2 Omnipresent (10)
7 Ruffian (4)
8 Conceptual framework (6)
10 Regret (3)
11 Leg bone (5)
13 Decay (3)
15 Long-sleeved linen vestment (3)
16 Irritate (4)
17 Moral precept of conduct (5)
20 Reptile (5)
21 Measuring stick (9)
22 Perhaps (5)
24 Kid leather (5)
26 Possesses (4)
27 Of recent origin (3)
29 In favour of (3)
30 Manuscript volume (5)
31 And so on (abbrev.) (3)
32 Constrictor (6)
34 The back of (4)
35 Brain (10)

DOWN

1 Die from lack of food (6)
2 Exclamation of disgust (3)
3 S. eastern country (5)
4 Member of native tribe in Peru (4)
5 Pass (8)
6 Attack with severe criticism (6)
8 Akin (3)
9 Deride (4)
12 Blighted (7)
14 Clock faces (5)
16 Become liable for (5)
18 Inducing sleep (8)
19 Weep (3)
20 Female relative (abbrev.) (3)
22 Tether (6)
23 Askew (4)
25 Steep bank under a rampart (6)
27 Not (prefix) (3)
28 To ski on snow by means of wedeln (5)
30 Poultry enclosure (4)
33 Sea eagle (3)

ACROSS

1 Lie (11)
6 Excreted matter (7)
9 Besides (3)
12 Ore of cobalt (9)
14 Long cloak with hood (6)
15 Temple (4)
16 Pronoun (3)
17 A single time (4)
18 Was a tool (anag.) (3)
19 River in central England (4)
20 Wily (3)
22 Island of Hawaii (4)
24 Reply (6)
25 Enthusiastic (9)
27 Turf (3)
28 Gyratory (5)
29 Hereditary anaemia (11)

DOWN

2 Compels to leave (6)
3 Bedouin (4)
4 Division of a long poem (5)
5 Sheets and blankets (10)
7 Spacious (9)
8 Terminal digit of the foot (3)
9 Having wings (4)
10 Denial (9)
11 A regenerate state (10)
13 Once more (4)
16 Cut and dried grass (3)
18 Insult (4)
20 Storage shelter (4)
21 Cavity in a body organ (6)
23 An excited or tumultuous state (5)
24 Some (3)
26 Matures or ripens (4)

24

ACROSS

1 Be unfaithful (6)
4 Republic of S. Africa (6)
7 Unflustered (9)
10 Grating (4)
11 19th letter of the Greek alphabet (3)
12 Snake-like fish (4)
13 Unwieldy ship (4)
15 Showy actions (5)
18 Golf clubs (5)
20 Having aches (4)
21 Cartel (4)
22 Part of a long poem (5)
24 Aquatic mammal (5)
26 Lace collar (4)
29 Regretted (4)
31 Bleat of a sheep (3)
32 Adult male beaver (4)
33 An act perpetrated by one nation upon another (9)
34 Glow from twilight (6)
35 Extra time (6)

DOWN

1 Bracelet (6)
2 Outside of cheese (4)
3 Early life (5)
4 Dreadful (5)
5 Sheltered side (4)
6 Gets up (6)
7 Foreigner (9)
8 Fake (4)
9 Extraction of flavour by boiling (9)
14 Thousand (pref.) (4)
16 Statute (3)
17 Norse god of thunder (4)
19 Decay (3)
22 Warship (6)
23 Not near (4)
25 Make rare (6)
27 German submarine (5)
28 Mortal (5)
30 Distribute cards (4)
32 Drill a hole (4)

ACROSS

1 Portuguese navigator (8)
5 Fresh-water fish (4)
8 Beer (3)
9 Soccer (8)
11 Travel on (4)
13 Respect (6)
15 Tenth month of the year (7)
16 Capital of Kansas (6)
19 Linen robe (3)
21 Before (3)
22 Tabs (6)
25 Deceived (7)
26 Join (6)
30 Short letter (4)
31 Pertaining to birds (8)
32 Sailor (3)
33 Depend (4)
34 Close (8)

DOWN

2 Guarantee (6)
3 Provided space between lines of type (6)
4 Egypt's river (4)
5 Slender missile (4)
6 Person to whom property is transferred (7)
7 To yield (4)
10 Proceed in a leisurely way (6)
12 Surround (5)
14 Foot covering (4)
17 Pecuniary gain (6)
18 Hebrew school (5)
19 Boundaries (7)
20 Combination of parties (4)
23 Heavenly body (6)
24 Misdemeanor (6)
27 Carry (4)
28 Ethereal (4)
29 Tramp (4)

26

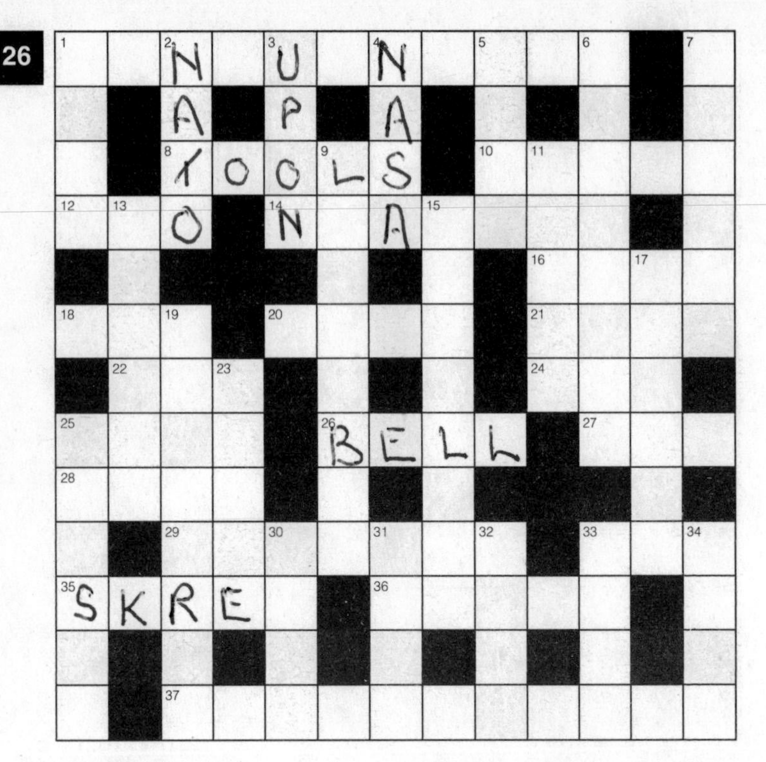

ACROSS

1 Bloodroot (11)
8 Implements (5)
10 Each day (5)
12 From (3)
14 Proximate (7)
16 Long narrow strip of fabric (4)
18 Wood sorrel (3)
20 Jumbled or mixed up (4)
21 Separate article (4)
22 Room with a harem (3)
24 Soak (3)
25 Thrash (4)
26 Ringing instrument (4)
27 Tap gently (3)
28 Doing nothing (4)
29 Branch of mathematics (7)
33 Woman's name (3)
35 Loose rock debris (5)
36 Bits of information (5)
37 Voluntary movement (11)

DOWN

1 Breaking waves (4)
2 Western pact (4)
3 Once ---- a time (4)
4 US space agency (4)
5 Advise (4)
6 Excited (8)
7 Disorder (6)
9 Subject to a levy (8)
11 Up and about (5)
13 Catalogue (6)
15 Warning (8)
17 Explosive device (6)
19 Moonstone (8)
23 White poplar tree (5)
25 Type of gasoline (6)
30 Notable adventure of exploit (4)
31 Cheat (4)
32 Great age (4)
33 Egyptian goddess of fertility (4)
34 Inspires dread (4)

ACROSS
1 Twining stem (4)
3 Weakness (8)
6 Mournful (7)
9 Slender freshwater fish (5)
12 Musical composition for one (4)
14 Specified person or thing (3)
15 Bag hung from a saddle (9)
17 Prissy (4)
18 Sparse fluid (3)
19 Bantu language (5)
21 Remuneration (3)
22 Authentic (4)
23 Horse bred for racing (9)
27 Adult males (3)
29 Holly (4)
30 Last letter ofthe Greek alphabet (5)
31 Saliva enzyme (7)
33 Sorrowful (8)
34 Abominable snowman (4)

DOWN
1 Waits (5)
2 Supplement (3)
3 Entertain (5)
4 Hologram (9)
5 A small island (4)
7 Variety of magnetite (9)
8 To hit a high ball (3)
10 Not limited by time (9)
11 Heavy (5)
13 Drinks (as a cat) (4)
16 Lush (9)
18 Gimmick (5)
20 Make healthy (4)
24 Brown-capped boletus mushroom (3)
25 Laud (5)
26 Boredom (5)
28 Islamic chieftain (4)
32 Some (3)

28

ACROSS

2 Biased (10)
7 Wise man (4)
8 Assails (6)
10 Oriental sash (3)
11 Register (5)
13 Tear (3)
15 Attach by stitches (3)
16 Veinlike deposit (4)
17 Outer coat of a seed (5)
20 Country bumpkin (5)
21 Shaped like a pitcher (9)
22 Regular course (5)
24 Reverence for God (5)
26 Goatskin bag for holding wine (4)
27 Oxlike African antelope (3)
29 Also (3)
30 Little pie (5)
31 Animal park (3)
32 Speaks (6)
34 Sicilian volcano (4)
35 Enrolment (10)

DOWN

1 Conduct (6)
2 Podded vegetable (3)
3 Levels (5)
4 Contest between two persons (4)
5 Native American (8)
6 Disperse (6)
8 To yield (3)
9 Periodic movement of sea (4)
12 Reverberating loudly (7)
14 Ridge (5)
16 Living in flowing water (5)
18 Partial sum (8)
19 Statute (3)
20 Yelp (3)
22 Dull (6)
23 Underground part of a plant (4)
25 Enlisted person in the US navy (6)
27 Fuel (3)
28 Useful (5)
30 Career golfers (4)
33 Wager (3)

29

ACROSS

1 Condition of being superior (11)
6 Pertaining to the mouth (7)
9 Choose (3)
12 Processes for choosing a government (9)
14 Finger (6)
15 Public baths (4)
16 Not sweet (3)
17 Large black bird (4)
18 Rank (3)
19 Storage shelter (4)
20 Allow (3)
22 Couple (4)
24 Diners (6)
25 Changeable (9)
27 Put down (3)
28 Sponsorship (5)
29 Ready-made (3-3-5)

DOWN

2 Armour for the knee (6)
3 Uncommon (4)
4 Swift (5)
5 Given to biting (10)
7 Globular (9)
8 Entirely (3)
9 Of the ear (4)
10 Lacking teeth (9)
11 Plant of the lily family (10)
13 Skein of thread (4)
16 A drunkard (3)
18 Spawning area of salmon (4)
20 Gentlewoman (4)
21 Move ungracefully (6)
23 Not appropriate (5)
24 Female sheep (3)
26 Rowing implements (4)

30

ACROSS

1 Cone-shaped (6)
4 Cordial (6)
7 Goatfish (9)
10 Sharp (4)
11 Single number (3)
12 Damn (4)
13 To bandage (4)
15 Run away to get married (5)
18 Edict of the czar (5)
20 State of the north-central United States (4)
21 An agitated state (4)
22 Monetary unit of Lesotho (5)
24 Cutting instrument (5)
26 Ladder step (4)
29 Grant temporary use of (4)
31 Born (3)
32 Small dabbling duck (4)
33 Lacking grace (9)
34 Free from obligation (6)
35 Show indistinctly (6)

DOWN

1 Biscuit (Amer.) (6)
2 Not shut (4)
3 Demobilization (5)
4 Physician (5)
5 Requirement (4)
6 Person included in a list (6)
7 Joining again (9)
8 Number less than ten (4)
9 Essays (9)
14 Dip into tea or coffee (4)
16 A trap for catching fish (3)
17 Jug (4)
19 Relatives (3)
22 Biblical dancing girl (6)
23 Leg joint (4)
25 Intertwine (6)
27 Unabridged (5)
28 Icy (5)
30 Musical percussion instrument (4)
32 Former Russian ruler (4)

ACROSS

1 Worship of Satan (8)
5 Spurt (4)
8 Industrious insect (3)
9 Internal (8)
11 Mountain range (4)
13 Infuriate (6)
15 Earache (7)
16 Diatribe (6)
19 Hug (anag.) (3)
21 Fish, e.g. lamprey (3)
22 East Indian fig tree (6)
25 Spiral (7)
26 For a short time (6)
30 Conjunction (4)
31 Exotropic (4-4)
32 Petroleum (3)
33 Whimsically comical (4)
34 Musical composition (8)

DOWN

2 Congenitally attached (6)
3 Inflammation of the eye (6)
4 Bog (4)
5 Massive wild ox (4)
6 Disentangle (7)
7 Male deer (4)
10 Commendation (6)
12 City in West Yorkshire (5)
14 Pleasing (4)
17 Live (6)
18 German underwater vessel (5)
19 Set free (7)
20 Frozen rain (4)
23 Objects from everyday life (6)
24 Remnant (6)
27 Command to stop a horse (4)
28 Inwardly (4)
29 Open vessel with handle and spout (4)

32

ACROSS

1 Of all forms (11)
8 Small antelope (5)
10 Striped african mammal (5)
12 Affirmative reply (3)
14 Account books (7)
16 Widespread (4)
18 Doctor (abbrev.) (3)
20 Capital of Shaanxi province, China (4)
21 Dutch cheese (4)
22 Colouring material (3)
24 Debutante (abbrev.) (3)
25 Large marine food fish (4)
26 Modify printed matter (4)
27 Not wet (3)
28 Upper Thames River in south-central England (4)
29 Raw fish appetizer (7)
33 Very skilled person (3)
35 Capital of Idaho (5)
36 Musical study piece (5)
37 Study of ants (11)

DOWN

1 Greasy (4)
2 Inner part of temple (4)
3 Thwart (4)
4 Sudden assault (4)
5 Exude slowly (4)
6 Sank to a lower level (8)
7 Head garland (6)
9 Vitamin deficiency disease (8)
11 Made a mistake (5)
13 Second book of the Bible (6)
15 Shoot-out (8)
17 Cloth (6)
19 Cynical disposition (8)
23 Relaxes (5)
25 Characteristic quality of a sound (6)
30 Change direction (4)
31 Cover with wax (4)
32 E.U. currency (4)
33 Aviation (prefix) (4)
34 Not difficult (4)

ACROSS
1 In bed (4)
3 Hermitic (8)
6 Enclose (7)
9 Prices paid (5)
12 Sea bird (4)
14 Study carefully (3)
15 Pertaining to Euclid (9)
17 To mend (4)
18 Vulgar, ill-bred fellow (3)
19 Pond scum (5)
21 Wrath (3)
22 Therefore (4)
23 Made arrangements (9)
27 Forfeit or sum paid into the pool in a card game (3)
29 Basic unit of heredity (4)
30 Boredom (5)
31 Normally (7)
33 Threshold (8)
34 Propend (4)

DOWN
1 Of an axis (5)
2 Indian dish (3)
3 Finished (5)
4 Pertaining to ancient Mycenae (9)
5 To the inside of (4)
7 Evil spirit (9)
8 Before (3)
10 Veal cutlet (9)
11 Long-billed sandpiper (5)
13 Nothing (inf.) (4)
16 Introductory studies (9)
18 Recurring series (5)
20 Traditional knowledge (4)
24 Oxlike African antelope (3)
25 Greek writer of fables (5)
26 Wood nymph (5)
28 Upon (4)
32 Disposed (3)

34

ACROSS

2 Talkative person (10)
7 Stead (4)
8 Teaching of the Buddha (6)
10 Illustrative craft (3)
11 Storage centre (5)
13 Outer edge (3)
15 Spore-bearing part of a moss capsule (3)
16 Turbine blade (4)
17 Aquatic opossum (5)
20 Powder from castor-oil plant (5)
21 Tuber (9)
22 Dropsy (5)
24 Basic (5)
26 Fine and delicate (4)
27 Slender metal fastener (3)
29 Earlier (3)
30 Source of cocoa (5)
31 Donkey (3)
32 Resembling cedar (6)
34 Vigour (4)
35 Woman who seduces (10)

DOWN

1 Indistinct (6)
2 Food regurgitated by a ruminant (3)
3 Farewell (5)
4 Authentic (Ger.) (4)
5 Soldiers' accommodation (8)
6 Chinese island (6)
8 Spanish title (3)
9 Prefix for small (4)
12 Commonplace (7)
14 Spacious (5)
16 Cleric (5)
18 Went before (8)
19 Hawaiian acacia (3)
20 Steal from (3)
22 Chooses (6)
23 Venture (4)
25 Wound (6)
27 Metal container for frying (3)
28 Mother-of-pearl (5)
30 A crocodile (inf.) (4)
33 Observation (abbrev.) (3)

ACROSS
1 Full of repetition (11)
6 Wedge-shaped (7)
9 Highly contagious viral disease (3)
12 Bother (9)
14 Woody tissue (6)
15 Calm (4)
16 Direct a gun (3)
17 Labour (4)
18 Energy (3)
19 Located near the ear (4)
20 Spanish hero (3)
22 ---- crop, short 1920's hairstyle (4)
24 Attic (6)
25 Growing old (9)
27 Make lace (3)
28 Pertaining to the ear (5)
29 Dizzy (11)

DOWN
2 Tranquil (6)
3 Abound (4)
4 Relative by marriage (5)
5 A woman sculptor (10)
7 Indifferent (9)
8 Large cask (3)
9 Fro (4)
10 Artificial (9)
11 Appropriate (10)
13 Radar screen element (4)
16 Help (3)
18 Bluish-white metallic element (4)
20 Price paid (4)
21 Intense dislike (6)
23 Instruct (5)
24 A wildebeest (3)
26 Relaxation (4)

36

ACROSS
1 Side of a hog (6)
4 Interruption (6)
7 Thin freshwater minnow (9)
10 Endure (4)
11 Ocean (3)
12 Vagrant (4)
13 Yellow of an egg (4)
15 Strange and mysterious (5)
18 Heron (5)
20 Skin eruption (4)
21 Obstacle (4)
22 Promised (5)
24 Lowermost deck (5)
26 Surfeit (4)
29 A narrow opening (4)
31 Father (3)
32 Mouth or mouth-like opening (4)
33 Wild with excitement (9)
34 Seventh planet (6)
35 A brownish orange (6)

DOWN
1 Gourmet (6)
2 Of you (archaic) (4)
3 Characteristic of a horse (5)
4 Garbage (5)
5 Nonsense (4)
6 Exertion (6)
7 Tropical American shrub (9)
8 Great age (4)
9 Sandglass (9)
14 Game of chance (4)
16 Frozen water (3)
17 Purposes (4)
19 Needlefish (3)
22 Hindu preserver (6)
23 Celestial body (4)
25 Forgiveness (6)
27 Farewell (5)
28 Decree (5)
30 Web-footed aquatic bird (4)
32 Eject from position (4)

ACROSS

1 Volume (8)
5 Division of a school year (4)
8 A religious belief of African origin involving witchcraft (3)
9 Splendour (8)
11 Comply (4)
13 To tickle (6)
15 Containing tin (7)
16 Cutting edges (6)
19 Yuk! (3)
21 Previous to (3)
22 Respect (6)
25 Feeling of vexation (7)
26 Moon of the planet Jupiter (6)
30 Ireland (4)
31 Affluent (8)
32 Some (3)
33 Bend (4)
34 Farewell (8)

DOWN

2 Introduce air into (6)
3 Conciliatory (6)
4 Cathedral city (4)
5 Hoot (4)
6 Reflux of the tide (7)
7 Monetary unit of Cambodia (4)
10 Contrive (6)
12 An agent of fermentation (5)
14 Not busy (4)
17 To rights (6)
18 Confused hand-to-hand fight (5)
19 Pertaining to the uterus (7)
20 Pile (4)
23 Entirely (6)
24 Monetary unit of Albania (6)
27 Mountain range (4)
28 Variety of chalcedony (4)
29 Inspires dread (4)

38

ACROSS

1 Attainments of a scholar (11)
8 Situated on an axis (5)
10 A toxic protein extracted from castor beans (5)
12 Armed conflict (3)
14 Diary (7)
16 Emperor of Rome 54–68AD (4)
18 Spasmodic muscular contraction (3)
20 Increases (4)
21 A country of southwest Asia (4)
22 Colouring material (3)
24 Large edible mushroom (3)
25 Scandinavian (4)
26 Title of respect for God (4)
27 Falsehood (3)
28 Sour (4)
29 Husband of an unfaithful wife (7)
33 Attempt (3)
35 Lad (Scot. dialect) (5)
36 A poplar (5)
37 Authoritative (11)

DOWN

1 Gradual (4)
2 Listen to (4)
3 Put down (4)
4 Depend (4)
5 Illustrious warrior (4)
6 Young pike (8)
7 Curse (6)
9 Large burrowing African mammal (8)
11 Using ions (6)
13 Yielding an acid (6)
15 Ball game (8)
17 Small sword (6)
19 Cynical disposition (8)
23 Assume (5)
25 Bird of prey (6)
30 A wooden shoe (4)
31 Blades used to row a boat (4)
32 Inhabitant of Denmark (4)
33 Large African antelope (4)
34 Howl (4)

39

ACROSS

1 Professional charges (4)
3 indefatigable (8)
6 Person obligated to another (7)
9 Put away papers (5)
12 Hence (4)
14 Irish Republican Army (3)
15 Bounded by three lines (9)
17 State in the W. United States (4)
18 Family name prefix (3)
19 Ledge for display (5)
21 Small child (3)
22 In place of (4)
23 Radiant (9)
27 Skill (3)
29 Russian emperor (4)
30 Muslim messiah (5)
31 First Russian astronaut (7)
33 Ensnarl (8)
34 Typographical error (inf.) (4)

DOWN

1 Rest on surface of a liquid (5)
2 Snow runner (3)
3 Between (5)
4 Laboured (9)
5 Visionary (4)
7 Cloth worn around hips (9)
8 Before (3)
10 Astronomical unit of length (9)
11 Intimidate (5)
13 Ancient France (4)
16 Something inserted (9)
18 Woman in charge of a household (5)
20 Colours (4)
24 Cigarette (slang) (3)
25 Salt of uric acid (5)
26 Latin American dance (5)
28 Shower (4)
32 Fitting (3)

40

ACROSS

2 Often (10)
7 Dominion (4)
8 Rebuke (6)
10 Annoy (3)
11 Stroll (5)
13 Tear (3)
15 A meadow (3)
16 Duration (4)
17 Ascends (5)
20 Efface (5)
21 Suffering from a chronic respiratory disease (9)
22 Awry (5)
24 Humiliate (5)
26 Saucy person (4)
27 Insect that lives in colonies (3)
29 Outside Broadcasts (Abbr.) (3)
30 Additional (5)
31 Eccentric (3)
32 Reduce to a lower grade (6)
34 Greek god of love (4)
35 Farseeing or shrewd (10)

DOWN

1 Sculptor (6)
2 Gave food (3)
3 The same as (5)
4 Reflected sound (4)
5 Treacle (8)
6 Exclamation to express joy (6)
8 A hot drink (3)
9 Intentions (4)
12 Section (7)
14 Set again (5)
16 Clan (5)
18 Man who sells goods (8)
19 Pigpen (3)
20 7th letter of the Greek alphabet (3)
22 Having no distinct feet (6)
23 Deride (4)
25 First-born (6)
27 A chopper (3)
28 Walk (5)
30 Inscribe (4)
33 Married (3)

ACROSS
1 Doubtful (11)
6 Affluent (7)
9 Weeding implement (3)
12 Canis Minor (9)
14 Tangle of logs (6)
15 Against (4)
16 Mouthpiece of a bridle (3)
17 An active volcano in Sicily (4)
18 Not good (3)
19 Off-Broadway theatre award (4)
20 Exclamation of surprise (3)
22 Irritate (4)
24 Concealed (6)
25 Thing of no importance (9)
27 General name for beer (3)
28 Slender graceful woman (5)
29 Exist together (11)

DOWN
2 Lawless person (6)
3 Puts down (4)
4 Fail at a premature stage (5)
5 Suffering from oppressive heat (10)
7 Republic in South America (9)
8 Sew (3)
9 Seize (4)
10 Capital of Scotland (9)
11 Self-centred (10)
13 Stated (4)
16 Exclamation of contempt (3)
18 Monetary unit of Thailand (4)
20 Pimples, especially on the face (4)
21 Former name of Sri Lanka (6)
23 Two-way teletypewriter service (5)
24 Inflammation of the eyelid (3)
26 Contraction of is not (4)

42

ACROSS
1 Ridged (6)
4 Captured (slang) (6)
7 A therapist who manipulates the skeleton (9)
10 Harbour (4)
11 Handwoven Scandinavian rug (3)
12 Pig sound (4)
13 Narrate (4)
15 Abnormally small person (5)
18 Body of salt water (5)
20 Longest river in the world (4)
21 Cat's sound of contenment (4)
22 Oxygen compound (5)
24 Hit with fist (5)
26 Partakes of food (4)
29 Peep (4)
31 Small Eurasian deer (3)
32 Smallest component (4)
33 Playact (9)
34 Rubbed out (6)
35 Pinching tool (6)

DOWN
1 Filed (6)
2 Expel (4)
3 Bring to bear (5)
4 Landlocked country in the Himalayas (5)
5 As a divisor of (4)
6 To become blacker (6)
7 Made arrangements (9)
8 Cry used to open a court (4)
9 Spend winter in dormant state (9)
14 Leap (4)
16 To free (3)
17 Run away (4)
19 French vineyard (3)
22 Resist (6)
23 Portico (4)
25 Hinder or impede (6)
27 Equipped (5)
28 Organization (5)
30 Malay dagger (4)
32 Islamic call to prayer (4)

43

ACROSS

1 Insurrection (8)
5 Split apart (4)
8 A single entity (3)
9 Disease causing inflammation of the nerves (8)
11 A State in the United States (4)
13 Resulting from mutation (6)
15 Proclaim with approval (7)
16 Able to move freely (6)
19 Atomic mass unit (3)
21 Permit (3)
22 Ill (6)
25 Triumph (7)
26 One given to empty or boastful talk (slang) (6)
30 Ancient Greek money (4)
31 Remote (8)
32 Large flightless bird (3)
33 River which flows into the Baltic Sea (4)
34 Fuss over a trifling matter (8)

DOWN

2 Deliver a sermon (6)
3 Spain and Portugal (6)
4 Harsh (4)
5 The basic core (4)
6 Dwell in (7)
7 Blood vessel (4)
10 Illuminate (6)
12 Opposite one of two (5)
14 Mountains in Asia (4)
17 Well-bred people (6)
18 Reused wool (5)
19 Inspiring awe (7)
20 Bone of the forearm (4)
23 European-style restaurant (6)
24 The Muse of astronomy (6)
27 Lying down (4)
28 Make indistinct (4)
29 Ball game (4)

44

ACROSS

1 Negligent (11)
8 Kingdom (5)
10 Foe (5)
12 Denial (3)
14 Chief Indian officer (7)
16 Look at amorously (4)
18 A photograph (slang) (3)
20 Beehive (4)
21 Demeanour (4)
22 Distress signal (3)
24 Tavern (3)
25 Portable shelter (4)
26 Ebony (4)
27 Two-wheeled horse carriage (3)
28 Information (4)
29 Uncommon (7)
33 Island of Denmark (3)
35 Norwegian dramatist (5)
36 Open space in a forest (5)
37 Remove oxygen from (11)

DOWN

1 To smooth clothes (4)
2 Breezy (4)
3 Contraction of it was (4)
4 Deprived of sensation (4)
5 Chilled (4)
6 Appearing (8)
7 One-fifth of the atmosphere (6)
9 Without luck (8)
11 Mother-in-law of Ruth (Old Testament) (5)
13 Got up (6)
15 Sanction (8)
17 Lenient act (6)
19 Confounded (8)
23 Rock (5)
25 Bright golden brown (6)
30 Remarkable (4)
31 Ill-favoured (4)
32 Alley (4)
33 Goat's milk cheese (4)
34 Greek goddess of victory (4)

ACROSS

1 Shank (4)
3 Treelike (8)
6 Gratuity (7)
9 Surmise (5)
12 An Afrikaner (4)
14 A lyric poem (3)
15 Severe diarrhoea (9)
17 Officiating priest of a mosque (4)
18 To travel or glide over snow (3)
19 A steam room (5)
21 Vase (3)
22 Ornamental fabric (4)
23 Illuminate (9)
27 Part of the verb to be (3)
29 Looked at (4)
30 Halogen element (5)
31 Place of residence (7)
33 Small banner (8)
34 Resting place (4)

DOWN

1 Yielded (5)
2 Dry (Fr.) (3)
3 Distrust (5)
4 Woman employed in a dairy (9)
5 Cooled below freezing (4)
7 Inexpert (9)
8 Fish eggs (3)
10 Made according to a formula (9)
11 A programme that is broadcast again (5)
13 Archaic name for Ireland (4)
16 Ignorance (9)
18 A caravansary (5)
20 Ethereal (4)
24 Colour (3)
25 Take as one's own (5)
26 Showy actions (5)
28 Roster (4)
32 Electrically-charged atom (3)

46

ACROSS

2 Meteorologist (10)
7 A person that uses (4)
8 Expects confidently (6)
10 Move quickly (3)
11 Courtyard (5)
13 Humble dwelling (3)
15 A thick creamy Indian stew (3)
16 Boss on a shield (4)
17 Put forth (5)
20 Son of Abraham (5)
21 Bulbous plant (9)
22 Sylvan (5)
24 Muslim messiah (5)
26 Admirable (4)
27 Top card (3)
29 Upper limb (3)
30 Huge (5)
31 Mischievous person (3)
32 Line on a weather map (6)
34 Soon (4)
35 Potato dish (4-6)

DOWN

1 Mouth of a gun barrel (6)
2 Lopsided (3)
3 In front (5)
4 Basic unit of currency in the EU (4)
5 Jumble (8)
6 Algae (6)
8 Sesame plant (3)
9 Brass wind instrument (4)
12 Cassava preparation (7)
14 Commerce (5)
16 Customary (5)
18 Immense (8)
19 Score in rugby (3)
20 Doctrine (3)
22 Visible spirit (6)
23 Rowing implements (4)
25 Baby (6)
27 Atmosphere (3)
28 Equip (5)
30 Clothes (4)
33 Owns or possesses (3)

1			2		3		4		5			6

ACROSS

1 Tree-dwelling Amazon monkey (6)
4 Deliver a sermon (6)
7 Hard-shelled pupa (9)
10 Depend (4)
11 Pull laboriously (3)
12 A reed stop in an organ (4)
13 Sly look (4)
15 Vacant (5)
18 Fertile area in a desert (5)
20 Saturate (4)
21 Pious platitudes (4)
22 Semi-synthetic material (5)
24 Cheerful (5)
26 Young guinea fowl (4)
29 Portion (4)
31 British Airports Authority (abbrev.) (3)
32 Frozen treats (4)
33 Airport (9)
34 Meriting trust (6)
35 Complain (6)

DOWN

1 False (6)
2 Wan (4)
3 Brief romantic affair (5)
4 Sandy bathing beach (5)
5 Way out (4)
6 Pester (6)
7 Waterclock (9)
8 Goes to law (4)
9 Physical matter (9)
14 Laugh loudly (4)
16 Also (3)
17 Pull abruptly (4)
19 Black bird (3)
22 Do again (6)
23 Glass ornament (4)
25 Animal with tusks (6)
27 Deep, lustrous black (5)
28 Behind time (5)
30 A technique used to relieve pain (4)
32 Officiating priest of a mosque (4)

48

ACROSS
1 Lack of respect (11)
6 Pompous (7)
9 Turf (3)
12 Sweatsuit worn by athletes (9)
14 Light turban (6)
15 Grass (4)
16 Knock vigorously (3)
17 Girl's name (4)
18 Valued mineral (3)
19 Periods of history (4)
20 Fish (3)
22 Capital of Norway (4)
24 God of the heavens (6)
25 Treat with aluminium (9)
27 Plant juice (3)
28 Breadth (5)
29 Frail boat (11)

DOWN
2 Decayed (6)
3 The sacred scriptures of Hinduism (4)
4 Uneven (5)
5 Pertaining to the esophagus (10)
7 Artless (9)
8 Literary or archaic before (3)
9 A large round wicker basket (4)
10 Vacation resort ranch (9)
11 Sister by marriage (10)
13 Stuff (4)
16 Crimson (3)
18 Thug (4)
20 Cut (4)
21 Remove silt from river (6)
23 Slap (5)
24 Type of submachine gun (3)
26 Certainly (archaic) (4)

49

ACROSS

1 Uncontrolled scrub fire (8)
5 Combustible matter (4)
8 Conclusion (3)
9 Card game (8)
11 Send forth (4)
13 Composed (6)
15 Intellectual (7)
16 Magistrate (6)
19 Expression of surprise (3)
21 Month (3)
22 Ensnare (6)
25 Ear ornament (7)
26 Cultivated area (6)
30 Sharpen (4)
31 Public and formal (8)
32 Arrest (3)
33 Thick fabric (4)
34 Unnecessary (8)

DOWN

2 River in W. central Africa (6)
3 Unreal (6)
4 Consumes (4)
5 Supply (4)
6 Effeminate (7)
7 Amend text (4)
10 Exercise book (Fr.) (6)
12 Dogma (5)
14 Examination (abbrev.) (4)
17 Medical (6)
18 Sound of a horse (5)
19 Endless (7)
20 Edible plant of the mustard family (4)
23 Confuse (6)
24 Yearly record (6)
27 Top-notch (4)
28 Something that is owed (4)
29 Midday (4)

50

ACROSS

1 School held in the evening (11)
8 Ooze out (5)
10 Small cabin (5)
12 Long dashes in text (3)
14 Failure to act (7)
16 To yield (4)
18 Possessive form of it (3)
20 Egyptian goddess of fertility (4)
21 Periods of history (4)
22 17th letter of the Greek alphabet (3)
24 Soak (3)
25 Narcotics agents (slang) (4)
26 Hardly cooked (4)
27 Loud noise (3)
28 To the leeward side (4)
29 Alas (7)
33 Urge (3)
35 Enamel (5)
36 Pile (5)
37 Person who cuts hair (11)

DOWN

1 Back of the neck (4)
2 Departs (4)
3 Dull sound (4)
4 Cook (4)
5 Island of Hawaii (4)
6 Literate (8)
7 Resounds (6)
9 Sweets (8)
11 Sore (5)
13 Resembling a mitre (6)
15 Theoretical (8)
17 Going out with (6)
19 Nagging (8)
23 Body of salt water (5)
25 Textile worker (6)
30 Sewing case (4)
31 Secondhand (4)
32 Cabbage-like plant (4)
33 Supplements (4)
34 Massive wild ox (4)

ACROSS

1 Group or band (4)
3 Having a nice smell (8)
6 Purplish red (7)
9 Steeps (5)
12 As previously given (4)
14 Prohibit (3)
15 Optical instrument (9)
17 Greek goddess of the rainbow (4)
18 Hawaiian food (3)
19 French for thank you (5)
21 Perceive with the eyes (3)
22 Sharp nail as on a cat (4)
23 Asset easily made liquid (4-5)
27 That is, namely (3)
29 Group of three people (4)
30 Fragrant resin (5)
31 Banal (7)
33 Real estate register (8)
34 Mild oath (4)

DOWN

1 The entire scale (5)
2 Command to a horse (3)
3 Caper (5)
4 Hypnotism (9)
5 Female German name (4)
7 Make French (9)
8 Fuss (3)
10 Ethiopia (9)
11 Reptile (5)
13 Heroic (4)
16 The study or science of language (9)
18 Annoy (5)
20 Water container (4)
24 Direct a gun (3)
25 Awake (5)
26 Give up (5)
28 Hip bones (4)
32 Female deer (3)

52

ACROSS

2 Dispute (10)
7 Upswept hairdo (4)
8 Real (6)
10 Nipple of a female mammal (3)
11 Narrow valley (5)
13 Furrow (3)
15 Male child (3)
16 Male parent (4)
17 Threads (5)
20 In front (5)
21 Chief magistrate of a shire (9)
22 Tearful (5)
24 Extreme (5)
26 Floating platform (4)
27 Antiquity (3)
29 Vessel built by Noah (3)
30 Pimp (5)
31 Superior quality vineyard (3)
32 Inborn (6)
34 Wise (4)
35 Thick soup or stew (10)

DOWN

1 Various (6)
2 Study carefully (3)
3 Influential person (5)
4 A single time (4)
5 Greedy (8)
6 Atilt (6)
8 To endure (3)
9 Distinctive quality (4)
12 Eyeglass for one eye (7)
14 Not appropriate (5)
16 Laminated rock (5)
18 Square not (8)
19 Wily (3)
20 Unit of mass (abbrev.) (3)
22 Ghost (6)
23 Acquire through merit (4)
25 Entertained (6)
27 Previous to (3)
28 Distributed cards (5)
30 Egyptian deity (4)
33 Powdery residue (3)

ACROSS

1 Lengthier (6)
4 Probably (6)
7 Lewdness (9)
10 Feat (4)
11 Electrically charged atom (3)
12 Cougar (4)
13 Once more (4)
15 Degenderize (5)
18 Collection of maps (5)
20 Ponder intently (4)
21 A leg joint (4)
22 Hindu social class (5)
24 Outmoded (5)
26 Exclamation of fright (4)
29 Peruse (4)
31 Akin (3)
32 New Zealand parrot (4)
33 Denial (9)
34 Originating in the mind (6)
35 Pines for (6)

DOWN

1 ------ lights, type of window (6)
2 Delighted (4)
3 A type of larva (5)
4 The sesame plant (5)
5 Speech defect (4)
6 Compositions (6)
7 Bed cover (9)
8 Charged particles (4)
9 Almost fatal (9)
14 Stick used by a magician (4)
16 Long period of time (3)
17 Radiograph (4)
19 Light meal (3)
22 Small destructive animals (6)
23 Petty criminal (4)
25 Stage plays (6)
27 Biblical son of Abraham (5)
28 Lustrous black (5)
30 Daily fare of food (4)
32 Japanese syllabic script (4)

54

ACROSS
1 Exhibiting radioactivity (11)
6 Female criminal (7)
9 Class (3)
12 Reduce acidity (9)
14 Broad avenue (6)
15 Jug, as it were (anag.) (4)
16 Biblical high priest (3)
17 Trigonometric function (4)
18 Ten decibels (3)
19 Continuous dull pain (4)
20 Monetary unit of Japan (3)
22 Loch (4)
24 Stableman (6)
25 Having the form of villi (9)
27 Distant but within sight (3)
28 Full of veins (5)
29 Tart lemon-flavoured carbonated drink (6-5)

DOWN
2 Draw idly (6)
3 Earthen pot (4)
4 Spanish accent placed over the letter 'n' (5)
5 Boldly assertive (10)
7 In name only (9)
8 Meadow (3)
9 Spectacular Hawaiian bird (4)
10 City on the Firth of Forth (9)
11 Make symmetrical (10)
13 Prison room (4)
16 Even (poet.) (3)
18 Flesh of a cow (4)
20 Body covering (4)
21 Metallic element (6)
23 High up (5)
24 Metal-bearing mineral (3)
26 Egg-shaped (4)

55

ACROSS

1 One who lives locally (8)
5 Australasian bird (4)
8 Freeze over (3)
9 Lay eggs (8)
11 Pleasing (4)
13 Small spots (6)
15 Aromatic herb (7)
16 Magistrate (6)
19 Longest division of geologic time (3)
21 Hawaiian acacia (3)
22 Chinese island (6)
25 Pertaining to the fingers (7)
26 Large drinking glass (6)
30 Authentic (4)
31 Dauntless (8)
32 Amphibian (3)
33 Restaurant (4)
34 A native of Europe (8)

DOWN

2 To show a different surface (6)
3 Demented (6)
4 Swallows (4)
5 Cows (4)
6 Bristle (7)
7 Show disgust or strong dislike (4)
10 Organized massacre (6)
12 Gravel ridge (5)
14 Highest point (4)
17 Halogen element (6)
18 Put forth (5)
19 Worn over the ears in cold weather (7)
20 Upper part of a glacier (4)
23 Female sibling (6)
24 Thin plate (6)
27 Water-soluble compound (4)
28 Allot (4)
29 Vex (4)

56

ACROSS

1 A medicine to restore health (11)
8 Pungent bulb (5)
10 To belch (5)
12 Also (3)
14 Stronghold (7)
16 Inner surface of the hand (4)
18 Lair (3)
20 Petty quarrel (4)
21 Urban district of SE England (4)
22 --- deer (3)
24 Lower limb (3)
25 Main island of Indonesia (4)
26 A piece of land or plot (4)
27 Decease (3)
28 Employs (4)
29 Gaily (7)
33 A single person or thing (3)
35 Small hand drum (5)
36 Not telling the truth (5)
37 Substitution (11)

DOWN

1 Rave (4)
2 Used to drive or frighten away (4)
3 Relating to the ear (4)
4 Female relative (4)
5 Chilled (4)
6 Strove to be equal (8)
7 Season before winter (6)
9 Waterproof paper (3-5)
11 Drive back (5)
13 Musical dramas (6)
15 Really (8)
17 Traditional saying (6)
19 11th month of the year (8)
23 Artist's support (5)
25 Fairly (6)
30 Incline (4)
31 Part of the hip (4)
32 Exclamation of fright (4)
33 Double curve (4)
34 Compass point (4)

ACROSS

1 Visage (4)
3 Adores (8)
6 Flogging (7)
9 Dried plum (5)
12 Prehistoric sculptural tomb (4)
14 Greek goddess of night (3)
15 Secret dungeon (9)
17 Part of a shield (4)
18 Fifth tone of the musical scale (3)
19 Ascend (5)
21 Strike lightly (3)
22 Woody plant (4)
23 Inherently (9)
27 Sin (3)
29 At that time (4)
30 Monetary unit of Finland (5)
31 Unload from a plane (7)
33 Succession (8)
34 Simpleton (4)

DOWN

1 Page in account book (5)
2 A letter appearing in Old Saxon (3)
3 Flinch (5)
4 Ninth month of the year (9)
5 Insignificant (4)
7 Subordinate (9)
8 Get (3)
10 Disliked (9)
11 Use energy (5)
13 Partly fermented grape juice (4)
16 Inducement (9)
18 Woolly ruminant mammal (5)
20 Wife of Jacob (Bib.) (4)
24 Beverage (3)
25 Join (5)
26 Aquatic mammal (5)
28 Advise (4)
32 Domesticated canine (3)

58

ACROSS

2 Tactless (10)
7 Relating to urine (4)
8 Persian musical instrument (6)
10 Not many (3)
11 A scrapbook (5)
13 Cretean peak (3)
15 Plant juice (3)
16 Tone (anag.) (4)
17 With ears (5)
20 Waterfall (5)
21 Person who arrives before others (9)
22 Paralyze (5)
24 Scoff (5)
26 Encourage in wrongdoing (4)
27 Jump on one foot (3)
29 Monetary unit of Bulgaria (3)
30 Covered on the inside (5)
31 Idiot (3)
32 Sayings (6)
34 Baking chamber (4)
35 Business activity (10)

DOWN

1 Irritate (6)
2 Slippery conditions (3)
3 Trades (5)
4 Officiating priest of a mosque (4)
5 Height (8)
6 Erring (6)
8 Drink by taking small swallows (3)
9 Image of a deity (4)
12 City or place of great luxury (7)
14 Sumptuous meal (5)
16 Merits (5)
18 Pertinent (8)
19 Not wet (3)
20 Expression of disgust (S. Afr.) (3)
22 Stately mansion (6)
23 Couched (4)
25 Purify (6)
27 Belonging to him (3)
28 Finnish money (5)
30 Sly look (4)
33 To make faces (3)

59

ACROSS

1 Merriment (6)
4 Breed of dog (6)
7 Capital of Romania (9)
10 Type of wood (4)
11 Advanced in years (3)
12 Monetary unit of W. Somoa (4)
13 Potpourri (4)
15 Full of reeds (5)
18 Norwegian name for Norway (5)
20 Enemies (4)
21 Small container (4)
22 Manila hemp plant (5)
24 Mountain spinach (5)
26 Inheritor (4)
29 Capital of Yemen (4)
31 Shelter (3)
32 Strike breaker (4)
33 Intersect (9)
34 Mode of standing (6)
35 River in SW Asia (6)

DOWN

1 A principal beam (6)
2 12th month of the Jewish calendar (4)
3 Lout (5)
4 Verily (Fr.) (5)
5 Expel (4)
6 Make equal (6)
7 Shameless (9)
8 Supporter (4)
9 Sojourn (9)
14 Upon (4)
16 Doctor (slang) (3)
17 Yes (4)
19 Belonging to us (3)
22 Subsides (6)
23 Fastens a knot (4)
25 Arrogance (6)
27 Evade (5)
28 Set again (5)
30 Inert gaseous element (4)
32 Male deer (4)

60

ACROSS
1 Mutual retaliation (11)
6 Tight embrace (4-3)
9 Viper (3)
12 Forceful (9)
14 Seaport in the S. Ukraine (6)
15 Inlets (4)
16 Flow back (3)
17 Until (4)
18 Third person singular present tense of have (3)
19 Diplomacy (4)
20 Beetle (3)
22 Type of hairdo (4)
24 Exertion (6)
25 Profitable (9)
27 Lock opener (3)
28 Containing metal (5)
29 Third-place winner (6-5)

DOWN
2 Rework (6)
3 Energy units (4)
4 Good-tasting (5)
5 Completely (10)
7 Filled with awe (9)
8 North American nation (3)
9 Bedouin (4)
10 Pertaining to fish (9)
11 Passive (10)
13 Recedes (4)
16 Organ of hearing (3)
18 Shout in derision (4)
20 Day of the Allied landing in France (4)
21 Afraid (6)
23 Primp (5)
24 Evening (3)
26 A ruler claiming descent from Muhammad (4)

ACROSS

1 Causing horror (8)
5 Male night out (4)
8 Monetary unit of Sweden (3)
9 Woman's negligee jacket (8)
11 Concern (4)
13 Instrument used in combat (6)
15 Elevations (7)
16 Summerhouse (6)
19 The States (Abbrev.) (3)
21 Fashionably up-to-date (3)
22 Communication (6)
25 Small Eurasian crow (7)
26 Having sound (6)
30 Sibilate (4)
31 Modern (2-2-4)
32 Falsehood (3)
33 Tree frog (4)
34 Historian (8)

DOWN

2 Military catapult (6)
3 Hovers (6)
4 Ship's company (4)
5 Caribbean dance music (4)
6 Caught (7)
7 Air (prefix) (4)
10 Incept (6)
12 Equip (5)
14 Test (4)
17 Exhausted (6)
18 Luxuriant (5)
19 Kitchen vessel (7)
20 Longest division of geologic time (4)
23 Partial antigen (6)
24 Desert plant (6)
27 Greasy (4)
28 Seaward (4)
29 Large brass wind instrument (4)

62

ACROSS
1 Attribution of a custom (11)
8 Small white heron (5)
10 Unit of magnetic induction (5)
12 Atmosphere (3)
14 Torn by inner conflict (7)
16 Small child (4)
18 Seed vessel (3)
20 Canned pork luncheon meat (4)
21 Land measure (4)
22 Swindle (3)
24 Definite article (3)
25 The acme (4)
26 Water (4)
27 Part of corn (3)
28 Midge (4)
29 Warlike (7)
33 21st letter of the Greek alphabet (3)
35 Banish (5)
36 Vestige (5)
37 Harmful (11)

DOWN
1 Girl's name (4)
2 Affirm with confidence (4)
3 Romanian dance (4)
4 Roman emperor 962–73 (4)
5 Monetary unit of Peru (4)
6 Hair on the upper lip (8)
7 Beard (6)
9 US equivalent of aubergine (8)
11 Group of witches (5)
13 Polygon having all angles equal (6)
15 Having the shape of a coin (8)
17 Violation of trust (6)
19 Great energy (8)
23 Flower segment (5)
25 Radiant (6)
30 Clarets (4)
31 Need to scratch (4)
32 Wash (4)
33 Basic unit of money in Uruguay (4)
34 Evils (4)

63

ACROSS

1 Portent (4)
3 Striated (8)
6 Lacking eyes (7)
9 One of two equal sections of a cone (5)
12 Made a court petition (4)
14 Organ of sight (3)
15 With force (9)
17 Let out (4)
18 Pressing of wine (Fr.) (3)
19 Small yeast-raised pancake (5)
21 Anger (3)
22 European (prefix) (4)
23 Diminution (9)
27 Dry (as of wine) (3)
29 The sheatfish (4)
30 Stenographer (abbrev.) (5)
31 Bartender (7)
33 Bullfighters (8)
34 Unit of linear measure (4)

DOWN

1 Follows orders (5)
2 Naught (3)
3 Cavity (5)
4 Arrange in a random manner (9)
5 Catch sight of (4)
7 Persuasive speech (9)
8 Source of light and heat (3)
10 Relevant (9)
11 Strange and mysterious (5)
13 Garden (4)
16 Wood used for cabinetmaking (9)
18 Category (5)
20 Part of ear (4)
24 High-pitched (3)
25 Former Russian rulers (5)
26 Exhausted (5)
28 Small ornamental ladies' bag (4)
32 Crafty (3)

64

ACROSS

2 Not blinking (10)
7 Evenings (Abbrev.) (4)
8 Experts (6)
10 Outcome (3)
11 Swear word (5)
13 Exclamation of surprise (3)
15 Male sheep (3)
16 Land measure (4)
17 Ethical (5)
20 Go into (5)
21 State of being obedient (9)
22 One of the United Arab Emirates (5)
24 Evade (5)
26 An object of worship (4)
27 Legal right (3)
29 Posed (3)
30 Zest (5)
31 Resinous deposit (3)
32 Pliable (6)
34 Lowest tides (4)
35 Deputy (10)

DOWN

1 Make amends (6)
2 Employ (3)
3 Yemen currency (5)
4 A brood of pheasants (4)
5 Tightly packed (8)
6 Flowing oil well (6)
8 Viper (3)
9 Noxious weed (4)
12 Ruby-coloured (7)
14 Clique (5)
16 The elbow (5)
18 Turn into a robot (8)
19 Wreath of flowers (3)
20 Conclusion (3)
22 Disperse (6)
23 Heritable land of the Teutonic people (4)
25 Unless (6)
27 Project (3)
28 Mouthlike opening (5)
30 Small biting black fly (4)
33 Social insect (3)

ACROSS

1 Area with coin-operated games (6)
4 Remove bones (6)
7 Very small painting (9)
10 Incline (4)
11 A false statement (3)
12 Amusement (4)
13 Tuberous root of the taro (4)
15 Governed (5)
18 Bury (5)
20 Looked at (4)
21 Plebeian (Abbrev.) (4)
22 A violent free-for-all (5)
24 European ermine (5)
26 Flat circular plate (4)
29 Ark builder (4)
31 Ocean (3)
32 Obstacle (4)
33 Imagined (9)
34 Group (6)
35 Morose (6)

DOWN

1 Person who fishes (6)
2 Related by blood (4)
3 Banish (5)
4 Outmoded (5)
5 A mass of floating ice (4)
6 Make beloved (6)
7 National emblem of Canada (5-4)
8 Helper (4)
9 Headed east (9)
14 Lubricates (4)
16 Organ of sight (3)
17 Feat (4)
19 Open mesh fabric (3)
22 Operated by hand (6)
23 Seaward (4)
25 The young of a male tiger and female lion (6)
27 Pineapple fibre (5)
28 Lawsuits (5)
30 Suspend (4)
32 Authenticating mark (4)

66

ACROSS
1 Education of both sexes (11)
6 4th president of the U.S. (7)
9 Aged (3)
12 Political union (Ger.) (9)
14 Revolve (6)
15 Falsehoods (4)
16 Constellation in the Northern Hemisphere (3)
17 Distinctive form of clothing (4)
18 Condensed moisture (3)
19 Raced (4)
20 Opening in a needle (3)
22 Overhanging lower edge of a roof (4)
24 Apportions (6)
25 Mandarin (9)
27 Cardinal number (3)
28 Employees (5)
29 Informal gathering (3-8)

DOWN
2 Synthetic (6)
3 Spore-bearing parts of a moss vessel (4)
4 Silk fabric (5)
5 Make pregnant (10)
7 Cleansing agent (9)
8 Single number (3)
9 Midwestern US State (4)
10 Impervious to dust (9)
11 Plant of the lily family (10)
13 Skein of thread (4)
16 Shelter (3)
18 English-born American Quaker (4)
20 Level (4)
21 Interweave (6)
23 Representative (5)
24 Tiny insect (3)
26 Small island (4)

ACROSS

1 Boundless (8)
5 Epic poetry (4)
8 Grade of wine (3)
9 Piercing (8)
11 Skin eruption (4)
13 Justice (6)
15 Lattice (7)
16 French exercise book (6)
19 Wrath (3)
21 A river in Scotland (3)
22 Intensity of hue (6)
25 English gold coin (7)
26 Subject to a penalty (6)
30 Shamrock island (4)
31 Delegate (8)
32 Chickpea dish (3)
33 Insignificant (4)
34 Large owl (8)

DOWN

2 Scrivener (6)
3 Inflammation of the eye (6)
4 Verge (4)
5 Beige (4)
6 Tract of grassland (7)
7 Banish (4)
10 Lively Spanish dance (6)
12 Many-headed monster in Greek mythology (5)
14 Quadrangle (4)
17 Men of courage (6)
18 Extent (5)
19 Inhabitant of Iran (7)
20 Large flightless Australian birds (4)
23 Picket (6)
24 Groove (6)
27 Official language of Pakistan (4)
28 Inwardly (4)
29 The goddess of youth (4)

68

ACROSS

1 Lying upon something else (11)
8 A colourless crystalline substance (5)
10 Clauses of a document (5)
12 Place (3)
14 Patella (7)
16 Sharp hissings sounds (4)
18 Not many (3)
20 Of thou (4)
21 Chief god of ancient Greece (4)
22 Corded cloth (3)
24 Very skilled person (3)
25 Hungarian sheepdog (4)
26 Not odd (4)
27 Flow back (3)
28 ---- of Wight (4)
29 Lattice (7)
33 Cloudlike mass (3)
35 Perch (5)
36 Long-continued practice (5)
37 Present everywhere (11)

DOWN

1 Exchange (4)
2 A secret plan (4)
3 Make account of (4)
4 Skin infection (4)
5 Heroic (4)
6 Toecap (8)
7 Valuate (6)
9 Little by little (8)
11 Shallow ornamental bowl (5)
13 Womb (6)
15 Critical explanation (8)
17 Indian village (6)
19 Affluent (4-2-2)
23 Wharves (5)
25 Penetrate (6)
30 Famous London college (4)
31 Aggregation (4)
32 Surfeit (4)
33 Comrade (4)
34 Spurt (4)

ACROSS

1 Insect larva (4)
3 Having two wives (8)
6 Neolithic stone implement (7)
9 Fenced areas (5)
12 Devours (4)
14 Age (3)
15 Gullible (9)
17 Roofing item (4)
18 Obsolete (Abbrev.) (3)
19 Started (5)
21 Regret (3)
22 Skin (4)
23 Inveterate (9)
27 Tavern (3)
29 A grandmother (4)
30 Favoured (5)
31 Most gruesome (7)
33 Finely chopped (8)
34 Grudging admiration (4)

DOWN

1 Arising from a gene (5)
2 Measure of sound (3)
3 East Indian pepper plant (5)
4 Former name for Ethiopia (9)
5 Untie (4)
7 Spend more than one can afford (9)
8 Monetary unit of Vietnam (3)
10 Allusion (9)
11 Serpent (5)
13 Skirt worn by ballerinas (4)
16 Without illusions (9)
18 Fertile desert tract (5)
20 Sicilian volcano (4)
24 Oxlike African antelope (3)
25 Stormed (5)
26 Eccentric (5)
28 Near (4)
32 Binary compound (suff.) (3)

70

ACROSS

2 Type of bet on horse races (10)
7 Small notch (4)
8 Quickly (6)
10 Unwell (3)
11 Blue of a clear sky (5)
13 Wine (Fr.) (3)
15 Partitive article (3)
16 Decoy (4)
17 Bell-shaped flower (5)
20 Small mountains (5)
21 Composite plant of the Alps (9)
22 Bet (5)
24 Choose (5)
26 Evenings (abbrev.) (4)
27 At a great distance (3)
29 Put on (3)
30 Pertaining to the ear (5)
31 To give vent (3)
32 Termination (6)
34 Killer whale (4)
35 Pipefish (10)

DOWN

1 Apply ointment (6)
2 West Indian popular music (3)
3 Public square (5)
4 At the bow of a vessel (4)
5 Agitate (8)
6 Makes amends (6)
8 Peer (3)
9 Rotate (4)
12 Abjure (7)
14 Seasons (5)
16 Cotton thread for hosiery (5)
18 French mathematician (8)
19 For each (3)
20 Hasten (3)
22 High-speed skiing (6)
23 River in central England (4)
25 Muslim headdress (6)
27 Stale air (3)
28 Jewish scholar (5)
30 Of, or relating to, the anus (4)
33 5th note in a musical scale (3)

ACROSS
1 Accept as true (6)
4 Albanian money (6)
7 Impossible to hear (9)
10 Having no light (4)
11 Floor covering (3)
12 Son of Isaac and Rebekah (4)
13 Preparatory school (abbrev.) (4)
15 Rotates (5)
18 Edict of the czar (5)
20 Muscle spasms (4)
21 Indigo (4)
22 Muse of lyric poetry (5)
24 Talent (5)
26 Person with great power (4)
29 W. Samoa money (4)
31 Professional (abbrev.) (3)
32 Misfortunes (4)
33 Embellish (9)
34 Highly seasoned stew (6)
35 Over there (6)

DOWN
1 Woollen braid (6)
2 Dip into hot drink (4)
3 Pound (5)
4 Completely (5)
5 World's longest river (4)
6 Reprimand (6)
7 Easily irritated (9)
8 Mend with rows of stitches (4)
9 Moving stairway (9)
14 Hoodlum (4)
16 Louse egg (3)
17 Native of Scotland (4)
19 Relatives (3)
22 One or the other of two (6)
23 Gambling game (4)
25 One who kisses (6)
27 Small fish (5)
28 Turbulent (5)
30 Ammunition (slang) (4)
32 Suppose (4)

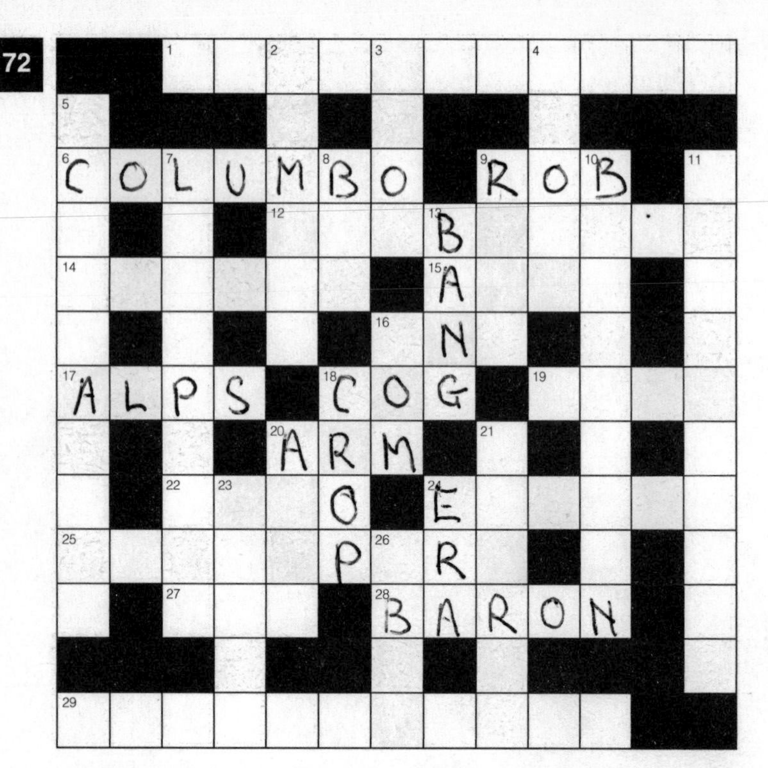

ACROSS
1 Pollute (11)
6 Capital of Sri Lanka (7)
9 Steal from (3)
12 Reference mark (9)
14 Dishevelled (6)
15 Inheritor (4)
16 As being (3)
17 Mountains (4)
18 Gear tooth (3)
19 Foolish (4)
20 Upper limb (3)
22 Character in Othello (4)
24 Resembling an echo (6)
25 Woman who has never borne a child (9)
27 Containing two or more eras (3)
28 Member of nobility (5)
29 Type of drop scone (11)

DOWN
2 Ant-eating Australian marsupial (6)
3 At another time (4)
4 Ruth's mother-in-law (bibl.) (5)
5 Scarlet fever (10)
7 Lover of words (9)
8 Implore (3)
9 Ostrich-like bird (4)
10 Place of confinement for slaves (9)
11 Doubt (10)
13 Dull explosive sound (4)
16 City in NW Iran (3)
18 Harvest (4)
20 Against (4)
21 Greek island in the Aegean Sea (6)
23 Loudly (5)
24 Period in history (3)
26 French clergyman (4)

ACROSS

1 Having three feet (8)
5 Swindle (4)
8 Young goat (3)
9 Powerfully explosive (8)
11 Asian Republic (4)
13 Clamour (6)
15 Hairy (7)
16 Makeshift (6)
19 Globe (3)
21 Covering for the head (3)
22 Uncovered (6)
25 Admire servilely (7)
26 Adhesive (6)
30 Typographical error (4)
31 Bewildered (8)
32 Comrade (3)
33 Blend (4)
34 Roundworm (8)

DOWN

2 Novice (6)
3 Make a contribution (6)
4 At the pitch written (music) (4)
5 Parody (4)
6 Small circle (7)
7 6th month of the Jewish calendar (4)
10 Barracks (6)
12 Thermoplastic yarn (5)
14 US State where Salt Lake City is the capital (4)
17 Fine white clay (6)
18 Most unfavourable (5)
19 Having an Oedipus complex (7)
20 Bill (4)
23 Inner shrine (6)
24 Be present at (6)
27 Class (4)
28 Chilled (4)
29 Open mouth wide (4)

74

ACROSS	
1	Become worse (11)
8	Emperor of Ethiopia (5)
10	Be silent (5)
12	Hard gemstone used in laser technology (3)
14	Fred -------, US singer and dancer (7)
16	Basic unit of heredity (4)
18	Racket (3)
20	People also called Danakil (4)
21	Central European river (4)
22	Exclamation of contempt (3)
24	Negative (abbrev.) (3)
25	Bones (4)
26	Vases (4)
27	A hanging end or thread (3)
28	Exchange for money (4)
29	Voluble talk (7)
33	Scarlet (3)
35	Young (5)
36	Dropsy (5)
37	Kill by electricity (11)

DOWN	
1	Punctually (4)
2	Chinese secret society (4)
3	Wrinkle (4)
4	Expel (4)
5	Against (4)
6	Went beyond the limit (8)
7	Sire (6)
9	The right to use another's property (8)
11	Inert elemental gas (5)
13	Fit for cultivation (6)
15	Put in order (8)
17	Invalidate (6)
19	Coccyx (8)
23	Shout of exultation (5)
25	Line on a weather map (6)
30	A tool similar to an axe (4)
31	Heave (4)
32	City in W. Nevada (4)
33	Rough earthenware (4)
34	Nap (4)

ACROSS

1 A structure for confining animals (4)
3 30th president of the US (8)
6 Altar boy (7)
9 Plentiful (5)
12 Greek goddess of strife (4)
14 High mountain (3)
15 Most tender (9)
17 Assuredly (archaic) (4)
18 Pronoun (3)
19 Virtual (5)
21 Mineral in rock (3)
22 Keep away from (4)
23 Travelling from place to place (9)
27 Kimono sash (3)
29 Caribbean dance music (4)
30 Island in the Bay of Naples (5)
31 Distinguished (7)
33 Shaped by a hammer (8)
34 Mown grass (4)

DOWN

1 Seashore (5)
2 Long, thin fish (3)
3 Provide food (5)
4 At least (9)
5 Audacity (4)
7 Legal right of possession (9)
8 Prior (3)
10 Rectory (9)
11 Lyric poem (5)
13 Egyptian goddess of fertility (4)
16 Of special beauty (9)
18 Ruin (5)
20 Until (4)
24 To freeze over (3)
25 Titled (5)
26 One of prodigious size and strength (5)
28 A leavened rum cake (4)
32 Naught (3)

76

1			2		3			4		5		6
7												
							8				9	
10				11		12				13		
			14		15				16			
17		18		19				20				
		21										
22	23							24				25
26					27		28					
29				30						31		
32									33			
									34			
35												

ACROSS

2 Flattered (10)
7 River in the Czech Republic (4)
8 Reproduction (6)
10 Label (3)
11 Ornamental coronet (5)
13 Deranged (3)
15 Less than two (3)
16 Hindu music (4)
17 Joyous (5)
20 Bumpkin (5)
21 Embitter (9)
22 Capital of Jordan (5)
24 Pierces with horn (5)
26 Fasteners (4)
27 Domesticated animal (3)
29 Wood sorrel (3)
30 Entrances (5)
31 Dry (as in wine) (3)
32 Of little width (6)
34 To the inside of (4)
35 Wanton (10)

DOWN

1 Dissepiment (6)
2 Place for sleep or rest (3)
3 A sound signal (5)
4 Ancient empire of Peru (4)
5 Knockout punch (8)
6 Skilfull (6)
8 Prior to (archaic) (3)
9 Leaf of a book (4)
12 Small ring (7)
14 Killer whales (5)
16 Rotating member (5)
18 Defensive mounds (8)
19 The passive, female principle in Chinese philosophy (3)
20 A hard synthetic gemstone (3)
22 Not divided into zones (6)
23 Transparent mineral silicate (4)
25 Zone (6)
27 Foot of an animal (3)
28 Characteristic rhythm (5)
30 Desert in E Asia (4)
33 Three-toed sloths (3)

77

ACROSS

1 Having no feet (6)
4 Roar (6)
7 Stamina (9)
10 Of the best quality (1-3)
11 Slender metal fastener (3)
12 11th letter of the Hebrew alphabet (4)
13 Objectives (4)
15 Livid (5)
18 Duck with soft down (5)
20 Sarcastic or bitter (4)
21 Illustrious warrior (4)
22 Crowbar (5)
24 Impertinence (5)
26 Way out (4)
29 Queue (4)
31 Affirmative reply (3)
32 Repair (4)
33 Member of a guild (9)
34 A narcotic (6)
35 Thorough view (6)

DOWN

1 To fill with horror (6)
2 Sand hill (4)
3 Magnifying glass used by jewellers (5)
4 Tasteless (5)
5 Deficiency (4)
6 Flat ring (6)
7 Impression (9)
8 Outer covering (4)
9 Anglo-Saxon magistrate (9)
14 Observed (4)
16 Diamonds (slang) (3)
17 Dreadful (4)
19 Wrath (3)
22 Female demon in Semitic folklore (6)
23 Bound (4)
25 Observation (6)
27 Yellow, gummy pentosan found in plant cells (5)
28 Flavour (5)
30 European (abbrev.) (4)
32 Urn (4)

78

ACROSS

1 Make external (11)
7 Deviating line (5)
9 Hotel (3)
12 Heavy quilt (9)
14 Sickness in the stomach (6)
15 24-hour periods (4)
16 Metallic element (3)
17 Gemstone (4)
18 Cereal grass (3)
19 A goatlike mammal of Asia (4)
20 Find the sum of (3)
22 Shakespearian villain (4)
24 In a correct manner (6)
25 Ornate (9)
27 Annoy by persistent fault-finding (3)
28 Italian city (5)
29 Good and bad times (3-3-5)

DOWN

2 Large soup dish (6)
3 Regretted (4)
4 Jitterbug dance (5)
5 Dealer in hardware (10)
7 Of or relating to the white race (9)
8 By way of (3)
9 Islamic republic in SW Asia (4)
10 Homesickness (9)
11 Comprehend (10)
13 Modifying literary works (4)
16 Small child (3)
18 Scent (4)
20 Highly excited (4)
21 Before this time (6)
23 Manila hemp plant (5)
24 Consumed (3)
26 Old (4)

ACROSS

1 Inhabitant of Canada (8)
5 Exchequer (4)
8 Supplement (3)
9 A scaly condition of the scalp (8)
11 Division of a school year (4)
13 Flaccid (6)
15 Small circle (7)
16 Occurring in spring (6)
19 Door opener (3)
21 Large body of salt water (3)
22 One who wantonly destroys property (6)
25 A coming (7)
26 Reproduction (6)
30 Individual facts (4)
31 Remove grease (8)
32 Church seat (3)
33 Crimsons and scarlets (4)
34 Instruction session (8)

DOWN

2 Loss of muscle coordination (6)
3 Hardens (6)
4 An unpleasant smell (4)
5 Cheese made from goat's milk (4)
6 Japanese art of arranging flowers (7)
7 Inhabitant of Serbia (4)
10 Dodged (6)
12 Spinal cord (prefix) (5)
14 Dregs (4)
17 Purify (6)
18 Overgrown with ivy (5)
19 Knotty (7)
20 An umbelliferous plant with edible roots (4)
23 Radiating light (6)
24 Feeling of sickness (6)
27 A tropical Asian evergreen tree (4)
28 Infectious tropical disease (4)
29 To eliminate or delete (4)

80

ACROSS

1 Fish-eating (11)
8 Parson's house (5)
10 A roughly built house (5)
12 Scottish river (3)
14 Exposure of the body to the sun (7)
16 Sod (4)
18 Hide of a small beast (3)
20 Cat sound (4)
21 Chinese dialect (4)
22 Albanian money (3)
24 Excellent, wonderful (slang) (3)
25 Repeat (4)
26 Lamented (4)
27 Born (3)
28 A thought (4)
29 Cut using forceful strokes (7)
33 7th letter of Greek alphabet (3)
35 A giant (5)
36 Music hall (5)
37 County in N. Ireland (11)

DOWN

1 Trudge (4)
2 Identical (4)
3 Hostelries (4)
4 Furnace (4)
5 Black-and-white whale (4)
6 Less than human (8)
7 Convert into wine (6)
9 Soft rustling sound (8)
11 Fragrant oil (5)
13 Banished (6)
15 Weighted (8)
17 Gnawing animal (6)
19 Statue support (8)
23 Australian marsupial (5)
25 Gaping grin (6)
30 Soon (4)
31 Tramp (4)
32 Feat (4)
33 Islamic chieftain (4)
34 Military force (4)

ACROSS

1 Device for converting sound waves (4)
3 Geniality (8)
6 Terse (7)
9 Of or relating to ships (5)
12 A river in NE France (4)
14 Vexation (3)
15 The day before this day (9)
17 Smoke combined with fog (4)
18 Light afternoon meal (3)
19 Stroll (5)
21 Forms of identification (abbrev.) (3)
22 Narrate (4)
23 Indispensable (9)
27 An early mathematical system (3)
29 Implement (4)
30 Boredom (5)
31 Decipher (7)
33 Small plume (8)
34 Excavates (4)

DOWN

1 Lacteal (5)
2 Self-esteem (3)
3 Wild rose (5)
4 Period of blissful harmony (9)
5 8th month of the Jewish calendar (4)
7 Conversion into cheese (9)
8 Food regurgitated by a ruminant (3)
10 The state of being pure (9)
11 Lexicon (5)
13 Basis (4)
16 Exclamatory oath (9)
18 A topic of discussion (5)
20 Too (4)
24 Grass-covered surface (3)
25 Choose (5)
26 Old stringed instruments (5)
28 The indigo plant (4)
32 A thin straight bar (3)

82

ACROSS

2 Extremely sacred (10)
7 Repetition of sound (4)
8 Blossom (6)
10 Sheep souund (3)
11 A descendant of Cain (5)
13 Chopping tool (3)
15 Small amount (3)
16 Lyric poems (4)
17 Evade (5)
20 Spinach (5)
21 Directed towards the north (9)
22 Diving bird (5)
24 Domineering (5)
26 Part of a test (4)
27 Derelict (3)
29 The sum of (3)
30 Founder of the Mogul Empire (5)
31 To and --- (3)
32 Checked (6)
34 A large crock or jar (4)
35 Deviation (10)

DOWN

1 Frail (6)
2 Former coin of France (3)
3 Cuff (5)
4 Dispose of money (4)
5 These days (8)
6 To flail (6)
8 Craze (3)
9 Executive officer (inf.) (4)
12 Container for bathing in (7)
14 Naturally-dried brick (5)
16 Lowermost deck (5)
18 Incessant (8)
19 Aforetime (3)
20 Golden globe (3)
22 Stared fiercely (6)
23 Travel on (4)
25 Petty officer in the US Navy (6)
27 Not good (3)
28 Thank you in French (5)
30 English monk (4)
33 Not (prefix) (3)

ACROSS
1 Gulp (6)
4 Moslem robe (6)
7 Flagrant (9)
10 Fine and delicate (4)
11 Fabled bird (3)
12 Long periods of time (4)
13 Having a toe (4)
15 Prices paid (5)
18 Move rhythmically (5)
20 Large, almost tailless, rodent (4)
21 Nimbus (4)
22 First prime minister of India (5)
24 Shouts (5)
26 Sullen (4)
29 Ambience (4)
31 Rage (3)
32 Summit of a small hill (4)
33 Recompense (9)
34 Required (6)
35 Country in N. Europe (6)

DOWN
1 Celtic language (6)
2 A hobgoblin (4)
3 Turn outwards (5)
4 Plant fluid (5)
5 A colour (4)
6 To bother or harass (6)
7 Part of the atmosphere (9)
8 Well-behaved (4)
9 Drowsy (9)
14 6 June, 1944 (1-3)
16 Sailor (3)
17 Gust of wind (4)
19 Malt beverage (3)
22 A white crystalline acid (6)
23 Mentor (4)
25 Furnish (6)
27 Greased (5)
28 Staff again (5)
30 Among (4)
32 Knot in wood (4)

84

ACROSS

1 Express by gesturing (11)
6 Flourish (7)
9 Inlet, bay or creek (3)
12 Wayfarer (9)
14 A parliamentary report (6)
15 Stratum (4)
16 Succeeded (3)
17 Large mop (4)
18 Dandy (3)
19 Two continuous curves (4)
20 Not (3)
22 Set of clothing (4)
24 The beginning (3-3)
25 Protestant of N. Ireland (9)
27 Sixth note in a musical scale (3)
28 Vast chasm (5)
29 Befitting a gentleman (11)

DOWN

2 Oozed (6)
3 Charged fragments (4)
4 Basic monetary unit of Sierra Leone (5)
5 Sudden termination (10)
7 Practice for performance (9)
8 Lever for rowing (3)
9 A blood vessel (4)
10 Extraordinary (9)
11 Priority in rank (10)
13 Cease (4)
16 Grievous distress (3)
18 Destiny (4)
20 Near (4)
21 East Indian fig tree (6)
23 Not fitting (5)
24 Small fish (3)
26 Disfigure (4)

ACROSS

1 Enchantment (8)
5 Converse (4)
8 Pig (3)
9 Underground graveyard (8)
11 To kill in a frenzy (4)
13 Infuriate (6)
15 Made empty (7)
16 Annul (6)
19 Unit of tone pitch (3)
21 Beetle (3)
22 Prejudiced (6)
25 A woman who serves drinks in a bar (7)
26 Pleasantly warm (6)
30 Otherwise (4)
31 Haughty (8)
32 Frozen dessert (3)
33 Plant in the mustard family (4)
34 Consisting of eight (8)

DOWN

2 Book of the Bible (6)
3 Pressed (6)
4 Deride (4)
5 Burn slightly (4)
6 A vassal (7)
7 Highly excited (4)
10 Sayings (6)
12 Boat spines (5)
14 Requirement (4)
17 Part of a saddle (6)
18 Diminish (5)
19 Wild cherry (7)
20 Remaining (4)
23 Nothing (6)
24 Whisky (6)
27 Potpourri (4)
28 Part of a plant (4)
29 Up-and-down toy (4)

86

ACROSS

1 Extending to the floor (5-6)
8 Urge forward (5)
10 Leers at (5)
12 Goad for driving cattle (3)
14 Flags (7)
16 Unit of nuclear energy (4)
18 Lake (Fr.) (3)
20 Snare (4)
21 Give advice to (4)
22 A young man (3)
24 Cover (3)
25 Extract of soybeans (4)
26 Church recess (4)
27 Unit of brightness (3)
28 Information (4)
29 Ruler of an empire (7)
33 Alkali (3)
35 Earlier (5)
36 Inhabitant of Iraq (5)
37 Farthest east (11)

DOWN

1 Beat with a whip (4)
2 Roman poet (4)
3 To abuse sexually (4)
4 Snake-like fish (4)
5 Alcoholic drink (4)
6 Breed of dairy cattle (8)
7 Suppose (6)
9 Weaken (8)
11 Knot (5)
13 Celtic paradise (6)
15 One that assumes a false identity (8)
17 Peculiarity (6)
19 Coffee stimulant (8)
23 Cathedral (5)
25 Scarf (6)
30 Experts (Inf.) (4)
31 Starchy food grain (4)
32 Shower (4)
33 Pool (4)
34 To prepare written material (4)

ACROSS

1 Cardinals collectively (11)
6 Part of the knee (7)
9 Roman goddess of plenty (3)
12 Inanimate (9)
14 Fickleness (6)
15 Coloured (4)
16 Blend (3)
17 Swift (4)
18 The least amount (3)
19 Jewish calendar month (4)
20 A type of dance (3)
22 Trick (4)
24 Volcano in Antarctica (6)
25 Double (9)
27 Average (3)
28 Get rid of insect pests (5)
29 Lying upon something else (11)

DOWN

2 Narrate (6)
3 Little devils (4)
4 Pass into disuse (5)
5 With skill (10)
7 Listen secretly (9)
8 No matter which (3)
9 Variety of chalcedony (4)
10 Bag hung from the side of a saddle (9)
11 Intrusive (10)
13 Revise typed matter (4)
16 Cleaning implement (3)
18 Wife of Heber the Kenite (4)
20 Male monarch or emperor (4)
21 Triple (6)
23 A decree or edict (5)
24 Supplement (3)
26 Notion (4)

88

ACROSS
2 Paralysis of a single limb (10)
7 American theatre award (4)
8 Pierce (6)
10 Until (prep.) (3)
11 Military chaplain (5)
13 Animal kingdom (pref.) (3)
15 Female rabbit (3)
16 Female child (4)
17 Automaton (5)
20 Area used for sports (5)
21 Aerogram (3-6)
22 Causing a mess (5)
24 Relaxed (5)
26 Send forth (4)
27 Give a nickname to (3)
29 Naught (3)
30 Pain or grief (5)
31 Mischievous person (3)
32 With iridium (6)
34 First man on earth (4)
35 Probability (10)

DOWN
1 Unsteady gait (6)
2 Encountered (3)
3 Wanderer (5)
4 Walk with a limp (4)
5 Cattle farmers (8)
6 Ring of colour (6)
8 A strong emotion (3)
9 Bereft (4)
12 Mournful (7)
14 Raise (5)
16 Big (5)
18 Legendary creature (8)
19 Attempt (3)
20 Had some food (3)
22 Servile (6)
23 Middle Eastern prince (4)
25 Slander (6)
27 What's Up ---? (3)
28 Extremely successful (slang) (5)
30 Clock face (4)
33 To move about restlessly (3)

1			2		3		4		5			6

ACROSS

1 Brooding hen (6)
4 Robbery at sea (6)
7 Unsettled (9)
10 Intend (4)
11 Idle or boastful talk (slang) (3)
12 Water holder (4)
13 Shades (4)
15 Give up (5)
18 Dither (5)
20 Dry, dryness (prefix) (4)
21 Positions (4)
22 8th letter of the Greek alphabet (5)
24 Support tower (5)
26 A difficult problem or question (4)
29 Father (4)
31 Social insect (3)
32 Poker stake (4)
33 Cut short (9)
34 Mistreats (6)
35 More warm-hearted (6)

DOWN

1 Ragtime dance (6)
2 A three-masted schooner (4)
3 Coarse (5)
4 Sphygmus (5)
5 A lecherous man (4)
6 Once each year (6)
7 Paying no taxes (3-6)
8 Children's book author (4)
9 A landlocked monarchy in SE Africa (9)
14 Come to a halt (4)
16 Permit (3)
17 Sketch (4)
19 Very cold (3)
22 Capital of Kansas (6)
23 Synchronize (abbrev.) (4)
25 One who needs (6)
27 Clock pointers (5)
28 Pile (5)
30 Weapons (4)
32 A great age (4)

90

ACROSS

1 Municipal body (4-7)
6 Person who visits (7)
9 Small seed (3)
12 A device for reading data from punched cards (9)
14 Loud shrill cry (6)
15 Sodium carbonate (4)
16 Acquire (3)
17 Sexual drive, libido (4)
18 Deranged (3)
19 Complacent (4)
20 Slippery as an --- (3)
22 Confront (4)
24 Distended (6)
25 The moment of landing (9)
27 Toilet (slang) (3)
28 Navajo dwelling (5)
29 Jukebox (11)

DOWN

2 Unsteady gait (6)
3 Restraint (4)
4 River nymph (5)
5 Disembowel (10)
7 Sad (9)
8 Tree of the genus Quercus (3)
9 Scheme (4)
10 Grouse (9)
11 Final destructive battle (10)
13 Secondhand (4)
16 Girl or woman (3)
18 Reward (4)
20 Resonant sound (4)
21 Elasticized cord (6)
23 In a cocked position (5)
24 Twain (3)
26 US state (4)

ACROSS

1 Commit to memory (8)
5 Robust or high-spirited young man (4)
8 A major division of geological time (3)
9 Hindu religious mendicant (8)
11 Relaxation (4)
13 Preserved (as in fruit) (6)
15 Commander of a fleet (7)
16 To become a pupa (6)
19 A long, narrow fish (3)
21 Adult male (3)
22 Crown (6)
25 Not asked (7)
26 Elevated land (6)
30 A skirt or coat of mid-calf length (4)
31 Prickly (8)
32 A marine fish (3)
33 A mound of sand deposited during the melting of glacial ice (4)
34 Inherent (8)

DOWN

2 Antelopes (6)
3 A Hebrew prophet of the eighth century B.C. (6)
4 Heroic (4)
5 Part of the verb to be (4)
6 Pertaining to the planet Uranus (7)
7 Portfolio (4)
10 Fastened with nails (6)
12 Having an edge (5)
14 Any of various double sulphates (4)
17 Rector (6)
18 Music hall (5)
19 Territory of an earl (7)
20 Incline (4)
23 Hymn (6)
24 Film comedian and director (6)
27 An unusual craving (4)
28 Helper (4)
29 Half (prefix) (4)

92

ACROSS
1 An arm of the Mediterranean (8-3)
8 Sound (5)
10 Caused by a virus (5)
12 Black bird (3)
14 Purposeless (7)
16 Demonstrative pronoun (4)
18 Belonging to us (3)
20 Duumbstruck (4)
21 Falsehoods (4)
22 Leave in water (3)
24 Sin (3)
25 Apiece (4)
26 Rhythmic swing (4)
27 Listening organ (3)
28 On the sheltered side (4)
29 In proportion (7)
33 Chop (3)
35 Coming after (5)
36 Obscure road (5)
37 State in the NE United States (5-6)

DOWN
1 Extent of space (4)
2 Wife or a rajah (4)
3 Capital of W. Samoa (4)
4 Separate article (4)
5 Rescue (4)
6 Scottish county (8)
7 Apportions (6)
9 Extraordinary (8)
11 Pineapple fibre (5)
13 Pertaining to a nerve (6)
15 Lawfulness (8)
17 Charge with gas (6)
19 Sensory nerve (8)
23 At that place (5)
25 Young eagle (6)
30 Ricelike grains of pasta (4)
31 Showing unusual talent (4)
32 Inspires dread (4)
33 Tree frog (4)
34 Elevated tract of open country (4)

		1		2		3			4			
5												
6		7			8			9		10		11
				12			13					
14							15					
						16						
17					18				19			
				20				21				
		22	23				24					
25						26						
		27				28						
29												

ACROSS

1 System of methods (11)
6 More than two (7)
9 Public house (3)
12 Processes for choosing a government (9)
14 Open (6)
15 Pre-Easter season (4)
16 Male cat (3)
17 Free from contamination (4)
18 Vulgar, ill-bred fellow (3)
19 One sixth of a drachma (4)
20 Wet spongy ground (3)
22 An elementary particle with a negative charge (4)
24 Theatrical dance (6)
25 Member of a secret society founded in N. Ireland (9)
27 Denial (3)
28 Republic in S. Asia (5)
29 July 14th in France (8-3)

DOWN

2 Rebuke (6)
3 Look at amorously (4)
4 Russian revolutionary leader (5)
5 Supposition (10)
7 Member of a church vestry (9)
8 Entirely (3)
9 Separate article (4)
10 Events worthy of note (9)
11 The act of scorching (10)
13 Lump of earth (4)
16 Insignia (3)
18 Fruit of the pine (4)
20 A hobgoblin (4)
21 Marked with bands (6)
23 Not appropriate (5)
24 Prohibit (3)
26 Factory (4)

94

ACROSS

2 Glow with heat (10)
7 Feathered creature (4)
8 US actress, Marilyn ------ (6)
10 Apex (3)
11 Shield (5)
13 Curve (3)
15 Daub (3)
16 Aid and ---- (4)
17 End of life (5)
20 Copper and zinc alloy (5)
21 Eulogist (9)
22 Soft (5)
24 Scores (5)
26 Run ---- (4)
27 Assistance (3)
29 Rent out (3)
30 Happen (5)
31 In place of (3)
32 Complete (6)
34 On top of (4)
35 Study of the mechanics of fluids (10)

DOWN

1 Diminished (6)
2 An artificial language (3)
3 Member of the dog family (5)
4 Entrance (4)
5 Seaport on NE Java (8)
6 Chooses (6)
8 Crowd (3)
9 Minerals (4)
12 Diabolical (7)
14 Pile (5)
16 Shaft shot from a bow (5)
18 Apportioned (8)
19 Tint (3)
20 Badly drained land (3)
22 4th letter of the Hebrew alphabet (6)
23 A sign (4)
25 Grief (6)
27 Top class flyer (3)
28 One of the UAE (5)
30 Whale (4)
33 Distress signal (3)

1			2		3		4		5			6

ACROSS
1 Towards the wind (6)
4 Elementary particle (6)
7 Merle (Fr.) (9)
10 Ill-favoured (4)
11 Button on a typewriter (3)
12 A nipple (4)
13 Healing wound (4)
15 Hoax (5)
18 Round edible bulb (5)
20 Malay dagger with a wavy blade (4)
21 Plot of ground (4)
22 Snake (5)
24 Earth (5)
26 Limbs (4)
29 Revolve (4)
31 Gamble (3)
32 Remote (4)
33 S. African diamond mine (9)
34 Leased (6)
35 Breed of dog (6)

DOWN
1 Abrupt increase (6)
2 Within (4)
3 Wharves (5)
4 Republic in N. Africa (5)
5 Fortified wine (4)
6 To make tidy (6)
7 Indication of failure (5-4)
8 Show disgust or strong dislike (4)
9 To make brittle (9)
14 To pass through a sieve (4)
16 An urban area (3)
17 Rock rich in silicon and aluminium (4)
19 Not (3)
22 Shooting star (6)
23 S-shaped curve (4)
25 Scrape off (6)
27 Grew less (5)
28 Leash (5)
30 Catalogue (4)
32 Air (prefix) (4)

96

ACROSS

1 Fastens a knot (4)
3 Wonderful (8)
6 Pertinent (7)
9 Less common (5)
12 Look at amorously (4)
14 Biblical high priest (3)
15 A spelling bee (9)
17 European (prefix) (4)
18 Doctrine (3)
19 Courtyard (5)
21 Narrow beam of light (3)
22 Mimics (4)
23 Tapered eating stick (9)
27 Bird related to the cuckoo (3)
29 Class (4)
30 Source of cocoa (5)
31 Breastbone (7)
33 Member of a lobby (8)
34 Damn (4)

DOWN

1 Spanish river (5)
2 Total (3)
3 Church council (5)
4 Energetic (9)
5 Christmas (4)
7 Person suffering from rheumatism (9)
8 Self-esteem (3)
10 Act of retorting (9)
11 Rising in ridges (5)
13 Monetary unit of Angola (4)
16 Surgical removal of fatty tissue (9)
18 Pertaining to the ileum (5)
20 Wan (4)
24 Roman goddess of plenty (3)
25 Small (Fr.) (5)
26 Tidily kept (5)
28 Western pact (4)
32 Do away with (3)

ACROSS

1 Harmony of sounds (8)
5 Hew (4)
8 To move forward by rowing (3)
9 The process of intertwining wool (8)
11 Obstacle (4)
13 Breathe in (6)
15 Pours off leaving sediment (7)
16 Flat-bottomed rowboat (Fr.) (6)
19 Spout (3)
21 Average (3)
22 Virgin (6)
25 Ominous (7)
26 Sitting (6)
30 Large mop (4)
31 Legal status of an alien (8)
32 Australian bird (3)
33 Formerly (4)
34 Ensnarl (8)

DOWN

2 Over there (6)
3 Narcotic (6)
4 Person who practices yoga (4)
5 A weighted weapon (4)
6 Wicker receptacle for documents (7)
7 Spoken (4)
10 Joined (6)
12 Class (5)
14 Tides that attain the least height (4)
17 Dutch navigator (6)
18 Gather (5)
19 Jitters (7)
20 Web-footed aquatic bird (4)
23 Hungarian monetary unit (6)
24 Fungous (6)
27 Beaker (4)
28 Adjoin (4)
29 Story (4)

98

ACROSS

1 Process of reclaiming (11)
8 Mock (5)
10 Sum (5)
12 Picas (3)
14 Large New Zealand reptile (7)
16 Showing unusual talent (4)
18 Donkey (3)
20 Social gathering for men (4)
21 Small dabbling duck (4)
22 And so on (abbrev.) (3)
24 Conclusion (3)
25 A water-soluble compound (4)
26 Hind part (4)
27 Old Saxon letter (3)
28 Russian for 'no' (4)
29 A country person (7)
33 Epoch (3)
35 Severe (5)
36 European country (5)
37 Displace (11)

DOWN

1 Agricultural implement (4)
2 Felines (4)
3 Border on (4)
4 Rectangular pier (4)
5 Very small quantity (4)
6 Note well (8)
7 Hebrew liturgical prayer (6)
9 Nourishes (8)
11 Deliver an oration (5)
13 Wretchedness (6)
15 Covering (8)
17 Climbing device (6)
19 Most precipitous (8)
23 Cook food (5)
25 Complete agreement (6)
30 Girl's name (4)
31 Helps (4)
32 Edible tuber (4)
33 Tropical American wildcat (4)
34 An axlike tool (4)

99

ACROSS
1 Bulky equipment (11)
6 Sentence containing all the letters of the alphabet (7)
9 Exclamation of contempt (3)
12 Obligation (9)
14 Respect (6)
15 Overdue (4)
16 Owns (3)
17 Undoing (4)
18 Musical note G (3)
19 Challenge (4)
20 Weep (3)
22 Catch sight of (4)
24 Football (6)
25 Hidden (9)
27 Add up (3)
28 Oneness (5)
29 Municipal body (4-7)

DOWN
2 Conference (6)
3 Russian parliament before 1917 (4)
4 Elevate (5)
5 Outward show (10)
7 Nourishment (9)
8 Direct a gun (3)
9 Leaning towards (4)
10 Series of ranks (9)
11 Make symmetrical (10)
13 Meaningless chatter (4)
16 Fireplace shelf (3)
18 Herb cultivated for food (4)
20 Raced (4)
21 12 constellations (6)
23 Covered with scales (5)
24 Indonesian money (3)
26 Hawaiian party (4)

100

ACROSS

2 Uproarious (10)
7 Motion picture (4)
8 Middle (6)
10 Nae (3)
11 Effort (5)
13 A jackdaw (3)
15 Consumed food (3)
16 Great ----, very large dog (4)
17 Celestial body (5)
20 Stinking (5)
21 Instrument for measuring rainfall (9)
22 Brittle (5)
24 The base of a number system (5)
26 Veinlike deposit (4)
27 13th letter of the Hebrew alphabet (3)
29 Room with a harem (3)
30 Made a hole (5)
31 Videlicet (abbrev.) (3)
32 Vessel for burning incense (6)
34 Automobile (abbrev.) (4)
35 Flexibility (10)

DOWN

1 Picturesque (6)
2 Hot brewed drink (3)
3 Secret organization (5)
4 Golf pegs (4)
5 Outmoded (8)
6 Boiled slowly (6)
8 Stimulus (3)
9 Wife of a rajah (4)
12 Totter (7)
14 Discontinue (5)
16 To clear of gas (5)
18 Ancient Indian drum (8)
19 Apex (3)
20 Soft animal hair (3)
22 Woman's close-fitting hat (6)
23 Travelled on (4)
25 City in Jiangsu province, China (6)
27 Moroccan (abbrev.) (3)
28 French for 'thanks' (5)
30 Strike forcibly (4)
33 Month (3)

ACROSS

1 Invertebrate creature (6)
4 Plant with colourful leaves (6)
7 Finishing touch (9)
10 Aloft (4)
11 Stretch (3)
12 Christian holiday celebrating the birth of Christ (4)
13 Scarf (4)
15 Vacant (5)
18 Paddled (5)
20 Mortgate (4)
21 Predatory black-and-white whale (4)
22 Steering device on a car (5)
24 Narrow joining pieces (5)
26 Drinks like an animal (4)
29 Requirement (4)
31 Open mesh fabric (3)
32 Cricket ground in London (4)
33 Represent pictorially (9)
34 Proscribe (6)
35 Judicial ruling (6)

DOWN

1 Instill (6)
2 Ebony (4)
3 Forest (5)
4 Quotes (5)
5 Sharp-sighted animal (4)
6 Drunk (6)
7 Done (9)
8 A cape on the northern extremity of Jutland (4)
9 Inclusive (9)
14 Wind instrument (4)
16 Bind (3)
17 Shout (4)
19 A perfect serve (3)
22 Manipulate (6)
23 Not closed (4)
25 Rarely (6)
27 Negatively charged ion (5)
28 Lieu (5)
30 Brief tape or recording of a musician (inf.) (4)
32 Near the ear (4)

102

ACROSS
1 Type of bread (4)
3 Midline sagittal cut (8)
6 Bring to a successful end (7)
9 Short and fat (5)
12 Otherwise (4)
14 Affirmative vote (3)
15 Occurring every ten years (9)
17 Bone of the forearm (4)
18 Two (Scots) (3)
19 Garlic-flavoured mayonnaise (5)
21 Male offspring (3)
22 Smeared with swampy mud (4)
23 Spanish dance (9)
27 Title of a knight (3)
29 Spoken (4)
30 Large sea (5)
31 Tank (7)
33 Resolution into simple elements (8)
34 A thickening base for sauces (4)

DOWN
1 Tartan (5)
2 Muhammad ---, US fighter (3)
3 Refuge (5)
4 Moving (9)
5 Cautious (4)
7 Looped bridle (9)
8 Biblical high priest (3)
10 Inhabitant of Damascus (9)
11 Long (5)
13 First king of Israel (4)
16 Asset easily made liquid (4-5)
18 Trunk of the human body (5)
20 8th month of the Jewish calendar (4)
24 Milky-looking liquid (3)
25 Alternative name (5)
26 Addition (5)
28 Image (4)
32 A black sticky substance (3)

ACROSS

1 Airdrop (8)
5 A small town (4)
8 Antecedent to (3)
9 One who takes over a plane (8)
11 Foliage unit (4)
13 Riddle (6)
15 Move in a gyrating fashion (7)
16 Plummet (6)
19 Writing fluid (3)
21 Latin for 'I' (3)
22 Meditate (6)
25 Explorer (7)
26 Look askance (6)
30 Legs of pork (4)
31 Practice (8)
32 A metric unit of volume (3)
33 A prong on a fork (4)
34 Convict (8)

DOWN

2 Bird enclosure (6)
3 Dissolute (6)
4 Ponder intently (4)
5 Delicatessen (4)
6 Aromatic herb (7)
7 Quantity of paper (4)
10 Go up (6)
12 Phase (5)
14 River in Egypt (4)
17 African country (6)
18 Resembling an ape (5)
19 Brutal (7)
20 Sharp (4)
23 Alternatives (6)
24 Minor (6)
27 Muslim judge (4)
28 Island (4)
29 A card or domino with three pips (4)

104

ACROSS

1 Person who writes pamplets (11)
8 One who wields an axe (5)
10 Tortilla topped with cheese (5)
12 Even (poet.) (3)
14 Examine closely (7)
16 Precious stones (4)
18 Evergreen tree (3)
20 Capital of Norway (4)
21 Smallest component (4)
22 Breach (3)
24 Extras (3)
25 Islamic chieftain (4)
26 Metallic element (4)
27 Wrest (3)
28 Hindu princess (4)
29 Clique (7)
33 Miles per hour (3)
35 Tally (5)
36 Capital of Ghana (5)
37 Telephone operator (11)

DOWN

1 Brownish purple (4)
2 Average (4)
3 Household (4)
4 Type of eagle (4)
5 Sicilian volcano (4)
6 Swiss dish (8)
7 Policies of Mao Zedong (6)
9 County in Scotland (8)
11 Pond scum (5)
13 Riddle (6)
15 Related by blood (8)
17 Test model (6)
19 Waterproof coat (8)
23 Earlier (5)
25 Rubbed out (6)
30 Small dabbling duck (4)
31 Incline (4)
32 Rebound (4)
33 Island in central Hawaii (4)
34 Heave (4)

ACROSS
1 Without emotion (11)
6 Floating leaf (7)
9 Unit of force equal to the force exerted by gravity (3)
12 Making use of only one hand (3-6)
14 Busty (6)
15 Crypt (4)
16 First woman (3)
17 Naive person (4)
18 Enemy (3)
19 Stately aquatic bird (4)
20 Metallic element (3)
22 Heritable land of the Teutonic people (4)
24 Military organizations (6)
25 Inflexible (9)
27 Long dashes in printed matter (3)
28 Requires (5)
29 A contracted state of the neck muscles, or wryneck (11)

DOWN
2 Benign tumour (6)
3 'The Venerable ----' Anglo-Saxon theologian (4)
4 Unfolds (5)
5 Transitory (10)
7 Weariness (9)
8 Either (3)
9 Open-mouthed stare (4)
10 Alpine plant (9)
11 Direct (10)
13 Possess (4)
16 Generation (3)
18 Type of pastry (4)
20 Labels (4)
21 Severe experience (6)
23 Relinquish (5)
24 One (Scot.) (3)
26 To reverse or erase (4)

106

ACROSS

2 Longitudinally (10)
7 Melody (4)
8 Algae (6)
10 Not in (3)
11 Stormed (5)
13 Adam's partner (3)
15 Young boy (3)
16 Get ready (4)
17 Semblance (5)
20 Wide awake (5)
21 Inflammation of the sclera (9)
22 Salivate (5)
24 Go into (5)
26 A strip of leather (4)
27 Become firm (3)
29 7th letter of the Greek alphabet (3)
30 Sorrow (5)
31 Medical practitioner (inf.) (3)
32 French painter (6)
34 Above or higher (4)
35 Shrub with edible blue-black berries (10)

DOWN

1 A loose, wrapped skirt (6)
2 Laboratory (abbrev.) (3)
3 Relating to the nose (5)
4 Head covering (4)
5 Concern (8)
6 Unless (6)
8 New English Dictionary (abbrev.) (3)
9 Above (4)
12 One of the archangels (7)
14 Annual horse meeting in England (5)
16 Shoot randomly (5)
18 Capable of being isolated (8)
19 Former measure of length (3)
20 Devoured (3)
22 Resides (6)
23 Network of nerves (4)
25 Catalogue (6)
27 Male child (3)
28 Hard drinker (5)
30 Throw down in a mass (4)
33 Plaything (3)

ACROSS

1 Outer edge (6)
4 Decrees (6)
7 Impossible to read (9)
10 Sea bird (4)
11 Encountered (3)
12 Executive (abbrev.) (4)
13 Mite (anag.) (4)
15 Fibber (5)
18 Misuse (5)
20 A war fought from 1899–1902 (4)
21 Snarl or growl (4)
22 Area used for sports (5)
24 Fenced areas (5)
26 Staffs (4)
29 Iridescent gemstone (4)
31 An item in an auction (3)
32 Hitch (4)
33 Position of notoriety (9)
34 Soft-nosed bullet (6)
35 To breathe out (6)

DOWN

1 Meagre (6)
2 Without value (4)
3 Fragrant resin (5)
4 Best of a group (5)
5 Doing nothing (4)
6 Coin (6)
7 Bigoted (9)
8 Obtains (4)
9 Running out (9)
14 Large indefinite number (4)
16 Not (prefix) (3)
17 Toothed machine part (4)
19 Bleating sound (3)
22 Professed (6)
23 Object of worship (4)
25 Person who signs (6)
27 Fuming sulphuric acid (5)
28 Crossing over a fence (5)
30 Told an untruth (4)
32 Retail store (4)

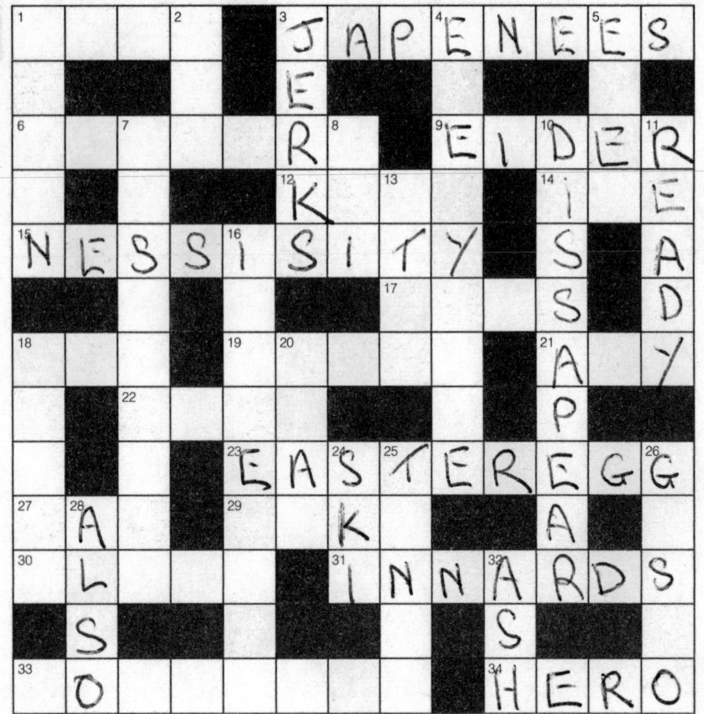

ACROSS
1 Willingly (4)
3 Inhabitant of Japan (8)
6 From within (2-5)
9 Large sea duck with soft plumage (5)
12 Gnarl (4)
14 A strong emotion (3)
15 Something necessary (9)
17 Every (Scot.) (4)
18 Dip in liquid (3)
19 Manila hemp plant (5)
21 Wield (3)
22 Wheel shaft (4)
23 Easter gift (6-3)
27 A creamy E. Indian stew (3)
29 Third Gospel (4)
30 Resin used in making varnishes and inks (5)
31 Entrails (7)
33 Beautiful (8)
34 A person noted for feats of courage (4)

DOWN
1 Get to know (5)
2 Fish appendage (3)
3 Tugs (5)
4 Bring an acetyl group into an organic molecule (9)
5 A clairvoyant (4)
7 Incompetent (9)
8 A black bird (3)
10 Vanish (9)
11 Prepared (5)
13 Located near the ear (4)
16 Squamous (9)
18 Slip (5)
20 Sweetheart (4)
24 Snow runner (3)
25 Is inclined (5)
26 Contraption (5)
28 Too (4)
32 Cinders (3)

ACROSS
1 Scission (8)
5 Great quantity (4)
8 Remuneration (3)
9 Flaming torch (8)
11 Large wading bird (4)
13 Floating (6)
15 Bind with chains (7)
16 Raise up (6)
19 Petroleum derivative (3)
21 Be seated (3)
22 Reflecting surface (6)
25 Bantu language (7)
26 Niggardly (6)
30 Detest (4)
31 South Pole explorer (8)
32 Prohibit (3)
33 Islet (4)
34 Located (8)

DOWN
2 The interior of a region (6)
3 Conciliatory (6)
4 Part of speech (4)
5 Expectorate (4)
6 Nightclub (7)
7 16th letter of the Hebrew alphabet (4)
10 Hair of an angora goat (6)
12 Grim (5)
14 Mountains (4)
17 Rugose (6)
18 Shatter (5)
19 Pertaining to an orbit (7)
20 Yearn (4)
23 French dance (6)
24 Assert (6)
27 Labels (4)
28 Hawaiian goose (4)
29 Tibetan oxen (4)

110

ACROSS

1 Fear of crowds (11)
8 Spores (5)
10 House made of ice (5)
12 Haunch (3)
14 Obedient (7)
16 Small blemish (4)
18 First note of a music scale (3)
20 Storklike bird (4)
21 Very small (4)
22 French for 'no' (3)
24 Wood sorrel (3)
25 S. American long-tailed monkey (4)
26 Rope fibre (4)
27 Encourage (3)
28 Genuine (4)
29 A hole dug to extract petroleum (3-4)
33 Acrimony (3)
35 Unrefined (5)
36 Sea mammals (5)
37 Impossible to exhaust (11)

DOWN

1 Ornamental brooch (4)
2 Clasp for a door (4)
3 Was indebted to (4)
4 A command (archaic) (4)
5 Vigour (4)
6 Aromatic West Indian tree that produces berries (8)
7 Condescending (6)
9 Gestures without speech (8)
11 Zest (5)
13 Prone to irony (6)
15 Costume (8)
17 Military catapult (6)
19 Greenhouse (8)
23 Lustrous (5)
25 Irritable (6)
30 Girl's name (4)
31 I saw ---- sitting on a seesaw (4)
32 Ultimate (4)
33 Islet (4)
34 Nestling (4)

111

ACROSS

1 Comradeship (11)
6 Napped (7)
9 Fluid formed in infected tissue (3)
12 Biological description of animals (9)
14 Raved (6)
15 Small rivulet (4)
16 Dance (3)
17 Back of neck (4)
18 Head covering (3)
19 Serum (pl.) (4)
20 Crowd (3)
22 Leader of a mosque (4)
24 Tricky (6)
25 Endurable (9)
27 Partake of food (3)
28 Statutory (5)
29 Means of supporting life (11)

DOWN

2 A mast (6)
3 Repeat (4)
4 The same as (5)
5 Spacecraft navigators (10)
7 Connoisseur of wine (9)
8 End of day (abbrev.) (3)
9 A conceited dandy (4)
10 Ill-humoured (9)
11 Study of the mechanics of fluids (10)
13 Clench (4)
16 Punch (3)
18 Prolonged unconsciousness (4)
20 Trading centre (4)
21 American state (6)
23 Repasts (5)
24 Beer (3)
26 Ink spot (4)

112

ACROSS
2 Existing at the time of birth (10)
7 An open vessel with handle and spout (4)
8 Fabric (6)
10 Playing card (3)
11 Person who explores caves (5)
13 Filled pastry crust (3)
15 Spanish noble (3)
16 Ponder (4)
17 Pertaining to a node (5)
20 Light brown in colour (5)
21 Statute (9)
22 Conceited (5)
24 Ages (5)
26 Comply (4)
27 To free (3)
29 Fur scarf (3)
30 Type of sheep (5)
31 Japanese scarf (3)
32 Vest (6)
34 Between (4)
35 Type of parakeet (10)

DOWN
1 Keep possession of (6)
2 Weep (3)
3 River nymph (5)
4 Close (4)
5 Quilting (8)
6 Believable (6)
8 Lair (3)
9 Immature herring (4)
12 Galvanic (7)
14 Handkerchief (5)
16 The spirit of a dead person (5)
18 Dead (8)
19 Put down (3)
20 Ocean (3)
22 Spider web (6)
23 Musical instrument (4)
25 Tending to skid (6)
27 Long-tailed rodent (3)
28 Performance (5)
30 To shift sail from side to another (4)
33 Ingot (3)

ACROSS
1 Sweeping implements (6)
4 Run aground (6)
7 Fearless (9)
10 Hold as an opinion (4)
11 Brown-capped mushroom (3)
12 Sewing box (4)
13 Joint between thigh and lower leg (4)
15 Portals (5)
18 Moving in a circular motion (5)
20 Ruin (4)
21 Highly excited (4)
22 Horn-shaped bone (5)
24 Food eaten between meals (5)
26 ---- Rhodes, British chef (4)
29 Deprived of sensation (4)
31 Snake (3)
32 Alcoholic drink of fermented honey (4)
33 Armchair (4-5)
34 Beat (6)
35 Excessively (6)

DOWN
1 Planted in soil (6)
2 Egg cell (4)
3 Pile (5)
4 Long-billed sandpiper (5)
5 A debauchee (4)
6 Hebrew prophet (6)
7 Airport (9)
8 Coin (4)
9 Daydreamer (9)
14 Edible ova of the hen (4)
16 Hurried (3)
17 Complacent (4)
19 Yonder (3)
22 Easy gallop (6)
23 Crocodile (abbrev.) (4)
25 One of a pair of organs (6)
27 An abyss (5)
28 Lout (5)
30 Strong woody fibre (4)
32 Microphone (4)

114

ACROSS

1 People in general (4)
3 Intersection (8)
6 Pictorial images (7)
9 Dinners (5)
12 Seaweed (4)
14 A device for catching fish (3)
15 Sends away (9)
17 A knife used as a weapon (4)
18 Sum charged (3)
19 Raccoon-like carnivore (5)
21 Exploit (3)
22 Peruse (4)
23 Wetting agent (9)
27 Perennial plant of the Andes (3)
29 Member of a Semitic people (4)
30 Demobilization (5)
31 Augmented (7)
33 Science of rocket design (8)
34 Group of birds (4)

DOWN

1 Cooked in hot oil (5)
2 Small cask (3)
3 Tugs (5)
4 Short-sleeved shirt (9)
5 Gawp (4)
7 Dutch town (9)
8 Affirmative reply (3)
10 Substance that suppresses ovulation (9)
11 Phase (5)
13 For fear that (4)
16 Incompetent (9)
18 Deluge (5)
20 River (4)
24 Arrest (3)
25 Type of dark wood (5)
26 This present day (5)
28 Large edible mackerel (4)
32 Beneath (prefix) (3)

115

ACROSS

1 Gathered needlework (8)
5 Headland (4)
8 Stout (3)
9 Ceremonial suicide (4-4)
11 Old monetary unit of Italy (4)
13 10th month of the Jewish calendar (6)
15 Entangle (7)
16 Large seabird (6)
19 Facing the stern (3)
21 Nevertheless (3)
22 Untied (anag.) (3)
25 Conveyance on a buoyant medium (i.e. air or water) (7)
26 Come into being (6)
30 Unit of linear measure (4)
31 Cat of unknown parentage (8)
32 Perceive with the eyes (3)
33 Street of stabling (4)
34 Dig frantically with the hands (8)

DOWN

2 A noxious atmosphere (6)
3 Relating to the iris of the eye (6)
4 Pluck (4)
5 Still (4)
6 Nutriment (7)
7 S. American country (4)
10 Drifting (6)
12 Alchemist's mercury (5)
14 Apart (4)
17 Tidily (6)
18 Short and fat (5)
19 Crew of an aircraft (7)
20 Abound (4)
23 Person in charge of a prison (6)
24 A painful swelling around a toe or fingernail (6)
27 Relaxation (4)
28 A dose of poems (anag.) (4)
29 Stems of wheat (4)

116

ACROSS
1 Data (11)
8 Tidal bore (5)
10 Pueblo indian village (5)
12 Not high (3)
14 A delivery by parachute (7)
16 Norse god of thunder (4)
18 Attach by stitches (3)
20 The objective case of they (4)
21 Class (4)
22 17th letter of the Greek alphabet (3)
24 Took nourishment (3)
25 To fly (4)
26 Belonging to oneself (4)
27 Conclude (3)
28 A single time (4)
29 Liturgical prayer (7)
33 Temper (3)
35 Reproach (5)
36 Relating to Asia (5)
37 Informal gathering (11)

DOWN
1 A false god (4)
2 Soared (4)
3 Wrinkle (4)
4 Affirm with confidence (4)
5 8th month of the Jewish calendar (4)
6 Novice (8)
7 Scanty (6)
9 Capital of Virginia (8)
11 Short surplice (5)
13 King of the fairies (6)
15 Humidity (8)
17 The first event in a series (6)
19 Very large (8)
23 Mountain nymph (5)
25 A ball game (6)
30 Something that is owed (4)
31 Shakespearian villain (4)
32 Shelter for honeybees (4)
33 Unit of length (4)
34 Islamic leader (4)

ACROSS

1 In a warlike manner (11)
6 Umbrella used as a sunshade (7)
9 Chopping tool (3)
12 Involved with theology (9)
14 Make amends (6)
15 Tolled (4)
16 Vessel or duct (3)
17 Make healthy (4)
18 The sun (3)
19 Discharge of a firearm (4)
20 Rank (3)
22 Frozen treats (4)
24 Self-conscious smile (6)
25 Lateral curvature of the spine (9)
27 River in Western Thailand (3)
28 Group of eight (5)
29 Blueberry (11)

DOWN

2 Person included in a list (6)
3 Doing nothing (4)
4 Native of saxony (5)
5 Theatre devoted to operas (5-5)
7 Emission of energy in the form of rays (9)
8 Unit of electrical resistance (3)
9 Exclamation of sorrow (4)
10 Oval (3-7)
11 Sculpture pedestal (10)
13 Articulate (4)
16 Pledge (3)
18 Indifferent (4)
20 Restraint (4)
21 Female sibling (6)
23 A sound (5)
24 Thus (3)
26 Old World tree of the genus Sorbus (4)

118

ACROSS

2 Completely (10)
7 Vegetable (4)
8 Milk and egg drink (6)
10 Tree of the genus Quercus (3)
11 Lake in Sierra Nevada (5)
13 Goad (3)
15 Besides (3)
16 A pile of combustibles (4)
17 Stuffed savoury vine leaf (5)
20 Waterproof hip boot (5)
21 Heart-shaped (9)
22 Witches gathering (5)
24 More recent (5)
26 Kill (4)
27 Small round pod vegetable (3)
29 Portable bed (3)
30 Accessible (5)
31 A health resort (3)
32 Dwells (6)
34 Wicked (4)
35 Liable to punishment (10)

DOWN

1 Out of one's own country (6)
2 Besides (3)
3 This present day (5)
4 Rim (4)
5 Type of melon (8)
6 Long pointed sable brush (6)
8 A marker used on magnetic tapes (3)
9 A barbarous person (4)
12 Cheer (7)
14 Surround (5)
16 Communion plate (5)
18 A lobe (8)
19 Statute (3)
20 Pallid (3)
22 Steep bank under a rampart (6)
23 Slovenly person (4)
25 Actually (6)
27 Step in ballet (3)
28 Freely (2-3)
30 Possessive pronoun (4)
33 Sum charged (3)

1			2		3 E	■	4		5			6
	■	■		■	A	■		■		■	■	
	■	7 C	R	O	S	8 S	B	E	A	9 M	■	
10				■	11 E			■	12			
	■		■	■	13 D	U	S	14 K	■		■	
15			16	17 Y	■		■	18	19 T			
■	■	20		A		■	21		U		■	■
22				R	■	23	■	24	G			25
	■		■	26 D	27		28	■	■		■	
29			30	■	31			■	32			
	■	33									■	
	■	■		■		■		■		■	■	
34						■	35					

ACROSS
1 Ice cream topped with syrup (6)
4 Vigorous (6)
7 Joist (9) ✓
10 Endure (4)
11 Flightless bird (3)
12 Infectious tropical disease (4)
13 Partial darkness (4) ✓
15 Eccentric (5)
18 Distinct parts (5)
20 Apart (4)
21 12th month of the Jewish calendar (4)
22 Monk (5)
24 Belief involving sorcery (5)
26 Feathers (4)
29 Golf stroke (4)
31 Not (Scot.) (3)
32 Glitch (4)
33 Small cake of compressed moist yeast (9)
34 Need for liquid (6)
35 Sullage (6)

DOWN
1 Parody (6)
2 Dreadful (poetic) (4)
3 Relaxed (5) ✓
4 A puzzle (5)
5 Donkey cry (4)
6 Expects confidently (6)
7 An assured fact (9)
8 Complacent (4)
9 Small shell-shaped cake (9)
14 Thousand (4)
16 More than one (3)
17 Three feet (4) ✓
19 Clumsy boat (3) ✓
22 Roman Catholic (6)
23 Hit sharply (4)
25 To bargain (6)
27 Beginning (5)
28 Narrow joining pieces (5)
30 Rip (4)
32 Slanting (4)

120

ACROSS
1 Cleaving tool with a heavy blade (4)
3 Friendly (8)
6 4th book of the Old Testament (7)
9 Pertaining to birth (5)
12 Economizes (4)
14 A Turkish unit of weight (3)
15 Esoteric (9)
17 Unbutton (4)
18 Fuss (3)
19 Hire cars (5)
21 Jelly (3)
22 Converse (4)
23 Warrant officer on a warship (9)
27 Abstract being (3)
29 Gnomes (4)
30 Humped rumiinant (5)
31 Hearing distance (7)
33 Inspiration (8)
34 Requirement (4)

DOWN
1 More delicate (5)
2 Spun by spiders (3)
3 Landed (5)
4 Harmony (9)
5 Unwanted discharge of fluid (4)
7 Miniature model of something (9)
8 To glide on snow (3)
10 Radiographic apparatus (9)
11 Trademark (5)
13 Ornamental needlecase (4)
16 Events worthy of note (9)
18 Member of the Nahuatl people of Mexico (5)
20 Smallest unit of matter (4)
24 Caricature (3)
25 Ruling by the stars (anag.) (5)
26 Lustrous (5)
28 Greenhorn (4)
32 Transgression (3)

121

ACROSS

1 Somewhat green (8)
5 Goad (4)
8 Fall behind (3)
9 Something that obstructs (8)
11 Organs of sight (4)
13 To rent to another (6)
15 Fixed in position (7)
16 Pertaining to a cause (6)
19 Pigpen (3)
21 To be in possession of (3)
22 Capital of Alaska (6)
25 Not confined in a cage (7)
26 Alter (6)
30 Grasp (4)
31 Understands (8)
32 Mountain-dwelling parrot (3)
33 German for 'Mr.' (4)
34 Imperil (8)

DOWN

2 Allow as a discount (6)
3 Rude (6)
4 Colours (4)
5 Plebeian (4)
6 Unlit (7)
7 S-shaped curve (4)
10 Tubular (6)
12 Shoulder scarf of fur (5)
14 US State (4)
17 Naked-faced Amazon monkey (6)
18 Expel (5)
19 Athletic shoe (7)
20 Active male cosmic principle in Chinese philosophy (4)
23 Forward (6)
24 Erase (6)
27 Food fish (4)
28 Close (4)
29 One of the Great Lakes (4)

122

ACROSS

1 Praiseworthy (11)
8 Cuban ballroom dance (5)
10 Ran swiftly (5)
12 A beverage made by steeping tea leaves in water (3)
14 Republic in S. Europe (7)
16 Insult (4)
18 Exclamation of suprise (3)
20 Small nail (4)
21 Alley (4)
22 Comrade (3)
24 Etcetera (3)
25 Red wine (4)
26 A single occurrence (4)
27 Play it by --- (3)
28 Whirlpool (4)
29 Youth serving as a page (7)
33 Encountered (3)
35 Dexterity (5)
36 Salt of uric acid (5)
37 Large flightless bird of Antarctic regions (4-7)

DOWN

1 Outer garment (4)
2 Silicate mineral (4)
3 A neat volcano (anag.) (4)
4 Dull (4)
5 Oxidize (4)
6 Increase (8)
7 Tolerate (6)
9 Halo (8)
11 Passageway (5)
13 Venomous snake (6)
15 A kidnapper (8)
17 Allow to go free (6)
19 To select personally (8)
23 Faithful (5)
25 Acquainted with (6)
30 Small secluded valley (4)
31 Collide with (4)
32 Aggregate of fibres (4)
33 List of available options (4)
34 Ripped (4)

ACROSS

1 Historic scientific study (11)
6 Protective covering for the knee (7)
9 Comforter or quilt (3)
12 Pertaining to fish (9)
14 Religious pilgrim (6)
15 Island of Hawaii (4)
16 A purse (3)
17 False god (4)
18 A saxophone (abbrev.) (3)
19 Portico (4)
20 Being at the middle (3)
22 Principal (4)
24 An upper room (6)
25 Examining carefully (9)
27 Born (3)
28 Tool for boring holes (5)
29 Asking (11)

DOWN

2 Metallic element (6)
3 Supports (4)
4 Reluctant (5)
5 Doubt (10)
7 Chief magistrate of as shire (9)
8 The atmosphere (3)
9 Dutch name of The Hague (4)
10 One who deals in poultry (9)
11 Physical exercises (10)
13 Cajole (4)
16 Not good (3)
18 Hyperbolic sine (4)
20 House rodents (4)
21 6th century Hebrew prophet (6)
23 Regions (5)
24 African antelope (3)
26 A Shakespeare villain (4)

124

ACROSS

2 Restlessness (10)
7 River in central England (4)
8 Name of God in the OT (6)
10 Positive confirmation (3)
11 Seat (5)
13 Gone by (3)
15 Viper (3)
16 Verge (4)
17 Foundation (5)
20 Effrontery (5)
21 Study of icons (9)
22 Had deep feelings for (5)
24 Gave a measured amount (5)
26 Parched (4)
27 Very busy insect (3)
29 Ballet step (3)
30 Zeal (5)
31 Bookmark (3)
32 Pliable (6)
34 Basic unit of money in Peru (4)
35 A tuning instrument (6-4)

DOWN

1 East Indian fig tree (6)
2 Writing fluid (3)
3 Military authority in Turkey (5)
4 8th month of the Jewish calendar (4)
5 These days (8)
6 Resounds (6)
8 Bark sharply (3)
9 Urges on (4)
12 Shock with wonder (7)
14 Cut into small cubes (5)
16 A fungal plant disease (5)
18 Apportionment (8)
19 A pole (3)
20 A person (3)
22 Little flap (6)
23 Spoken (4)
25 Ruins (6)
27 Skill (3)
28 Japanese gateway (5)
30 Soon (4)
33 Hasten (3)

1	2				3		4	■	5	6	7	

ACROSS
1 Short opera (8)
5 Deep wound (4)
8 Climbing vine (3)
9 Tumour of the liver (8)
11 Orange skin (4)
13 Insanity (6)
15 Eighth sign of the Zodiac (7)
16 Silkworm covering (6)
19 Find the sum of (3)
21 And not (3)
22 Shooting star (6)
25 Tranquil (7)
26 Prejudice against old people (6)
30 Restraint (4)
31 Apothegm (8)
32 Inquire of (3)
33 Weapons (4)
34 Artillery fragments (8)

DOWN
2 Deliver a sermon (6)
3 Small-time (3-3)
4 Near the anus (4)
5 To grimace (4)
6 Pilot (7)
7 Synchronize (4)
10 Scrape off (6)
12 Approaching death (5)
14 On high (4)
17 Agree (6)
18 Sully (5)
19 Belief that there is no God (7)
20 Improvised bed (4)
23 A man who forces his attentions of women (6)
24 Dishevel (6)
27 Equipment (4)
28 Append one's signature (4)
29 Aggregate (4)

126

ACROSS

1 Narcotics agent (slang) (4)
3 Snobbish conduct (8)
6 Licentious (7)
9 Fulcrum for an oar (5)
12 US film acress, Lillian ---- (4)
14 Colour of blood (3)
15 Centesimal (9)
17 **Of the highest quality** (1-3)
18 Purulence (3)
19 Indian statesman and leader (5)
21 Open mesh fabric (3)
22 Affectedly dainty (4)
23 Tightly clustered (9)
27 Not either (3)
29 Wan (4)
30 Wood nymph (5)
31 Rag-dolls (7)
33 Greek dish with aubergine (8)
34 Used to refer to people in general (4)

DOWN

1 Whinny (5)
2 Sound of a dove (3)
3 Phase (5)
4 Bathing facilities (9)
5 Dominion (4)
7 Residence of monks (9)
8 Cover (3)
10 To get one's bearing (9)
11 Decree (5)
13 Celestial body (4)
16 Apostates (9)
18 Strike repeatedly (5)
20 Slippery fish (4)
24 Georg Simon ---, German physicist (3)
25 A tumour composed of muscle tissue (5)
26 Exalt (5)
28 Ricelike grains of pasta (4)
32 To place (3)

ACROSS

1 Man who sells merchandise (8)
5 A design of small, delicate figures (4)
8 Vietnamese currency unit (3)
9 Suitable for wear (8)
11 Fillet or border (4)
13 Written symbol (6)
15 Base (7)
16 Servile (6)
19 Made warm or hot (3)
21 Male child (3)
22 Before this time (3-3)
25 Brutal bully (7)
26 Snakes (6)
30 Cut of meat (4)
31 Laudatory notice (8)
32 The finish (3)
33 Energy units (4)
34 Hidden (8)

DOWN

2 Take vengeance for (6)
3 Capable of being moved (6)
4 Festive season (4)
5 Discharge of a firearm (4)
6 Made of baked clay (7)
7 Underground mammal (4)
10 Start again (6)
12 Muse of lyric poetry (5)
14 Recedes (4)
17 Delighted (6)
18 Monarchy in the Himalayas (5)
19 Course (7)
20 A trip with visits (4)
23 Furrow or groove (6)
24 Villain (6)
27 A particularly energetic person (4)
28 Completes (4)
29 Starch used in puddings (4)

128

ACROSS

1 Given to flirting (11)
8 Basic monetary unit of Denmark (5)
10 Nothing (5)
12 A heavy barge used for freight (3)
14 American hunting hound (7)
16 Growl (4)
18 An intricate network (3)
20 To smile broadly (4)
21 Probability (4)
22 Laboratory (abbrev.) (3)
24 Metallic element (3)
25 Passport endorsement (4)
26 To go by (4)
27 Fish related to the flounder (3)
28 Kiln for drying hops (4)
29 Religious festival (4-3)
33 Plural for eye (old English) (3)
35 Prolonged pain (5)
36 Not appropriate (5)
37 Embroidery (11)

DOWN

1 Aquatic vertebrate (4)
2 Distasteful (4)
3 Norse god of thunder (4)
4 Placed a golf ball (4)
5 Soup pasta (4)
6 Magnificent (8)
7 Not these (6)
9 Autopsy (8)
11 Bar (5)
13 Colonial marine hydroids (6)
15 Musician who plays in a group (8)
17 Congenitally attached (6)
19 Obsolete wind instrument (8)
23 Wand (5)
25 Nimble (6)
30 Small harplike musical instrument (4)
31 Contest between 2 persons (4)
32 An umbelliferous plant (4)
33 Small ornamental ladies' bag (4)
34 Trim (4)

ACROSS

1 Examine in detail (11)
7 Facial features (5)
9 As well as (3)
12 Brother of Hannibal (9)
14 Arrival (6)
15 Exclamation to portray minor accident (4)
16 Move through the air (3)
17 Sacks (4)
18 Floor covering (3)
19 Flat tableland with steep sides (4)
20 Magazine (abbrev.) (3)
22 Labour (4)
24 Picnic (6)
25 Rhizome (9)
27 17th letter of the Greek alphabet (3)
28 Inspire anew (5)
29 Milking cows (5-6)

DOWN

2 The Sustainer (Hindu) (6)
3 Disrespectful back talk (4)
4 Small assemblage (5)
5 On the starboard side (10)
7 One who guides a ship (9)
8 Erode (3)
9 A system of weights (4)
10 Something obscene (9)
11 Old-fashioned (3-7)
13 Dunce (4)
16 Cigarette (3)
18 Germinated grain used in brewing (4)
20 Fermented paste made from cooked soybeans (4)
21 Small auk (6)
23 Opposite one of two (5)
24 *Oxalis tuberosa* (3)
26 Grampus (4)

130

ACROSS

2 Skilled (10)
7 Doubtful, uncertain (4)
8 Brawn (6)
10 American who founded Wall Street (3)
11 Wise man (5)
13 To absorb food (3)
15 To free (3)
16 Sandy tract (4)
17 Foster (5)
20 Duck with soft down (5)
21 Birth (9)
22 Modify (5)
24 Marshgrass (5)
26 Low-quality diamond (4)
27 French for wine (3)
29 Domesticated canid (3)
30 Open to bribery (5)
31 Destiny (3)
32 Talisman (6)
34 Related by blood (4)
35 Soap for leather (10)

DOWN

1 Noon (6)
2 John ---, English Parliamentarian (3)
3 Academy award (5)
4 Pal (4)
5 Went beyond limit (8)
6 Move unsteadily (6)
8 Central (3)
9 Alley (4)
12 Skin of a young goat (7)
14 Not appropriate (5)
16 Gambler (5)
18 Undisputed (8)
19 Get (3)
20 Dashes half the width of an em (3)
22 Nervous anxiety (6)
23 Adverse fate (4)
25 Stretch forth (6)
27 Animal doctor (3)
28 Tortilla topped with cheese (5)
30 Face concealment (4)
33 Doze (3)

131

ACROSS

1 Borders (6)
4 Head nurse (6)
7 Humorous (9)
10 A long distance (4)
11 Devour (3)
12 Scorch (4)
13 Ostrichlike bird (4)
15 Long for (5)
18 Roost (5)
20 Layer (4)
21 Norwegian city (4)
22 An outsider (5)
24 Just won (5)
26 Spawn (4)
29 Used to express sorrow (4)
31 Edge (3)
32 ---- bomb, nuclear weapon (4)
33 Intensity of light (9)
34 Wooden tap in a cask (6)
35 A variety of chicory (6)

DOWN

1 Ceremonial prayer (6)
2 Austrian river (4)
3 Guide (5)
4 Strike hard (5)
5 Soft thick nub in yarn (4)
6 Vulgarity (6)
7 Rabid (9)
8 Goatlike Asian mammal (4)
9 Deputy (9)
14 Alcove (4)
16 Kind of wild barley (3)
17 A rare wild goose (4)
19 Antiquity (3)
22 Fortification made of tree branches (6)
23 Against (4)
25 Cheek depression (6)
27 Reflect (5)
28 Room (5)
30 Chanted (4)
32 Sour (4)

132

ACROSS

1 To jar (4)
3 Painting medium (8)
6 Withdraw (7)
9 Collection of maps (5)
12 Absent (4)
14 A large pot for making coffee or tea (3)
15 Self-styled (Fr.) (9)
17 Native of Thailand (4)
18 Louse egg (3)
19 Religion founded in Persia in 1863 (5)
21 And not (3)
22 Rode the river (anag.) (4)
23 Absolute (9)
27 Biblical high priest (3)
29 Mountain goat (4)
30 Pertaining to the voice (5)
31 Skyway (7)
33 Undo your seatbelt (8)
34 Area for recreation (4)

DOWN

1 Tugs (5)
2 Rocky pinnacle (3)
3 Black and white predatory whales (5)
4 Toy (9)
5 Close (4)
7 Having three atoms in a molecule (9)
8 US airline (acronym) (3)
10 Mexican Christmas lantern (9)
11 Scoff (5)
13 Rectangular (4)
16 Stupid (9)
18 A hilly desert region of S. Israel (5)
20 Type of horse (4)
24 Afternoon meal (3)
25 Banish (5)
26 Harsh squeaky sound (5)
28 Something for temporary use (4)
32 One circuit (3)

ACROSS
1 Musical wind instrument (8)
5 Duration (4)
8 Atomic mass unit (acronym) (3)
9 Until now (8)
11 Handle of a weapon or tool (4)
13 Tidily (6)
15 A female heir (7)
16 Grab (6)
19 Spout (3)
21 Day before (3)
22 Immigration of Jews to Israel (6)
25 The outdoors (4-3)
26 Abut (6)
30 Snare (4)
31 Weakness (8)
32 The cassowary (3)
33 To a smaller extent (4)
34 Farewell (8)

DOWN
2 Checked (6)
3 Strong forward rush (6)
4 Black bone (anag.) (4)
5 African weaver bird (4)
6 Mimic (7)
7 Ponder (4)
10 The game of hurling (6)
12 Greek goddess of fortune (5)
14 Greyish-brown eagle (4)
17 Wide street (6)
18 Capital of Morocco (5)
19 Jitters (7)
20 Cab (4)
23 Absence of passion (6)
24 One who pities (6)
27 Endure (4)
28 Literary work (4)
29 Temple (4)

134

ACROSS

1 Nimble (11)
8 Craze (5)
10 Hinged door (5)
12 Denial (3)
14 Increase in size (7)
16 Title of honour for bishops (4)
18 To yield (3)
20 Form of wrestling (4)
21 Tailless amphibian (4)
22 A flat Indian bread (3)
24 Immeasurably long period of time (3)
25 Not final or absolute (4)
26 Overly precious or nice (4)
27 Soviet secret police (3)
28 Continuous dull pain (4)
29 Moulting (7)
33 An edible fungus (3)
35 Cowboy display (5)
36 Seaport in NW Israel (5)
37 Esteemed (11)

DOWN

1 Incline (4)
2 Malodorous (4)
3 Harmony (4)
4 Gemstone (4)
5 A goatlike mammal (4)
6 Appointment book (8)
7 Decapitate (6)
9 Commercial production of goods (8)
11 Impure form of quartz (5)
13 Not accented (6)
15 Deficiency of oxygen (8)
17 Bracelet (6)
19 Done for (6-2)
23 Daughter of your brother or sister (5)
25 Of little width (6)
30 Bird of peace (4)
31 Fired a gun (4)
32 Vocalize melodically (4)
33 Roman censor (4)
34 Snub-nosed dogs (4)

ACROSS

1 Practical (11)
6 Occurring every 4th day (7)
9 Old English letter (3)
12 Make into a ritual (9)
14 Killick (6)
15 Tall woody plant (4)
16 Metal container (3)
17 Part of the eye (4)
18 Exclamation of contempt (3)
19 Scottish Celt (4)
20 Parched (3)
22 Indian city (4)
24 Dealer in textiles (6)
25 Word of four letters (9)
27 Ingest food (3)
28 Unite (5)
29 Sensible (11)

DOWN

2 Security round (6)
3 Is not (4)
4 Name (5)
5 Composure (10)
7 To adapt (9)
8 A melody or tune (3)
9 Acquire through merit (4)
10 Series of ranks (9)
11 Not relating to any religion (10)
13 State in the W. United States (4)
16 Small, low island (3)
18 Boast (4)
20 Damn (4)
21 Cause to remember (6)
23 Elegance (5)
24 Adult male (3)
26 Uncouth (4)

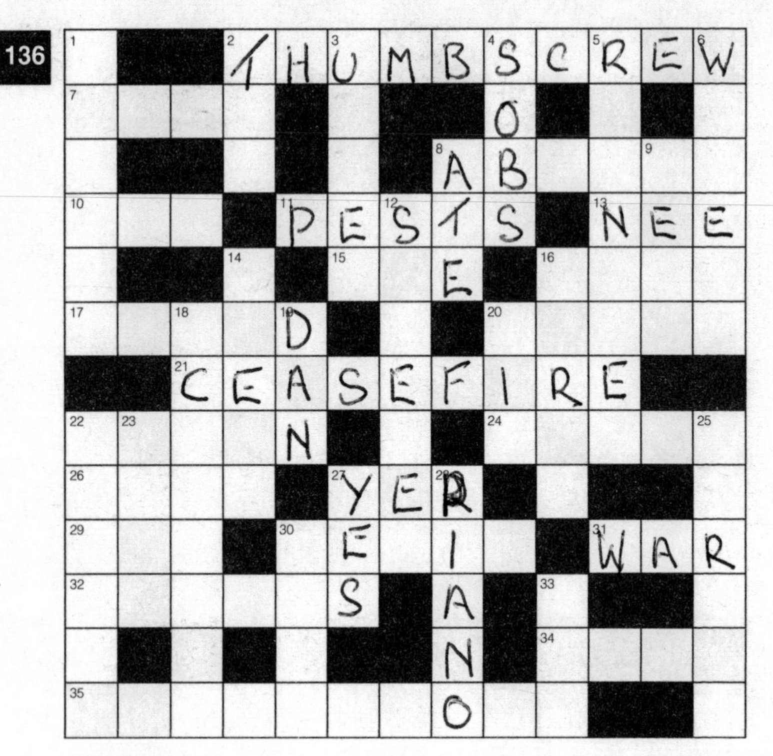

ACROSS

2 Instrument of torture (10)
7 Bone of the forearm (4)
8 Sudden (6)
10 To the stern (3)
11 Nuisances (5)
13 Maiden name (3)
15 Admiration (3)
16 High, eminent (4)
17 Antelope (5)
20 Sullen (5)
21 Truce (9)
22 Extraterrestrial (5)
24 Fabric hand-dyeing technique (5)
26 Husks or pods (4)
27 Yes (inf.) (3)
29 Sailor (3)
30 Adapted to a dry environment (5)
31 Armed conflict (3)
32 Likenesses (6)
34 A crossbar used on draught animals (4)
35 Simpleton (10)

DOWN

1 Undergo mutation (6)
2 Faucet (3)
3 Pale green mosslike lichen (5)
4 Weeps (4)
5 Small circle (8)
6 Boggy (6)
8 Had a meal (3)
9 Highest point (4)
12 Janitor (7)
14 Leg joints (5)
16 Pertaining to the ear (5)
18 Precipitation containing pollution (4-4)
19 Proficiency level at judo (3)
20 Akin (3)
22 Energetic activity (6)
23 Rich soil (4)
25 Core (6)
27 Affirmative (3)
28 Musical instrument (5)
30 Stranger (prefix.) (4)
33 Swindle (3)

ACROSS

1 Fastened with nails (6)
4 Small lump (6)
7 Throughout the world (9)
10 Building for storing hay (4)
11 Large container (3)
12 Level (4)
13 Otherwise (4)
15 The present occasion (5)
18 Fenced areas (5)
20 Score (4)
21 Debutantes (inf.) (4)
22 Thaws (5)
24 Approaching death (5)
26 Exclamation of fright (4)
29 Uncommon (4)
31 Your grandmother (3)
32 Heavily spiced stew (4)
33 Comprehensible (9)
34 Wrinkled (6)
35 Merchant (6)

DOWN

1 Imperfect ear of corn (6)
2 Large cat (4)
3 Research deeply (5)
4 Efts (5)
5 Past tense of bid (4)
6 Antelopes (6)
7 Cowboys (9)
8 Broad valley (4)
9 Capable of being turned inside out (9)
14 Having eyes (4)
16 Baby's bed (3)
17 Not difficult (4)
19 To endure (3)
22 Mutter (6)
23 Petty quarrel (4)
25 A peanut (6)
27 Accustom (5)
28 To make into law (5)
30 Resound (4)
32 Earthenware pot (4)

138

ACROSS

1 Scheme (4)
3 An artificially created jet of water (8)
6 Horizon (7)
9 Beastly (5)
12 A wild goat (4)
14 Digit at the end of the foot (3)
15 Subsidiary (9)
17 Highly excited (4)
18 Drunkard (3)
19 Small jazz band (5)
21 Not in (3)
22 Pelt (4)
23 Negotiator (9)
27 Burmese monetary unit (3)
29 Contraction of is not (4)
30 Plant used as a dye (5)
31 Spoke (7)
33 At whatever time (8)
34 Indefinite (4)

DOWN

1 Unleavened dough (5)
2 Nothing (3)
3 Ultimate (5)
4 Female goat (5-4)
5 As a divisor of (4)
7 Person who sails a yacht (9)
8 Period of history (3)
10 Dinosaur (9)
11 Unicellular fungi used for fermenting (5)
13 Graceful and intelligent riding horse (4)
16 Slashed (9)
18 Slender graceful woman (5)
20 Singles (4)
24 African antelope (3)
25 Aquatic mammal (5)
26 Woman's one-piece garment (5)
28 Informal yes (4)
32 Old Saxon letter (3)

ACROSS
1 Haughty (8)
5 Walking stick (4)
8 Exploit (3)
9 Remains of something ruined (8)
11 Flightless South American bird (4)
13 Visions (6)
15 Proposed (7)
16 Cylindrical (6)
19 Jamaican popular music (3)
21 Part of the verb to do (3)
22 Barrister (6)
25 Fixed in position (7)
26 Message (6)
30 Moral obligation (4)
31 Mountain climber (8)
32 Feminine pronoun (3)
33 Lock openers (4)
34 Writer of literary works (8)

DOWN
2 Purefy or refine (6)
3 Military catapult (6)
4 Sledge (4)
5 Remedy (4)
6 Feeling guilty (7)
7 Large E. Indian tree (4)
10 Dilapidated (6)
12 Trembling poplar (5)
14 Regretted (4)
17 Typewriter tape (6)
18 To lose blood (5)
19 Of dark complexion (7)
20 A great age (4)
23 Middle earbone (6)
24 Explosions (6)
27 Trick (4)
28 Affirmative votes (4)
29 Matron (4)

140

ACROSS
1 Tenant under a lease (11)
8 Standard of perfection (5)
10 Behaved (5)
12 Perception (3)
14 Unrealistic person (7)
16 Back of the neck (4)
18 Implore (3)
20 Mature (4)
21 Mark left by a healed wound (4)
22 6th letter of the Hebrew alphabet (3)
24 Even (poet.) (3)
25 Unit of money in Uruguay (4)
26 Helps (4)
27 To dip lightly into water (3)
28 Nasal phlegm (slang) (4)
29 Skin of animal (7)
33 Sorrowful (3)
35 Monument (5)
36 Not appropriate (5)
37 Restore to a unified state (11)

DOWN
1 Slender (4)
2 Related by blood (4)
3 Looked at (4)
4 Leer (4)
5 Small drink of liquor (4)
6 Went over again (8)
7 Totter (6)
9 Archaeological object (8)
11 Perfume with incense (5)
13 Cricken team (6)
15 Town in NE Scotland (8)
17 Republic in C. America (6)
19 Gaslight chandelier (8)
23 Elector (5)
25 Human mind (6)
30 Opposed to (4)
31 Injure (4)
32 Sturdy wool fibre (4)
33 Portico (4)
34 Plunge headfirst into water (4)

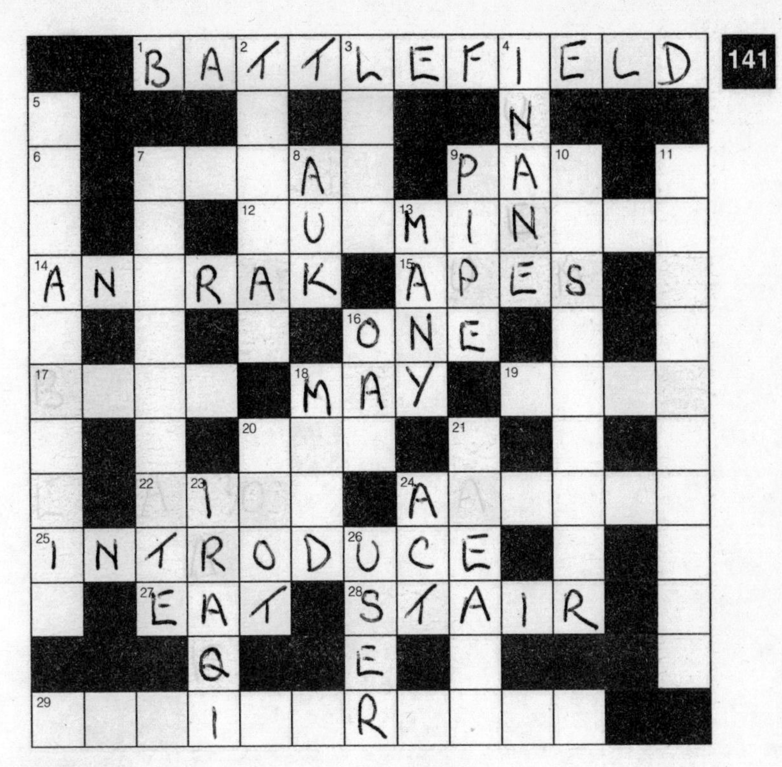

ACROSS
1 Area of contention (11)
6 Of certain seeds having a tuft (5)
9 Texture of baby food (3)
12 Topmost (9)
14 Parka (6)
15 Primates (4)
16 Single number (3)
17 ---- of March (15th in the Roman calendar) (4)
18 Fifth month (3)
19 Give food to (4)
20 The lunar new year in Vietnam (3)
22 River in N. England (4)
24 Slowly (6)
25 Acquaint (9)
27 Take nourishment (3)
28 Step (5)
29 Circumlocution (11)

DOWN
2 Male cat (6)
3 Recline in a relaxed manner (4)
4 Silly (5)
5 Of high moral or intellectual value (10)
7 Collaborate (9)
8 Diving bird (3)
9 A tube devised for smoking (4)
10 Wayfarer (10)
11 Point of view (10)
13 Numerous (4)
16 Cereal grass (3)
18 Reward (4)
20 Horse's gait (4)
21 Standards of perfection (6)
23 Citizen of Iraq (5)
24 Statute (3)
26 A person who makes use of something (4)

142

1			2		3			4		5		6
7												
							8				9	
10				11		12				13		
			14		15				16			
17		18		19				20				
		21										
22	23							24				25
26					27		28					
29				30						31		
32									33			
									34			
35												

ACROSS

2 Flag signalling quarantine (10)
7 Untie (4)
8 Agree (6)
10 Front area from the waist to the knees (3)
11 King of Troy (5)
13 A vase (3)
15 To play the part of (3)
16 Melody (4)
17 Energetic (5)
20 Snap (5)
21 Headlong (9)
22 Jargon (5)
24 Give up (5)
26 Triumphs (4)
27 Influenza (3)
29 Newt (3)
30 Edible red seaweed (5)
31 To increase speed of (3)
32 Make less sensitive (6)
34 Inspires dread (4)
35 Countless (10)

DOWN

1 Coarse jute fabric (6)
2 Teenage lout (3)
3 7th sign of the zodiac (5)
4 Objective case of who (4)
5 Free from error (8)
6 E. Egyptian village (6)
8 Small domesticated feline (3)
9 Relating to urine (4)
12 An avalanche (7)
14 Unfolds (5)
16 Upbeat (5)
18 Apparition (8)
19 A hard synthetic gemstone (3)
20 Weep (3)
22 European country (6)
23 Animate existence (4)
25 Contrive (6)
27 Amusement (3)
28 Long-continued practice (5)
30 Sandy tract (4)
33 Vessel or duct (3)

ACROSS

1 Attractive (6)
4 Ball game with 2 teams of 11 players (6)
7 The manner of conducting oneself (9)
10 Acting part (4)
11 Title of a knight (3)
12 Heating fuel (4)
13 Girl's name (4)
15 Pertaining to the moon (5)
18 Tooth (5)
20 Crustacean (4)
21 English monk (4)
22 Grey (5)
24 Pertaining to birth (5)
26 Specks (4)
29 Eruption of pimples (4)
31 A type of deer (3)
32 Manager (4)
33 Old female cat (9)
34 Make beloved (6)
35 Make less hard (6)

DOWN

1 Pale yellow liquid (6)
2 Fencing sword (4)
3 Rising agent for bread (5)
4 Scurry (5)
5 Brilliantly executed stratagem (4)
6 Roof timber (6)
7 Whitening (9)
8 A small container (4)
9 Fullness (9)
14 End of a prayer (4)
16 A metric unit of area equal to 100 square metres (3)
17 S. African monetary unit (4)
19 Office Document Architecture (acronym) (3)
22 A ruffian (6)
23 Ancient Greek colonnade (4)
25 Wound (6)
27 Abalone (5)
28 Vends (5)
30 One of the Great Lakes (4)
32 Punch (4)

144

ACROSS

1 Summit of a hill (4)
3 Ice lolly (8)
6 Visual (7)
9 Attribute to (5)
12 Seaweed (4)
14 Metal-bearing mineral (3)
15 Child (9)
17 Helper (4)
18 Pair (3)
19 Averages (5)
21 Sesame plant (3)
22 Pre-Easter season (4)
23 Emotional dependency (9)
27 Wet spongy ground (3)
29 Identical (4)
30 Rendezvous (5)
31 Adage (7)
33 Winged staff carried by Mercury (8)
34 Stratum (4)

DOWN

1 Eccentric (5)
2 21st letter of the Greek alphabet (3)
3 Mountains (5)
4 Act of surprising (9)
5 Sly look (4)
7 Needless repetition in different words (9)
8 Permit (3)
10 Anticipation (9)
11 Drive back (5)
13 Incline (4)
16 Vigorously active (9)
18 Distrust (5)
20 Volcano (4)
24 Ampere (abbrev.) (3)
25 Roman goddess of agriculture (5)
26 Cavalry sword (5)
28 Grampus (4)
32 Veterinarian (abbrev.) (3)

145

ACROSS

1 A dirge (8)
5 Small mountain (4)
8 The cardinal number (3)
9 Maker of fine scents (8)
11 S-shaped moulding (4)
13 Disfigure (6)
15 Medley (7)
16 Large seabird (6)
19 Period of human life (3)
21 Drinking cup (3)
22 Creased and wrinkly (6)
25 Beggars collectively (7)
26 Diacritic mark (6)
30 Unskilled labour (4)
31 Abroad (8)
32 Social insect living in organized colonies (3)
33 Verge (4)
34 Lightest element (8)

DOWN

2 Wintry (6)
3 Electric resistance (6)
4 Unit of linear measure (4)
5 Horse's foot (4)
6 Entering (7)
7 Sly look (4)
10 Precede (6)
12 Show emotion (5)
14 Examination (4)
17 Pokes gently (6)
18 Small assemblage (5)
19 Lasting through all time (7)
20 Rebekah's first-born twin son (Gen. 25:25) (4)
23 Rely (6)
24 A series of decorative arches (6)
27 Drink of fermented honey and water (4)
28 Poker stake (4)
29 Foolish nonsense (4)

ACROSS

1 Ungratefulness (11)
8 Scoundrel (5)
10 Farm bird (5)
12 Turf (3)
14 One's own person (7)
16 A flower (4)
18 Front part of an apron (3)
20 Challenge (4)
21 Extremely (4)
22 Away from usual place (3)
24 Head of corn (3)
25 Hyperbolic sine (4)
26 Stare open-mouthed (4)
27 Sheep ---, bloodsucking fly (3)
28 Verge (4)
29 Side by side (7)
33 Move with great speed (3)
35 Confused fight (5)
36 Republic in W. Africa (5)
37 Of smart appearance (4-7)

DOWN

1 A wading bird (4)
2 Castrate (4)
3 Too (4)
4 Lazy (4)
5 Exhort (4)
6 Zealous environmentalist (8)
7 Tiny (6)
9 Ensnarl (8)
11 An oily fruit (5)
13 Any opium-like substance (6)
15 Embarrassed (8)
17 Not real (6)
19 Small house (8)
23 A satellite of Jupiter (5)
25 Lecture (6)
30 True (4)
31 Highly excited (4)
32 Cap of Scottish origin (4)
33 Grange (4)
34 Small enclosed garden (4)

147

ACROSS

1 Obedient (11)
6 Carrion-eating stork (7)
9 Duration of life (3)
12 Little or Lesser Bear (4-5)
14 Fit for cultivation (6)
15 Spawning area of salmon (4)
16 Is able to (3)
17 Facility (4)
18 To put on (clothing) (3)
19 Faded and dull in appearance (4)
20 Centre of our planetary system (3)
22 Freshwater fish (4)
24 A single section as in a blackberry (6)
25 No longer infectious (9)
27 Cash on Delivery (acronym) (3)
28 Proverb (5)
29 Restrained (11)

DOWN

2 Cloud of interstellar gas (6)
3 Literary or musical work (4)
4 Chilly (5)
5 Inconsequential (10)
7 Ecstatic (9)
8 Monetary subunit in Denmark (3)
9 So be it (4)
10 Stamina (9)
11 Bishop of the highest rank (10)
13 Wild goat (4)
16 To swindle (3)
18 Contest between 2 people (4)
20 Gust of wind (4)
21 Eighth part of a circle (6)
23 Got up (5)
24 Besides (3)
26 Compass point (4)

148

ACROSS

2 Temperate (10)
7 Beehive (4)
8 Very drunk (inf.) (6)
10 Devour (3)
11 Having two feet (5)
13 Small Vietnamese coin (3)
15 Spring month (3)
16 Sliding lock (4)
17 Sudden pains (5)
20 Provide proof (5)
21 Growing in swamps (9)
22 Elects (5)
24 Inflict (5)
26 Apart (4)
27 Cram (3)
29 Soak (3)
30 Gannet (5)
31 Lacking water (3)
32 Mental deficiency (6)
34 Melody (4)
35 Treelike in form (10)

DOWN

1 Dormant state (6)
2 Copy (3)
3 Curtain fabric (5)
4 Blend (4)
5 Outbuilding (8)
6 Not rough (6)
8 Turkish governor (3)
9 Baby powder (4)
12 Page for page (7)
14 Awry (5)
16 French market town (5)
18 Act of nodding one's head (8)
19 Female sibling (inf.) (3)
20 Pledge (3)
22 Diverse (6)
23 Was indebted to (4)
25 Data input device (6)
27 Happiness (3)
28 Administrative region of SE China (5)
30 Mark left by a wound (4)
33 Block up (3)

ACROSS
1 Red dye (6)
4 Playful (6)
7 Absolute (3-3-3)
10 Car for hire (4)
11 A youth (3)
12 Persian fairy (4)
13 Engage in prayer (4)
15 Large sea duck (5)
18 Anaesthetic (5)
20 Capital of Yemen (4)
21 Shower (4)
22 Supple (5)
24 Expression of encouragement (5)
26 Male ruler of a duchy (4)
29 Highly excited (4)
31 Naught (3)
32 Emanation (4)
33 The period of being a novice (9)
34 Cure (6)
35 Entangle (6)

DOWN
1 Pot (6)
2 Island in central Hawaii (4)
3 Skin on the upper part of the head (5)
4 Seaport of Mecca (5)
5 Brilliantly executed stratagem (4)
6 Simpler (6)
7 Result of oxidizing (9)
8 Not any (4)
9 Technical skill (9)
14 Yes (4)
16 Old Saxon letter (3)
17 Grass (4)
19 Bind (3)
22 Thinner (6)
23 Parody (4)
25 Vitality (6)
27 Oneness (5)
28 Ignore (5)
30 Clotted blood (4)
32 Smallest component (4)

150

ACROSS

1 Aromatic herb (4)
3 Temporary activity (8)
6 Pertaining to an osculum (7)
9 Domesticates (5)
12 Unspecified in number (4)
14 Female sheep (3)
15 Child (9)
17 Encourage in wrongdoing (4)
18 Place (3)
19 Muslim messiah (5)
21 Method (3)
22 Wildcat (4)
23 Flight altitude barometer (9)
27 European Monetary System (abbrev.) (3)
29 Ripened plant ovule (4)
30 African pastoral people (5)
31 Legal dissolution of a marriage (7)
33 Cairn (8)
34 Used to refer to people in general (4)

DOWN

1 Given to moods (5)
2 19th letter of the Greek alphabet (3)
3 Gather (5)
4 Rare metallic element (9)
5 Ship's company (4)
7 Innumerable (9)
8 Decay (3)
10 Water from melted snow (9)
11 Slightly ill (5)
13 A meadow (4)
16 Room for indoor sports (9)
18 Introduction (5)
20 Wheel shaft (4)
24 Spread out for drying (3)
25 Utterly stupid person (5)
26 Full of reeds (5)
28 Mackerel shark (4)
32 Often (3)

ACROSS
1 Greatness (8)
5 Indifferent (2-2)
8 Choose (3)
9 Rancher (8)
11 Secondhand (4)
13 Domain of a baron (6)
15 Plunder (7)
16 Country (6)
19 Albania (abbrev.) (3)
21 Yonder (3)
22 Read from the Torah (6)
25 Examine closely (7)
26 Come into being (6)
30 US garden (4)
31 Cat of unknown parentage (8)
32 Envisage (3)
33 Poisonous evergreen shrubs (4)
34 Unrestricted power in government (8)

DOWN
2 The muse of astronomy (6)
3 Vigour (6)
4 Post (4)
5 Tart (4)
6 Constituent of blood serum (7)
7 Type of gun (4)
10 Icily (6)
12 Approaching death (5)
14 Apart (4)
17 A boyish girl (6)
18 Domestic cat (5)
19 Crew of an aircraft (7)
20 Aromatic fragrance (4)
23 Grommet (6)
24 Continuously (6)
27 Relaxation (4)
28 Lyric poems (4)
29 The Orient (4)

152

ACROSS

1 Marketed in finished condition (5-2-4)
8 Musical composition (5)
10 Pertaining to the kidneys (5)
12 Name you were born with (3)
14 Lubricated (7)
16 Depend (4)
18 Segment of a circle (3)
20 Boss on a shield (4)
21 Greek goddess (4)
22 Exclamation of surprise (3)
24 Even (poet.) (3)
25 Open ended (4)
26 Shelter for honeybees (4)
27 A river in Scotland (3)
28 Germinated grain used in brewing (4)
29 Dry partially (7)
33 Heretofore (3)
35 Monetary unit of the Soviet Union (5)
36 Each day (5)
37 Remove oxygen from (11)

DOWN

1 Shower (4)
2 Land measure (4)
3 Active male cosmic principle (4)
4 Reed instrument (4)
5 Pays attention (4)
6 Portrayed (8)
7 Spreads out (6)
9 Bar (8)
11 Strange and mysterious (5)
13 Moon of the planet Jupiter (6)
15 Skin emollient (8)
17 Consisting of lines (6)
19 Parturition (8)
23 The number system with base 8 (5)
25 Develop (6)
30 Memorandum (4)
31 Unnamed day on which an operation is to be launched (1-3)
32 Exclamation of fright (4)
33 Jaguarundi (4)
34 N. German river (4)

ACROSS
1 Christ (4-2-5)
6 Having many feet (7)
9 John ---, common person (3)
12 Traveller (9)
14 Ill will (6)
15 Basic monetary unit of Uruguay (4)
16 10th letter of Hebrew alphabet (3)
17 Sibilate (4)
18 Container used for cooking (3)
19 Remain (4)
20 Prefix "beneath" (3)
22 Smallest component (4)
24 Acetic acid as a solvent (6)
25 Surmountable (9)
27 Erode (3)
28 Loft (5)
29 Ancient Incan city (5-6)

DOWN
2 Japan (6)
3 Probability (4)
4 Golf clubs (5)
5 Theatre devoted to operas (5-5)
7 Scene (9)
8 Implement used to propel a boat (3)
9 Feat (4)
10 Vain (9)
11 Attends the bride (10)
13 Small blemish (4)
16 Teenage lout (3)
18 Cougar (4)
20 Category (4)
21 Pertaining to vinegar (6)
23 Instruct (5)
24 High-pitched (3)
26 Indonesian resort island (4)

154

ACROSS

2 Conformity (10)
7 Ourselves (4)
8 Slowly (6)
10 A clever remark (3)
11 Soft, crinkled fabric (5)
13 Black tropical American cuckoo (3)
15 Chopping tool (3)
16 Inquires (4)
17 Recess in a wall (5)
20 Brag (5)
21 Work performed by hand (9)
22 Antelope (5)
24 Tilted (5)
26 Departed (4)
27 Japanese money (3)
29 Mythical sea monster (3)
30 Smallest piece of Hebrew money (5)
31 Pronoun (3)
32 Standards of perfection (6)
34 ---- of Wight (4)
35 Dressing (10)

DOWN

1 Lecture (6)
2 Powdery residue (3)
3 Venomous snake (5)
4 City person (inf.) (4)
5 Seaport in southern Japan (8)
6 Self-centered person (6)
8 Barbary --- (3)
9 Appends one's signature (4)
12 One that excites (7)
14 Baron (5)
16 Main artery (5)
18 Court of equity (8)
19 Conclusion (3)
20 Fur scarf (3)
22 Conceit (6)
23 Nobleman (4)
25 Become taut (6)
27 Affirmative reply (3)
28 Girl's name (5)
30 Small secluded valley (4)
33 Drift (3)

ACROSS
1 US sharpshooter (6)
4 Kinky (6)
7 Irrational zeal (9)
10 An aromatic ointment (4)
11 Male sheep (3)
12 Factory (4)
13 Person in authority (4)
15 Gambler (5)
18 Inert elemental gas (5)
20 Affirm with confidence (4)
21 Malarial fever (4)
22 Consumed (5)
24 Loft nest (5)
26 Piece of work (4)
29 Covetousness (4)
31 Fever (inf.) (3)
32 Indicating personality traits (4)
33 Easter offering (6-3)
34 Arachnid (6)
35 Signatory (6)

DOWN
1 Uncovered (6)
2 Burden (4)
3 Desire (5)
4 Ascend (5)
5 Wander (4)
6 Small sandpiper (6)
7 A spirant (9)
8 Hindmost part of an animal (4)
9 Tarrying (9)
14 Narrative of heroic exploits (4)
16 The day before (3)
17 Hire (4)
19 Anguish (3)
22 Happenings (6)
23 ---- of Man (4)
25 Intertwine (6)
27 Later (5)
28 Turkish monetary unit (5)
30 36 inches (4)
32 Highly excited (4)

156

ACROSS

1 Lame movement (4)
3 Treat with medicine (8)
6 Measurement in yards (7)
9 Nocturnal tropical lizard (5)
12 Exultation (4)
14 Help (3)
15 Worker in livery stable (9)
17 Stratum (4)
18 Unit expressing intensity of sound (3)
19 Rope with running noose (5)
21 Seed-bearing spike of corn (3)
22 Conjunction (4)
23 Poisonous mushroom (9)
27 Vase (3)
29 Inwardly (4)
30 Desert region in S Israel (5)
31 Region in NW Italy (7)
33 Passing (8)
34 8th letter of the Hebrew alphabet (4)

DOWN

1 Faithful (5)
2 Cushion (3)
3 Humid (5)
4 Resourceful (9)
5 Polynesian carved image (4)
7 Disgusting (9)
8 Tree (3)
10 Crossroads (Fr.) (9)
11 Smell (5)
13 Has a meal (4)
16 Kinfolk (9)
18 Started (5)
20 Soon (4)
24 Entirely (3)
25 Approaching death (5)
26 Percolate (5)
28 True (4)
32 Exclamation of disgust (3)

ACROSS
1 Bodily exertion (8)
5 Mineral found in thin sheets (4)
8 Unwell (3)
9 Untidy (8)
11 Tides that attain the least height (4)
13 Woman who practices yoga (6)
15 One's own person (7)
16 Resembling an ape (6)
19 A free right to lands (3)
21 Greek goddess of dawn (3)
22 Dishevel (6)
25 Stopping (7)
26 Knapsack (6)
30 Reverberation (4)
31 Salad or cooking oil (5-3)
32 Sheep ---, a wingless bloodsucking fly (3)
33 Circular course (4)
34 Submission to fate (8)

DOWN
2 Benzene (6)
3 Breathe in (6)
4 Whirlpool (4)
5 Chinese dynasty (4)
6 Inflammation of the ileum (7)
7 Family (4)
10 Sign of the zodiac (6)
12 Softly (5)
14 Off-Broadway theatre award (4)
17 Sweet dessert (6)
18 Post (5)
19 To a greater distance (7)
20 Bone of the forearm (4)
23 Portray (6)
24 Metamorphic rock (6)
27 Distasteful (4)
28 Predict (4)
29 Blunder (4)

158

ACROSS

1 Mixture (11)
8 Money (5)
10 Sweetheart (5)
12 Zero (3)
14 Lodging houses (7)
16 Seek out a supplement (anag.) (4)
18 Outer edge (3)
20 Ashy substance (4)
21 Great in quantity (4)
22 Dance making light clicks (3)
24 Sick (3)
25 Hyperbolic sine (4)
26 Imperial unit of length (4)
27 Lacking in strictness (3)
28 Continent (4)
29 Unintelligent (7)
33 One that commands (3)
35 Tied (5)
36 Pile (5)
37 Office of a lieutenant (11)

DOWN

1 Maize (4)
2 Large shopping complex (4)
3 Irritate (4)
4 Monkeys (4)
5 ---- of Skye, Inner Hebrides (4)
6 Dolt (8)
7 Subject to a penalty (6)
9 Member of a Rotary Club (8)
11 Fragrant resin (5)
13 Inflammation of the iris (6)
15 Poisonous (8)
17 Cream cake (6)
19 Afflicted with insanity (8)
23 Facet (5)
25 Young salmon (6)
30 Doing nothing (4)
31 Contraction of is not (4)
32 Acquire through merit (4)
33 Related by blood (4)
34 A low, heavy horse cart (4)

ACROSS

1 3-dimensional vision (11)
6 Give an account (7)
9 Statute (3)
12 Interrupt at intervals (9)
14 Migratory grasshopper (6)
15 Capital of Italy (4)
16 Vietnam (3)
17 Short letter (4)
18 Date of birth (abbrev.) (3)
19 Container for water (4)
20 Transgression (3)
22 Skin complaint (4)
24 Happenings (6)
25 Profitable (9)
27 Small cask (3)
28 Slow (5)
29 Frail boat (11)

DOWN

2 Pass by (6)
3 Level (4)
4 Sac-like cavity with only one opening (5)
5 Favourable (10)
7 Usually oval course for racing (9)
8 Exclamation of contempt (3)
9 Smallest unit of matter (4)
10 Martial art (9)
11 Munificence (10)
13 Crustacean (4)
16 Not (prefix) (3)
18 Daily fare of food (4)
20 Obstacle (4)
21 Take vengeance for (6)
23 Harsh squeaky sound (5)
24 First woman (3)
26 Evils (4)

160

ACROSS

2 Favouring a republic (10)
7 Hamburg's river (4)
8 Hold fast (6)
10 Alcoholic liquor (3)
11 Leg of lamb (5)
13 Dry (as in wine) (3)
15 A sheep in its second year (3)
16 Created (4)
17 Hippopotamus (abbrev.) (5)
20 Parlour game (5)
21 Top roof timber (9)
22 Dog-like African mammal (5)
24 Small, round and shiny (5)
26 Stand at ---- (4)
27 To finish first (3)
29 Curve (3)
30 Person who dresses stones (5)
31 Roman goddess of plenty (3)
32 Wearing a veil (6)
34 Exude slowly (4)
35 Australian aboriginal instrument (10)

DOWN

1 Fireside (6)
2 Soak (3)
3 Lapwing (5)
4 Spoils of plunder (4)
5 Roman capital of Palestine (8)
6 Family members (6)
8 Gear tooth (3)
9 Spawning area of salmon (4)
12 First book of the Bible (7)
14 Thorn (5)
16 Men (5)
18 Abstract (8)
19 Room within a harem (3)
20 Male swan (3)
22 Lifted with great effort (6)
23 Lively (4)
25 Last past (old English) (6)
27 Roll of bank notes (3)
28 Wanderer (5)
30 Lake or pond (4)
33 Sound of a dove (3)

1			2		3		4		5			6
		7				8				9		
10					11				12			
					13			14				
15			16	17				18	19			
		20					21					
22						23		24				25
				26	27		28					
29			30		31				32			
		33										
34							35					

ACROSS

1 Somewhat old (6)
4 Impassiveness (6)
7 Articles of glass (9)
10 Fruit of the fir tree (4)
11 --- dance (3)
12 Pull abruptly (4)
13 Sicilian volcano (4)
15 The devil (5)
18 Snicker (5)
20 Colours (4)
21 Musical composition for one (4)
22 Seaweed (5)
24 Toss (5)
26 Ceases living (4)
29 Lean (4)
31 Condensed moisture (3)
32 Equipment (4)
33 Sucrose obtained from cane (4-5)
34 Showing courage (6)
35 Gallows (6)

DOWN

1 Snow leopards (6)
2 ---- of Dogs (4)
3 Speed (5)
4 Dam extending across the Nile (5)
5 Askew (4)
6 Federal soldier in the Civil War (6)
7 Fawning (9)
8 Third son of Adam (4)
9 One another (9)
14 On the top (4)
16 Diving bird (3)
17 Requirement (4)
19 Biblical high priest (3)
22 Situation comedy (inf.) (6)
23 Professional charges (4)
25 Large stinging wasp (6)
27 Standard of perfection (5)
28 Moved back and forth (5)
30 An innocent (4)
32 Clothes (4)

162

ACROSS

1 Radar screen element (4)
3 N American aquatic turtle (8)
6 Exhibiting chemical changes (7)
9 Ships floors (5)
12 Drinking vessels (4)
14 One circuit (3)
15 Maintain a house (9)
17 Shank (4)
18 Exclamation to startle (3)
19 Japanese poem (5)
21 North American deer (3)
22 Haul (4)
23 Girl employed to care for children (9)
27 Red fruit of the hawthorn (3)
29 Overlay with wood (4)
30 Boredom (5)
31 Male turkey (7)
33 Gate at the back of a wagon (8)
34 Marked by an elegant or exclusive manner (4)

DOWN

1 Expanse of sand (5)
2 21st letter of the Greek alphabet (3)
3 Dense (5)
4 Picea rubens (3-6)
5 Every (4)
7 The moment of landing (9)
8 Stimulus (3)
10 Narrow escape (9)
11 Electric discharge (5)
13 Quarter bushel (4)
16 Improving (9)
18 Wash (5)
20 Fit of shivering (4)
24 Manipulate (3)
25 Slant (5)
26 Bowler hat (5)
28 Old Indian coin (4)
32 Mouthpiece of a bridle (3)

ACROSS
1 Flagstaff (8)
5 Prophet (4)
8 Appreciation (3)
9 To pair or couple (8)
11 Ireland (4)
13 Exclamation of joy (6)
15 Artificial mound (7)
16 Make lighter (6)
19 Georg Simon ---, German physicist (3)
21 Synthetic garnet (3)
22 Acrid taste (6)
25 2nd month of the Jewish calendar (7)
26 Exclusively (6)
30 Droops (4)
31 Stand up to (8)
32 Haunch (3)
33 Wharf (4)
34 Put in order (8)

DOWN
2 Legitimate (6)
3 Detestable (6)
4 Nervously irritable (4)
5 Ooze (4)
6 Device to keep out noise or water (7)
7 One of the Great Lakes (4)
10 Nothing (6)
12 Not ever (5)
14 Indolently (4)
17 Suds (6)
18 Vast chasm (5)
19 Earache (7)
20 Blackbird (4)
23 Clown (6)
24 Immature insects (6)
27 Island of Hawaii (4)
28 Catch sight of (4)
29 Indian exercise method (4)

164

ACROSS
1 Unrelenting (11)
8 Cotton thread used for hosiery (5)
10 Evade (5)
12 Petroleum (3)
14 Benevolent demon (7)
16 Bachelor party (4)
18 Mineral spring (3)
20 Migrant farm worker (4)
21 Major European waterway (4)
22 Insect (3)
24 The Lion (3)
25 Winged (4)
26 Man's name (4)
27 Bill (3)
28 Small yeast cake (4)
29 A dirigible (7)
33 Old Saxon letter (3)
35 Area used for sports (5)
36 Showy actions (5)
37 Assenting (11)

DOWN
1 Type of hairstyle (4)
2 Drop (4)
3 Flower (4)
4 Chilled (4)
5 Separate article (4)
6 Glove made from mail (8)
7 Remove silt from river (6)
9 Having misfortune (8)
11 Scoundrel (5)
13 African antelope (6)
15 Hermitic (8)
17 On board (6)
19 Blue-green algae (8)
23 Habituate (5)
25 The rank of an abbott (6)
30 Rabble (4)
31 German 'mister' (4)
32 Entreaty (4)
33 Sewing case (4)
34 Detest (4)

ACROSS

1 Incorporating sound and vision (11)
6 Informal (7)
9 Furrow (3)
12 Will (9)
14 Moisten (6)
15 Fencing sword (4)
16 Spout (3)
17 Part of speech (4)
18 Deranged (3)
19 Noteworthy achievement (4)
20 To hit a ball high (3)
22 Steps descending to a river (4)
24 Nosy (6)
25 Treason (9)
27 Have regrets about (3)
28 The telling of lies (5)
29 Trivial (11)

DOWN

2 On the right side (6)
3 Probability (4)
4 Foam (5)
5 Having three teeth (10)
7 Soft, white cheese (9)
8 Evening (3)
9 Engrossed (4)
10 See-sawing (10)
11 Expert in strategy (10)
13 Placed a golf ball (4)
16 Punch (3)
18 Lepidopterous insect (4)
20 Ornamental fabric (4)
21 Irritating (6)
23 Piece of flat land by a river (5)
24 Peer (3)
26 Otherwise (4)

166

ACROSS
2 Supplements (10)
7 Garden tools (4)
8 Theatre district (6)
10 Peculiar (3)
11 Demobilization (5)
13 A young boy (3)
15 Penpoint (3)
16 Division of a hospital (4)
17 Stately (5)
20 Hanging limply (5)
21 Growing in swamps (9)
22 Favoured (5)
24 Desolate (5)
26 Entrance (4)
27 Apex (3)
29 Animal doctor (inf.) (3)
30 Give merit (5)
31 Sever (3)
32 Simple life form (6)
34 Woman's name (4)
35 Surgical removal of the thymus gland (10)

DOWN
1 Crowd (6)
2 Viper (3)
3 Communion plate (5)
4 A negligible amount (4)
5 Cave in (8)
6 Of inferior quality (6)
8 Steal from (3)
9 Tarpaulin (4)
12 Citizen army (7)
14 Bay (5)
16 Conditional (5)
18 Pertaining to hearing (8)
19 Carried out (3)
20 To throw in a high arc (3)
22 Scholar (6)
23 As previously given (4)
25 Rucksack (6)
27 Two (Scots) (3)
28 First (5)
30 French clergyman (4)
33 Lock opener (3)

1			2		3	■	4		5			6

ACROSS

1 Antipathetic (6)
4 A small inflamed elevation of the skin (6)
7 Progeny (9)
10 Female relative (4)
11 Class (3)
12 Therefore (4)
13 The lowest tide (4)
15 Anesthetic (5)
18 Passageway (5)
20 Extent of space (4)
21 Betting terms (4)
22 Section of a wall (5)
24 Echo location (5)
26 Male cosmic principle in Chinese philosophy (4)
29 On the sheltered side (4)
31 Formerly known as (3)
32 Seaward (4)
33 Perilous (9)
34 A sampler of food (6)
35 Seller of women's underwear (6)

DOWN

1 Related through males (6)
2 Floating platform (4)
3 Reddish dye (5)
4 Fur trimmed coat (5)
5 A window division (4)
6 Convert into code (6)
7 With one hand (9)
8 Entreaty (4)
9 Crassitude (9)
14 Cushions (4)
16 Before (3)
17 Depend (4)
19 Artificial language (3)
22 Monkey nut (6)
23 Leg joint (4)
25 Person who reads (6)
27 Wrath (5)
28 Ancient Hebrew coin (5)
30 The Orient (4)
32 Diving birds (4)

168

ACROSS

1 Hint (4)
3 Native tree (8)
6 Republic in S. Europe (7)
9 Capital of Morocco (5)
12 An agitated state (4)
14 Old English letter (3)
15 Learning (9)
17 Single, light metallic sound (4)
18 Covering for the head (3)
19 Mine prop (5)
21 Fish eggs (3)
22 Fencing sword (4)
23 Kinfolk (9)
27 Monetary unit of Romania (3)
29 Cut to required size (4)
30 African pastoral people (5)
31 Put in place (7)
33 Resident of Athens (8)
34 Woodwind instrument (4)

DOWN

1 Pursue (5)
2 Period of history (3)
3 Narrowest part of torso (5)
4 Two weeks (9)
5 Mild oath (4)
7 Abundant (9)
8 Long-tailed bird of the Cuckoo family (3)
10 Fashionable district in London (9)
11 At that place (5)
13 Very small quantity (4)
16 Something inserted (9)
18 Single stem (5)
20 Noble (4)
24 Falsehood (3)
25 Capital of Jordan (5)
26 Kid leather (5)
28 Compass point (4)
32 Forfeit paid into a pool (3)

ACROSS

1 Wretched coward (8)
5 Vex (4)
8 1 (3)
9 Haul under the bottom of a ship (8)
11 Middle Eastern bread (4)
13 Gloss (6)
15 Long journey (7)
16 Smooth (6)
19 Globe (3)
21 Everything (3)
22 Entertained (6)
25 Conveyance on air or water (7)
26 Stir to action (6)
30 Used to indicate a specified place (4)
31 Yellow crystalline fungicide (8)
32 Ampere (abbrev.) (3)
33 Votes in favour (4)
34 Guardianship (8)

DOWN

2 Exaggerate (6)
3 Catapult (6)
4 Without value (4)
5 Washes the floor (4)
6 First (7)
7 Festive occasion (4)
10 Not winners (6)
12 Shaft shot from a bow (5)
14 A water-soluble compound (4)
17 Malfunction (6)
18 Swindler (5)
19 End result (7)
20 Waistband (4)
23 Edible nut (6)
24 Milk and egg drink (6)
27 Radiograph (4)
28 Little devils (4)
29 Way out (4)

170

ACROSS

1 Device for controlling speed (11)
8 Battery terminal (5)
10 River in Zambia (5)
12 Little drink (3)
14 Most tidy (7)
16 Little island (4)
18 Exploit (3)
20 Prima donna (4)
21 So be it (4)
22 A ram (3)
24 Annoy by persistent fault-finding (3)
25 Remnants of shells (4)
26 Profane expression (4)
27 Catch someone (inf.) (3)
28 Plant whose sap is used in cosmetics (4)
29 Inactive (7)
33 Gymnasium (abbrev.) (3)
35 Capital of Idaho (5)
36 Instruct (5)
37 Impregnated with menthol (11)

DOWN

1 Skills (4)
2 Fellow (4)
3 Large cat (4)
4 Ostrich-like bird (4)
5 Gratuity (4)
6 Someone who travels by raft (8)
7 Kingdom in N. Europe (6)
9 Desiring (8)
11 Pertaining to Asia (5)
13 Place in position (6)
15 Serving to pull or draw (8)
17 Bequest (6)
19 Rare-earth metallic element (8)
23 Entreaties (5)
25 A small, glass ball (6)
30 Observed (4)
31 Irritate (4)
32 British nobleman (4)
33 Steps used by bathers (4)
34 Temperate (4)

171

ACROSS

1 A hopeless or desperate enterprise (7-4)
6 Animate (7)
9 Relatives (3)
12 Inanimate (9)
14 Guard against assault (6)
15 Abominable snowman (4)
16 Golfers mound (3)
17 Part of the eye (4)
18 A failure (3)
19 Encourage in wrongdoing (4)
20 Appropriate (3)
22 Long periods of history (4)
24 Castrated man (6)
25 Remove moisture from (9)
27 Posed (3)
28 Australian cockatoo (5)
29 Position of greatest advancement (7-4)

DOWN

2 Steep-sided valley (6)
3 Possesses (4)
4 Robbery (5)
5 Double (4-6)
7 Highness (9)
8 Finish (3)
9 Joint between the thigh and lower leg (4)
10 Small brush for cleaning fingernails (9)
11 Sweetheart (10)
13 Having eyes (4)
16 Exclamation of contempt (3)
18 Flat circular plate (4)
20 Truth (4)
21 Engaged in active combat (6)
23 Cheerful (5)
24 7th letter of Greek alphabet (3)
26 Full of eager anticipation (4)

172

ACROSS
2 Oil extracted from flax (8-3)
7 Consecrated (4)
8 Makeshift (6)
10 A clumsy person (3)
11 Wise man (5)
13 Hurried (3)
15 Slack (3)
16 Soft cheese (4)
17 Banish (5)
20 Damp (5)
21 Northern part of a country (9)
22 Zeal (5)
24 Songs for two (5)
26 Noisy (4)
27 Stale air (3)
29 Impair (3)
30 Outmoded (5)
31 A fairy (3)
32 Military weapon (6)
34 Wheel shaft (4)
35 Very small (5-5)

DOWN
1 A ceremonial chair (6)
2 Alkali (3)
3 Pertaining to the nose (5)
4 Examination (abbrev.) (4)
5 Countermand (8)
6 Young lion (6)
8 Blend (3)
9 Raised platform (4)
12 Jewish dietary laws (7)
14 Deluge (5)
16 Additional pay (5)
18 Harden (8)
19 Sin (3)
20 Deranged (3)
22 All but (6)
23 Horse colour (4)
25 Dagger (6)
27 At a great distance (3)
28 Farm birds (5)
30 Repudiate (4)
33 24 hours (3)

173

ACROSS
1 Marked with bands (6)
4 Chat (6)
7 Geographical dictionary (9)
10 Indolently (4)
11 Destiny (3)
12 Escaping fluid (4)
13 Thick slice (4)
15 Go into (5)
18 Misuse (5)
20 Goddess of the rainbow (4)
21 Anonymous (abbrev.) (4)
22 Board (5)
24 Language spoken in S. China (5)
26 Told an untruth (4)
29 Sullen (4)
31 Impair (3)
32 Remarkable (4)
33 Petitioner (9)
34 Involve (6)
35 Shred (6)

DOWN
1 Barium sulfate (6)
2 Horse cart without sides (4)
3 Affairs of honour (5)
4 Short surplice (5)
5 Christmas (4)
6 Bookmaker (inf.) (6)
7 Viscid (9)
8 Tribute (4)
9 Unemployed (9)
14 Financial institution (4)
16 Before (3)
17 Small rivulet (4)
19 Feather scarf (3)
22 Hawk (6)
23 Resound (4)
25 Line on a weather map (6)
27 Urge forward (5)
28 Tendency (5)
30 Wrinkle (4)
32 A mechanical part or module (4)

174

ACROSS
1 Cook (4)
3 Until now (8)
6 Baby (7)
9 Cleric (5)
12 Hollow in the earth (4)
14 Affirmative vote (3)
15 One billionth of a meter (9)
17 Seaward (4)
18 To be away from (3)
19 Small hand drum (5)
21 Permit (3)
22 Ornamental needlecase (4)
23 Unmarked by trails (9)
27 System for developing potential (3)
29 Small piece of land surrounded by water (4)
30 Contempt or disdain (5)
31 Officer of military police (7)
33 Haughty (8)
34 A crystallized mineral (4)

DOWN
1 Small house (5)
2 Minor falsehood (3)
3 Therefore (5)
4 Bag worn over one shoulder (9)
5 Salver (4)
7 Public declaration (9)
8 Cereal grass (3)
10 Spanish gentleman (9)
11 Refute by evidence (5)
13 Flesh of a calf (4)
16 Pertaining to the morning (9)
18 Giants (5)
20 Gives views publicly (4)
24 High mountain (3)
25 Goddess of tillage (5)
26 Collection of Hindu aphorisms (5)
28 Mark left by a healed wound (4)
32 Vitality (3)

ACROSS

1 Unkempt (8)
5 Undoing (4)
8 Besides (3)
9 Flounce (8)
11 Lump of earth (4)
13 Believable (6)
15 Belly (7)
16 Logic (6)
19 By way of (3)
21 Miles per hour (abbrev.) (3)
22 A stimulating drink (6)
25 Obsequies (7)
26 Squirts (6)
30 Listen to (4)
31 Tegument (8)
32 Single number (3)
33 Rectangular pier (4)
34 Dawn (8)

DOWN

2 Round and plump (6)
3 The throat (6)
4 Howl (4)
5 Tiered shelves (4)
6 Let loose (7)
7 Image of a deity (4)
10 Having extraordinary strength (6)
12 Decaying (5)
14 Separate article (4)
17 Become visible (6)
18 Embarrass (5)
19 Vagabond (7)
20 Ethereal (4)
23 View in detail (6)
24 Narrow headband (6)
27 Unskilled labourer (4)
28 Extent of space (4)
29 Gust of wind (4)

176

ACROSS
1 Gymnastic event (7-4)
8 Horizontal (5)
10 Merits (5)
12 Honey (3)
14 Spirit (7)
16 Republic in W. Africa (4)
18 Positive reply (3)
20 Type of sheepdog (4)
21 Ellipsoidal (4)
22 Arrest (3)
24 Corded cloth (3)
25 Tramp (4)
26 Chinese 2-stringed instrument (4)
27 Fit out (3)
28 Water jug (4)
29 Say again (7)
33 Period of human life (3)
35 Botch (5)
36 Trades (5)
37 Sommelier (4-7)

DOWN
1 Projecting edge (4)
2 Recline in a relaxed manner (4)
3 Hub (4)
4 Long fish (4)
5 Paradise (4)
6 Besides (8)
7 Firearm (6)
9 Edible (8)
11 Participant (5)
13 Before this time (6)
15 Air plant (8)
17 Open-mouthed (6)
19 Portable electric jigsaw (8)
23 Made a hole (5)
25 Recluse (6)
30 Before long (4)
31 Increases (4)
32 Calm (4)
33 On the sea (4)
34 Looked up and down (4)

ACROSS

1 Expiatory (11)
6 European weasel (7)
9 Exclamation (3)
12 Tending to absorb (9)
14 Frail (6)
15 Purchases (4)
16 Blood relation (inf.) (3)
17 Rocks (4)
18 Small bird (3)
19 Collar fastener (4)
20 An island of Denmark (3)
22 Journey (4)
24 Occurring in spring (6)
25 Involved with theology (9)
27 A battering device (3)
28 Hirsute (5)
29 Limitless (11)

DOWN

2 To mould again (6)
3 Performs (4)
4 Game played with an oval ball (5)
5 Office of an apostle (10)
7 Breed of sheep (9)
8 To endure (3)
9 An extinct wild ox (4)
10 Indecision (9)
11 Self-contained (10)
13 Notice of someone's death (4)
16 Transgression (3)
18 Typographical error (4)
20 Thin layer (4)
21 Prescription (6)
23 Highways (5)
24 By way of (3)
26 Clarified butter (4)

178

ACROSS

2 Spurious (10)
7 Writing fluids (4)
8 Separates metal from ore (6)
10 Title of a knight (3)
11 Farewell (5)
13 Occupied a seat (3)
15 Finale (3)
16 Liquid secreted by the liver (4)
17 Hamlet (5)
20 Move rhythmically (5)
21 Area of authority (9)
22 Protruberance (5)
24 Performance (5)
26 Divisions of geological time (4)
27 Formerly named (3)
29 Become firm (3)
30 Stuffed savoury vine leaf (5)
31 Jellylike substance (3)
32 Having a tail (6)
34 Contentment (4)
35 Windshield (10)

DOWN

1 Semi-hard light yellow cheese (6)
2 Viper (3)
3 Oxygen compound (5)
4 Edible roots (4)
5 Capital of Finland (8)
6 Person included in a list (6)
8 Turf (3)
9 Body powder (4)
12 Unbeliever (7)
14 Steep, rugged rocks (5)
16 Salted, smoked meat from a pig (5)
18 Offering made to a deity (8)
19 Filled pastry crust (3)
20 Part of verb to do (3)
22 Confer (6)
23 Carbamide (4)
25 Oesophagus (6)
27 Incline head (3)
28 Show emotion (5)
30 Debutantes (inf.) (4)
33 A bog or marsh (3)

ACROSS
1 Deprived (6)
4 Venerate (6)
7 Having no appetite (9)
10 Wreath encircling the helmet of a knight (4)
11 Posed (3)
12 Sardine (4)
13 Greek god of love (4)
15 Indian form of address (5)
18 Brawny (5)
20 Islamic chieftain (4)
21 Fog (4)
22 Tidily kept (5)
24 Impertinence (5)
26 Greek goddess of strife (4)
29 Learned (4)
31 Biblical high priest (3)
32 Lamprey (4)
33 Female traitor (9)
34 Non-resident doctor (6)
35 Asexual (6)

DOWN
1 Conductor's rods (6)
2 Sea eagle (4)
3 Brief (5)
4 Right (5)
5 Face concealment (4)
5 Vigour (6)
7 Person who practices alchemy (9)
8 British nobleman (4)
9 Interprets (9)
14 Front part of the leg (4)
16 Mischievous child (3)
17 Sever with the teeth (4)
19 Exploit (3)
22 Doll with a topknot (6)
23 Slant (4)
25 Simpler (6)
27 Prevail (5)
28 Seductively beautiful woman (5)
30 A member of an Iroquoian people (4)
32 Biblical name (4)

180

ACROSS

1 Vineyards (4)
3 Polish (8)
6 Ointment (7)
9 Legal (5)
12 Mentor (4)
14 High priest (3)
15 A musician (9)
17 City of N. India (4)
18 Law enforcement agency (3)
19 Black-and-white bearlike mammal (5)
21 Irish Republican Army (3)
22 Sleeps briefly (4)
23 The day before (9)
27 Atomic mass unit (3)
29 Headland (4)
30 Rope with running noose (5)
31 Country in N. Africa (7)
33 Wrinkles (8)
34 Sharp (4)

DOWN

1 Enumerate (5)
2 Former French coin (3)
3 Scorch (5)
4 Upbraid (9)
5 Ardour (4)
7 Oily (9)
8 Mild reproof (3)
10 Remaining part (9)
11 7th sign of the Zodiac (5)
13 Peruse (4)
16 Nonsense (9)
18 Mortal (5)
20 In the direction of the ocean (4)
24 Fitness centre (3)
25 Informs (5)
26 Hope for (5)
28 Broad, shallow volcanic crater (4)
32 American deer (3)

ACROSS

1 Sheets and pillowcases (8)
5 Growl (4)
8 King (3)
9 Raiment (8)
11 In bed (4)
13 Modest (6)
15 Very small fish (7)
16 Dwarfed tree (6)
19 Past tense of do (3)
21 Classical drama of Japan (3)
22 An author (6)
25 Outlast (7)
26 Upper house of the US Congress (6)
30 Pace (4)
31 Stray moggie (5-3)
32 Application (3)
33 Speak rudely to (4)
34 S. American turnover (8)

DOWN

2 Choux pastry cake (6)
3 Caught (slang) (6)
4 Near (4)
5 Metric unit of mass (4)
6 Inept (7)
7 Jump in figure skating (4)
10 Delicate morsel of food (6)
12 Relinquish (5)
14 On top of (4)
17 European country (6)
18 Native of Switzerland (5)
19 Gloom (7)
20 Something owed (4)
23 Coarse jute fabric (6)
24 Marked by danger (6)
27 Sewing case (4)
28 Large tailless primates (4)
29 Overhanging lower edge of a roof (4)

182

ACROSS
1 Easily angered (3-8)
8 Used for branding (5)
10 Desert in Israel (5)
12 Hole punch for leather (3)
14 Abounding (7)
16 English-born US Quaker (4)
18 Slender bar (3)
20 Spoken (4)
21 Comply (4)
22 Animal covering (3)
24 Battle (3)
25 Design of small, delicate figures (4)
26 TV award (4)
27 Alcoholic beverage (3)
28 Weapons (4)
29 Skin of a young goat (7)
33 In favour of (3)
35 Quilt or duvet (Aus.) (5)
36 Proverb (5)
37 Anthology (11)

DOWN
1 Tree frog (4)
2 Rear portion (4)
3 Small island in a lake (4)
4 Attitude (4)
5 Wife of a rajah (4)
6 Carrier for leftover food (5-3)
7 Distinctive uniform (6)
9 Proximity (8)
11 Equip (5)
13 Low-frequency speaker (6)
15 Dairy worker (8)
17 More spooky (6)
19 A dolt (German) (8)
23 Gum (5)
25 Become sad (6)
30 Lower portion of a wall (4)
31 Bushy plant of salt marshes (4)
32 Back of the neck (4)
33 Persian fairy (4)
34 Egg cell (4)

ACROSS
1 Quality of being higher in rank (11)
6 Severe or stern (7)
9 Residue of fire (3)
12 Moving restlessly (9)
14 Any opium-like substance (6)
15 Scottish Gaelic (4)
16 Wily (3)
17 French river (4)
18 Young goat (3)
19 To peel (4)
20 Minor untruth (3)
22 Mimics (4)
24 Chooses (6)
25 Blatant (9)
27 Sorrowful (3)
28 Of scrawny build (5)
29 Light, flimsy boat (11)

DOWN
2 Put in front (6)
3 Grass (4)
4 Corrodes (5)
5 Evil spirit (10)
7 Vessels propelled by wind (9)
8 To free (3)
9 Ethereal (4)
10 Series of ranks (9)
11 Offensive action (10)
13 Castrate (4)
16 Akin (3)
18 Embrace (4)
20 A bitter quarrel (4)
21 Swindle (6)
23 Trick (5)
24 Christmas ---, night before (3)
26 Certainly (archaic) (4)

184

ACROSS

2 Employees (10)
7 Size of type (4)
8 From what place (6)
10 Fuss (3)
11 Number of warships (5)
13 Sea monster (3)
15 To finish (3)
16 Spoiled child (4)
17 Adjusted pitch (5)
20 Hauls (5)
21 Silvery, ductile metal (9)
22 Plentiful (5)
24 Huge (5)
26 Small salmon (4)
27 Acquire (3)
29 Feline pet (3)
30 Roman god with two faces (5)
31 Stick for snooker (3)
32 Tooth covering (6)
34 Affirm with confidence (4)
35 Three-cornered (10)

DOWN

1 Directed upwards (6)
2 Used to be (3)
3 Firearm (5)
4 The real thing (Ger.) (4)
5 An unbroken view (8)
6 Chooses (6)
8 Marry (3)
9 Steep, rugged rock (4)
12 Animate (7)
14 Greeting (5)
16 European brown bear (5)
18 One of the 12 tribes of Israel (8)
19 Owing (3)
20 Excavate (3)
22 Take or receive (6)
23 Grumble (4)
25 Belonging to them (6)
27 A girl (inf.) (3)
28 Pertaining to a tube (5)
30 Sturdy twilled fabric (4)
33 Ingot (3)

1			2		3	■	4		5			6
	■	■		■		■		■		■	■	
	■	7				8				9	■	
10				■	11			■	12			
	■		■	■	13			14	■		■	
15			16	17	■		■	18	19			
■	■	20				■	21				■	■
22					■	23	■	24				25
	■		■	26	27		28	■	■		■	
29			30	■	31			■	32			
	■	33									■	
	■	■		■		■		■		■	■	
34						■	35					

ACROSS

1 Box for valuables (6)
4 Having webbed feet (6)
7 Neuron (5-4)
10 Female servant (4)
11 Took nourishment (3)
12 Old Spanish coin (4)
13 Veinlike deposit (4)
15 African ground squirrel (5)
18 Flower segment (5)
20 Egyptian goddess of fertility (4)
21 Polynesian carved image (4)
22 Emblem (5)
24 Perfume with incense (5)
26 Agreement (4)
29 Untie (4)
31 Female kangaroo (3)
32 Former Russian ruler (4)
33 Mistaken (9)
34 Uncover (6)
35 Jewish festival (6)

DOWN

1 Blend (6)
2 Give food to (4)
3 Competitor (5)
4 Tied (5)
5 Having little hair (4)
6 Register (6)
7 Complete darkness (9)
8 English public school (4)
9 Strength of constitution (9)
14 Heroic (4)
16 Exploit (3)
17 Fool (4)
19 Supplement (3)
22 Dishevel (6)
23 Image (4)
25 Implant deeply (6)
27 Sun-dried brick (5)
28 Numbers 13 through 19 (5)
30 Ricelike grains of pasta (4)
32 Protruding tooth (4)

186

ACROSS

1 Travel on (4)
3 Soccer (8)
6 Divine (7)
9 Norse god of winds (5)
12 Plant with sword-shaped leaves (4)
14 Fahrenheit (abbrev.) (3)
15 Reduce to fibres (9)
17 Finishes (4)
18 Spasmodic muscular contraction (3)
19 Picture border (5)
21 Rod used in snooker (3)
22 Group of three people (4)
23 Swelling (9)
27 Vietnamese monetary unit (3)
29 Placed a golf ball (4)
30 Boredom (5)
31 Ship sunk by an iceberg (7)
33 Industrious (8)
34 Protruberance (4)

DOWN

1 Stormed (5)
2 Old measure of length (3)
3 Yogi (5)
4 Condition of being stretched (9)
5 Old Italian money (4)
7 Apostasy (9)
8 Period of history (3)
10 In private life (3-6)
11 Wild Asian dog (5)
13 Separate article (4)
16 Proper (9)
18 Tax (5)
20 Lecherous man (4)
24 Encountered (3)
25 Decree (5)
26 Greek goddess of fortune (5)
28 Against (4)
32 Bristle of barley (3)

1	2				3		4	■	5	6	7	
■		■	■	■		■		■	8			■
9			10					■	11			12
■		■		■		■	13	14				
15							■		■		■	
■		■		■		■	16		17			
18	■	19		20	■	■	■	21			■	
22						■	23	■		■	24	■
	■		■		■	25						
26	27		28		29	■		■		■		■
30				■	31							
■	32			■		■		■	■	■		■
33				■	34							

ACROSS

1 Festive gathering (8)
5 Individual structure (4)
8 Communist (3)
9 Aquatic rodent (8)
11 Chilled (4)
13 Sweet liquid secreted by flowers (6)
15 Lodger (7)
16 Litter of pigs (6)
19 Constricting snake (3)
21 Darling Buds of --- (3)
22 Edible pale-bluish mushroom (6)
25 Entreat (7)
26 Least polite (6)
30 Melody (4)
31 Destroy by fire (8)
32 River of NW Germany (3)
33 Anger (4)
34 From nothing (8)

DOWN

2 S. American river (6)
3 Someone who evaluates manuscripts (6)
4 Dash (4)
5 Relating to urine (4)
6 Plant gland (7)
7 Notion (4)
10 Composite plant (6)
12 Destroy by immersion (5)
14 A test (4)
17 Arranged like rays (6)
18 African musical instrument (5)
19 Narrow, half-rounded moulding (7)
20 Helps (4)
23 An archer (6)
24 Seed-bearing plant organ (6)
27 Colourless crystalline compound (4)
28 Appease (4)
29 Make weary (4)

188

ACROSS

1 Hand tool (11)
8 An award (5)
10 Unable to relax (5)
12 Haunch (3)
14 Endless (7)
16 Ascend (4)
18 Roman goddess (3)
20 Evils (4)
21 Responsibility (4)
22 Deed (3)
24 9th letter of Hebrew alphabet (3)
25 Bloodsucking insect (4)
26 Noxious weed (4)
27 Floor covering (3)
28 Hindu princess (4)
29 Loss of the sense of smell (7)
33 Even (poet.) (3)
35 Artery (5)
36 Concluded (5)
37 Pertaining to upright posture (11)

DOWN

1 Member of Indian sect (4)
2 Hind part (4)
3 Broad (4)
4 Vex (4)
5 Blood vessel (4)
6 Easy chair (8)
7 Fashions (6)
9 Sporting competitors (8)
11 Fortune-telling cards (5)
13 Antelope with enormous leaps (6)
15 Confine (8)
17 Seam where two bones are fused (6)
19 Synopsis (8)
23 Spoil (5)
25 Monastery (6)
30 Building for drying hops (4)
31 Note (4)
32 Way in (4)
33 Prepare for publication (4)
34 An informer (slang) (4)

ACROSS

1 Degree of response (11)
6 Hours of daylight (7)
9 Donkey (3)
12 A designer of gadgets (9)
14 Unadorned and simple (6)
15 Native of Arabia (4)
16 Turkish governor (3)
17 A canine tooth (4)
18 Bleating sound (3)
19 Continuous dull pain (4)
20 Average (3)
22 Part of the eye (4)
24 An organism (6)
25 Receptive (9)
27 Girl's name (3)
28 Scenes (5)
29 Pun (4-2-5)

DOWN

2 Horse sounds (6)
3 Decorated cake (4)
4 Roman goddess of the hearth (5)
5 Functioning as an adjective (10)
7 A measuring implement (9)
8 Blossom of the hawthorn (3)
9 Ethereal (4)
10 Greasy (10)
11 Priority in rank (10)
13 Greek goddess of the earth (4)
16 Drinking area (3)
18 Strong woody fibre (4)
20 Hollow-stemmed (4)
21 Shooting star (6)
23 Prepared (5)
24 Black cuckoo (3)
26 Acknowledge (4)

190

ACROSS

2 Dutch city (10)
7 Wheel shaft (4)
8 Small restaurant (6)
10 Arrest (slang) (3)
11 A sign or symbol (5)
13 Pronoun (3)
15 Sink under weight (3)
16 Exchange (4)
17 Salivate (5)
20 Hold or express as an opinion (5)
21 Weatherboard (9)
22 Rational (5)
24 Eats (5)
26 Parched (4)
27 Vitality (3)
29 Make an offer in auction (3)
30 Oilcan (5)
31 Period of history (3)
32 Glacial epoch (6)
34 A river in West Yorkshire (4)
35 Supplications (10)

DOWN

1 Doomed (6)
2 Male humans (3)
3 Upbeat part of a measure (5)
4 Irritate (4)
5 Occuring throughout a city (8)
6 Company of actors (6)
8 Large (3)
9 Horse of mixed colour (4)
12 Confusion (7)
14 Not hollow (5)
16 A bout of fun or drinking (5)
18 The West (8)
19 A young man (3)
20 Idiot (3)
22 Likely to change (6)
23 Relating to urine (4)
25 Declared (6)
27 Contend (3)
28 French for thank you (5)
30 A double S-shaped curve (4)
33 Possesses (3)

ACROSS

1 Umbrella (slang) (6)
4 Jumble facts (6)
7 Shut in due to cetain weather condition (9)
10 Emerald ---- (4)
11 Of recent origin (3)
12 Lees (anag.) (4)
13 Without (4)
15 Effeminate male (5)
18 Musical drama (5)
20 Charge payable for permisison to pass (4)
21 Obtained from urine (4)
22 Small salamanders (5)
24 Go into (5)
26 Impetus (4)
29 Recess (4)
31 Be in debt (3)
32 Cooking chamber (4)
33 Parts of the universe capable of supporting life (9)
34 Christian festival (6)
35 Womb (6)

DOWN

1 Enlargement of toe joint (6)
2 Solitary (4)
3 Gapes (5)
4 Adult (5)
5 Mysterious poem (4)
6 Excrement (6)
7 Obliquely (9)
8 Legume (4)
9 Sleuth (9)
14 Annoyed (4)
16 Portable bed (3)
17 Another (4)
19 Slender metal fastener (3)
22 Subtle difference (6)
23 Gape (4)
25 Renovates (6)
27 One that fails to win (5)
28 First PM of India (5)
30 Authentic (4)
32 Wreath encircling a helmet (4)

192

ACROSS
1 Against (4)
3 Mulberry tree (8)
6 Connecting (7)
9 Misuse (5)
12 Nobleman (4)
14 Pinch (3)
15 Craven (9)
17 Expensive (4)
18 Sash worn on a kimono (3)
19 Progressive emaciation (5)
21 Roman goddess of plenty (3)
22 A nobleman (4)
23 Miserly (9)
27 Pronoun (3)
29 Metal fastener (4)
30 Hindu religious teacher (5)
31 Unconventional person (7)
33 Plant with small spiky flowers (8)
34 Long or rambling story (4)

DOWN
1 Metallic compound (5)
2 Group (3)
3 Tendon (5)
4 No sense of pain (9)
5 Taking effect at a specified date (law) (4)
7 A woman who has never borne a child (9)
8 Goad for driving cattle (3)
10 Pathless (9)
11 Fencing swords (5)
13 Travelled on horse back (4)
16 Every eight years (9)
18 Vows (5)
20 Melody (4)
24 Castrated male cat (3)
25 Beam of light (5)
26 Territory in NW Canada (5)
28 Female sheep (4)
32 Attempt (3)

ACROSS

1 Sweater (8)
5 It was (4)
8 Japan's curency (3)
9 Parallel hill lines on maps (8)
11 Crown of the head (4)
13 Not native (6)
15 Adjacent (7)
16 Principal ore of lead (6)
19 Idiot (3)
21 And not (3)
22 Showered (6)
25 Profitable (7)
26 Method (6)
30 Japanese rice beer (4)
31 Precision (8)
32 Finish first (3)
33 Is not (4)
34 Word game (8)

DOWN

2 Containing uranium (6)
3 Consisting of words (6)
4 Flower (4)
5 An error in keyed work (4)
6 The state of the atmosphere (7)
7 Against (4)
10 A South China Sea island (6)
12 Showy actions (5)
14 Capital of Shaanxi province, China (4)
17 Someone that gives credit (6)
18 Copper and zinc alloy (5)
19 Waterproof fabric (7)
20 Festive occasion (4)
23 4th sign of the zodiac (6)
24 Pertaining to the cheek (6)
27 Infectious tropical disease (4)
28 Portable shelter (4)
29 Floor coverings (4)

194

ACROSS

1 Intimacy (11)
8 Flowers (5)
10 Antelope (5)
12 Hire out (3)
14 Burn without flame (7)
16 French clergyman (4)
18 Globe (3)
20 Hold as an opinion (4)
21 Categorise (4)
22 Rainy (3)
24 Weeding implement (3)
25 Edible tropical Asian plant (4)
26 Metallic element (4)
27 Small cask (3)
28 Way out (4)
29 Torment (7)
33 Powdery residue (3)
35 Fragrant resin (5)
36 Relating to the ileum (5)
37 Increasing in heat (11)

DOWN

1 Thwart (4)
2 Auction room or trade centre (4)
3 To a smaller extent (4)
4 Too (4)
5 Frozen (4)
6 An annual publication (8)
7 Total sum of money allocated (6)
9 Peculate (8)
11 Strap (5)
13 Cerumen (6)
15 A fragrant yellow essential oil (8)
17 Breeches (6)
19 Disease due to lack of vitamin B (8)
23 Pole (5)
25 Shipworm (6)
30 Flat circular plate (4)
31 Phial (4)
32 Limbs (4)
33 Continuous dull pain (4)
34 Grove (4)

ACROSS
1 Inescapable (11)
6 Female red grouse (7)
9 Turf (3)
12 In a different place (9)
14 Paste made from seasame seeds (6)
15 A city in central China (4)
16 Label (3)
17 Epic poetry (4)
18 Portuguese equivalent of Don (3)
19 Stepped (4)
20 Not wet (3)
22 Musical instrument (4)
24 Expulsion (6)
25 Indifferent (9)
27 Nevertheless (3)
28 Directed towards a goal (5)
29 Having little courage (11)

DOWN
2 Greek goddess (6)
3 Admits (4)
4 Hawaiian greeting (5)
5 Supperficial knowledge (10)
7 Study of snakes (9)
8 Biblical high priest (3)
9 Drink greedily (4)
10 Resembling a treelike crystalised mineral (9)
11 Long for (10)
13 Test (4)
16 Plaything (3)
18 Sedement in a liquid (4)
20 A thing of small value (4)
21 Cherry stone(6)
23 Desolate (5)
24 First number (3)
26 Highest volcano in Europe (4)

196

ACROSS

2 Sorcery (10)
7 Indolently (4)
8 Shrew (6)
10 Jelly (3)
11 Customary(5)
13 Captive soldier (3)
15 Abstract being (3)
16 Duration (4)
17 Musical composition (5)
20 Small mountains (5)
21 Serving to educate (9)
22 Young fowl (5)
24 Hindu ascetic (5)
26 Barbarous person (4)
27 Nectar-gathering insect (3)
29 Biblical high priest (3)
30 Corridors (5)
31 Haul (3)
32 Hopple (6)
34 Very dark colour (4)
35 Moroccan city (10)

DOWN

1 Delay (6)
2 A side issue (3)
3 Spring up (5)
4 Drudge (4)
5 Wrestled (8)
6 Buffoons (6)
8 Duct (3)
9 Score (4)
12 Disentangle (7)
14 Become confused (5)
16 9th Jewish month (5)
18 Inflammation of a nerve (8)
19 Not in (3)
20 Belonging to him (3)
22 Resembling poetry (6)
23 Look at amorously (4)
25 Relax (6)
27 Ban (3)
28 Like an elf (5)
30 Aromatic plant (4)
33 Meadow (3)

ACROSS
1 Illegible handwriting (6)
4 Club (6)
7 Reconciliation (9)
10 Class (4)
11 Leg (inf.) (3)
12 ---- of Knowledge, Garden of Eden (4)
13 Biblical twin (4)
15 Ivory (5)
18 Wanderer (5)
20 Furniture wood (4)
21 Thrust with a knife (4)
22 Twilight (5)
24 Lowermost deck (5)
26 Sewing case (4)
29 Ardent (4)
31 Tavern (3)
32 Obstacle (4)
33 Travelling bag (9)
34 Short and blunt (6)
35 Dried grape (6)

DOWN
1 Group of seven (6)
2 Poker stake (4)
3 Rope to guide a horse (5)
4 Punctuation mark (5)
5 Slight hollow (4)
6 Fable (6)
7 Papal (9)
8 Not difficult (4)
9 Tremulant (9)
14 Until (4)
16 NZ parrot (3)
17 Identical (4)
19 Lever for rowing (3)
22 Eats grass (6)
23 Crescent-shaped figure (4)
25 Plump bird (6)
27 Liable to tip over (5)
28 Bury (5)
30 Paint unskilfully (4)
32 Japanese liquor (4)

198

ACROSS
1 New Orleans music (4)
3 Small, round and shiny (8)
6 Little wing (7)
9 Plinth (5)
12 Having a sound mind (4)
14 Petroleum (3)
15 Child (9)
17 Smallest component (4)
18 Also (3)
19 Hindu loincloth (5)
21 Long period of time (3)
22 Trademark (4)
23 Improving (9)
27 Unit of energy (3)
29 Rip (4)
30 Perhaps (5)
31 Agent of retribution (7)
33 Suburbs collectively (8)
34 Unemployment cheque (4)

DOWN
1 Jewish collectively (5)
2 One of a sharp series of twists and turns (3)
3 Consecrate (5)
4 Abandonment (9)
5 Wife of Shiva (4)
7 Study of the nerves (9)
8 Cheap and vulgar (3)
10 Make-up (9)
11 Small and sprightly (5)
13 Trim (4)
16 Gadget inventor (9)
18 Emblem (5)
20 Sharpen (4)
24 Chinese dynasty (3)
25 Area used for sports (5)
26 Gadget (5)
28 Rough earthenware (4)
32 Ovum (3)

ACROSS
1 Perforate (8)
5 Half burnt coal (4)
8 Romanian money (3)
9 Shop of a pawnbroker (8)
11 Increases (4)
13 Metallic element (6)
15 Flexible (7)
16 Easily bent (6)
19 A playing card (3)
21 Indian dish (3)
22 Security (6)
25 Dispute (7)
26 On fire (6)
30 Italian money (4)
31 A minor work (8)
32 Printer's measures (3)
33 Low growing plant (4)
34 Unnecessary (8)

DOWN
2 Convenient for use (6)
3 Upward (6)
4 Public exhibition (4)
5 Edible mollusc (4)
6 Having an Oedipus complex(7)
7 African antelope (4)
10 Subtle difference (6)
12 One who shapes metal (5)
14 Immature herring (4)
17 Medical (6)
18 Customary (5)
19 States as a fact (7)
20 Engrave with acid (4)
23 Small tube (6)
24 Greek god of winds (6)
27 Stead (4)
28 Deep wound (4)
29 Ripped (4)

200

1		2		3		4		5		6	■	7
	■		■		■		■		■		■	
	■	8			9		■	10	11			
12	13		■	14			15				■	
■		■	■	■		■		■	16		17	
18		19	■	20				■	21			
■	22		23	■		■		■	24			■
25				■	26				■	27		
28				■		■		■	■	■		■
	■	29		30		31		32	■	33		34
35					■	36					■	
	■		■		■		■		■		■	
	■	37										

ACROSS
1 Traitorous (11)
8 Modify (5)
10 Defamation (5)
12 Greek letter(3)
14 Eyelash cosmetic (7)
16 Land measure (4)
18 Airport code for Dallas (3)
20 Close (4)
21 Witty remark (4)
22 Music concert (3)
24 Information technology system (acronym) (3)
25 Hyperbolic sine (abbrev.) (4)
26 Narrow strip of fabric (4)
27 Join to something else (3)
28 Garment of Rome (4)
29 Remove obstruction (7)
33 Find the sum of (3)
35 Experiment (5)
36 Uncultivated country (5)
37 Expeditiously (11)

DOWN
1 Demonstrative adjective (4)
2 Son of Isaac (4)
3 Stuff (4)
4 Gobbles up (4)
5 Earthen pot (4)
6 Moderately acute (8)
7 Dormant state (6)
9 Pertaining to a parent (8)
11 Resident of Iraq (5)
13 Slowly (6)
15 Shell of a turtle (8)
17 Dared(6)
19 Pasta (8)
23 Republic in W. Africa (5)
25 Declared (6)
30 Hitch (4)
31 Was indebted to (4)
32 Cabbage like plant (4)
33 Entrance (4)
34 Repudiate (4)

		1		2		3			4			
5												
6		7			8			9		10		11
				12			13					
14							15					
						16						
17					18				19			
				20				21				
		22	23				24					
25						26						
		27				28						
29												

ACROSS
1 Expecting the worst (11)
6 Risk (7)
9 Plant juice (3)
12 Lasting a moment (9)
14 Bean (6)
15 Demeanour (4)
16 Drag (3)
17 Waste time aimlessly (4)
18 Bodily vessel (3)
19 S-shaped (4)
20 Go astray (3)
22 Inquires (4)
24 Intense fear (6)
25 Hidden (9)
27 Marker (3)
28 Concerned with a specific subject (5)
29 Disease of the heart (11)

DOWN
2 Resembling a slum (6)
3 Separate article (4)
4 Internal USA territory (5)
5 President's office (4-6)
7 Confers with others (9)
8 Fish embryo (3)
9 To sneak (4)
10 Eulogy (9)
11 Make symmetrical (10)
13 Aussie birds (4)
16 Thrash (3)
18 Passport endorsement (4)
20 Timber at ship stern (4)
21 A cardinal(6)
23 Parboil (5)
24 Spread out for drying (3)
26 Torch (4)

202

ACROSS

2 Covered with Parmesan (10)
7 Give counsel (4)
8 Flightless NZ parrot (6)
10 Not on (3)
11 Plant louse (5)
13 To ban from entry (3)
15 Juice (3)
16 Crazy (inf.) (4)
17 Result (5)
20 Streamlined (5)
21 Instruct (9)
22 Anti-aircraft artillery (5)
24 Fermenting agent (5)
26 Lubricate (4)
27 A physician (inf.) (3)
29 Gone by (3)
30 Company motifs (5)
31 Vital force (Chinese) (3)
32 Film comedian and director (6)
34 Water (4)
35 Hot-air bath (10)

DOWN

1 Furrow (6)
2 Clothes fastener (3)
3 Harvests (5)
4 Delighted (4)
5 Blue-green algae (8)
6 Parka (6)
8 Animal hide (3)
9 Leaf of a book (4)
12 Defeated (7)
14 Dolt (5)
16 Glowing coal (5)
18 Region bordering the coast (8)
19 A moose (3)
20 Pig's home (3)
22 Scales (6)
23 Sled (4)
25 Having three parts (6)
27 Put on (3)
28 Raccoon-like animal (5)
30 Attic (4)
33 Bad actor (3)

ACROSS

1 Eccentric (6)
4 Flexible (6)
7 Playfully jocular (9)
10 Snare (4)
11 Destiny (3)
12 Alter position (4)
13 Lees (4)
15 Rotating mechanism (5)
18 Articles in a newspaper (5)
20 ---- vera, Mediterranean plant (4)
21 Person addicted to drugs (4)
22 Botch (5)
24 Be silent (5)
26 Finely powdered earth (4)
29 Tiny amount of money (4)
31 Pod vegetable (3)
32 Particles (4)
33 Lightweight folding chair (4-5)
34 To call together (6)
35 40th US President (6)

DOWN

1 Brooding hen (6)
2 Fellow (4)
3 Give up (5)
4 Connecting series of rooms (5)
5 Sulk (4)
6 Antelopes (6)
7 Bizarre (9)
8 Move briskly (4)
9 Take to below freezing (9)
14 Essential point (4)
16 Advanced in years (3)
17 Crucifix (4)
19 Hot beverage (3)
22 A psychic (6)
23 Employs (4)
25 16th-century French silver coin (6)
27 Higher (5)
28 Potato (inf.) (5)
30 Sharp to the taste (4)
32 Very small amount (4)

204

ACROSS

1 A petty quarrel (4)
3 Bitterness of nature (8)
6 Weapon storage (7)
9 Cadge (5)
12 Roof overhang (4)
14 Sum charged (3)
15 A soldier (9)
17 Small area surrounded by water (4)
18 Universal distress signal (3)
19 Finnish monetary unit (5)
21 Doze (3)
22 Melt (4)
23 For immediate use (5-4)
27 Possesses (3)
29 Authentic (4)
30 All (mus.) (5)
31 Hindu deity (7)
33 Red wood (8)
34 Unit of linear measure (4)

DOWN

1 Precisely (inf.) (5)
2 Also (3)
3 Land measures (5)
4 Vastness (9)
5 Pleasing (4)
7 Investigation into financial means (5-4)
8 Sweet potato (3)
10 Composer (9)
11 Agitated (3-2)
13 Futile (4)
16 Leaving (9)
18 Vision (5)
20 Water carrier (4)
24 Diving bird (3)
25 Bowler hat (5)
26 Antelope with twisted horns (5)
28 Presence (4)
32 Asian condiment (3)

1	2				3		4	■	5	6	7	

ACROSS

1 Occurring in all places (4-4)
5 Verge (4)
8 Afternoon meal (3)
9 Japanese dish (8)
11 Puts into service (4)
13 Large venomous snake (6)
15 To recover (7)
16 Average (6)
19 Sole (3)
21 Title of respect (3)
22 Noon (6)
25 Close friend (7)
26 Squirts (6)
30 Before long (4)
31 Harden (8)
32 Alimentary canal (3)
33 Pancake made from rice flour (4)
34 Emaciated (8)

DOWN

2 Accustoms (6)
3 Sloping letter (6)
4 Make changes to text (4)
5 A case for small articles (4)
6 Hopelessness (7)
7 Greek goddess of the earth (4)
10 Away from the coast (6)
12 Fishhook line (5)
14 Pips on a domino (4)
17 Baby's nappy (6)
18 Gather (5)
19 Having a distinctive smell (7)
20 Not difficult (4)
23 Pamper (6)
24 A wide, deep collar (6)
27 ---- stick, child's plaything (4)
28 Rectangular pier (4)
29 Drinks slowly (4)

206

ACROSS

1 Overcrowded (11)
8 Not suitable (5)
10 Excrete (5)
12 As well as (3)
14 Nose opening (7)
16 Adjoin (4)
18 Boy (3)
20 Sets of tools (4)
21 Not any (4)
22 Docket (3)
24 Hit lightly (3)
25 Soybean (4)
26 Peruse (4)
27 Convert into leather (3)
28 Acute lung injury (acronym) (4)
29 Act of reuniting (7)
33 Peculiar (3)
35 Apparel (5)
36 Trail (5)
37 Wife of a marquess (11)

DOWN

1 Brief (4)
2 A hodgepodge (4)
3 Asian prince (4)
4 Fragments (4)
5 Above (4)
6 A riverboat for freight (8)
7 Sagacious (6)
9 Elementary particle (8)
11 Huge (5)
13 Speaker (6)
15 Person who makes a will (8)
17 Owing (6)
19 Reverie(8)
23 Tenuous substances (5)
25 Make unhappy (6)
30 Someone who employs something (4)
31 Intense irritation (4)
32 Western pact (4)
33 Migrant farm worker (4)
34 Puts on (4)

		1		2		3			4			
5												
6		7			8			9		10		11
				12			13					
14							15					
						16						
17					18				19			
				20				21				
		22	23				24					
25						26						
		27				28						
29												

ACROSS

1 Dispossess (11)
6 Spear-shaped (7)
9 Ocean (3)
12 Fit to be vended again (9)
14 Unlock (6)
15 Bell-shaped flower (4)
16 Young dog (3)
17 Analogous (4)
18 Precious mineral (3)
19 Piece of land surrounded by water (4)
20 Hawaiian acacia (3)
22 Bone of the forearm (4)
24 Bureau (6)
25 Bony structures (9)
27 Shoot a marble (3)
28 Member of the Tanoan people (5)
29 Lines of verse with no pause (11)

DOWN

2 Opalescent (6)
3 Lyric poems (4)
4 Standard of perfection (5)
5 Stiffness in the joints (10)
7 Nickname (9)
8 9th letter of the Hebrew alphabet (3)
9 Slide (4)
10 Ethiopia (9)
11 Bygone times (10)
13 Metal used as a hardener (4)
16 Small green vegetable (3)
18 Capricorn (4)
20 Understood (4)
21 Disgusting (6)
23 S. American ruminant (5)
24 Tropical black bird with a long tail (3)
26 Native of Oklahoma (slang) (4)

208

ACROSS

2 Extremely sacred (10)
7 To the inside of (4)
8 Old Scottish coin (6)
10 If and only if (3)
11 Envelop in fog (5)
13 Long-tailed rodent (3)
15 Wield (3)
16 Beat up (4)
17 Renown (5)
20 Speed (5)
21 Horizontal plant stem (9)
22 Nymph (5)
24 Brag (5)
26 Baking chamber (4)
27 Porcino mushroom (3)
29 Unit of weight (3)
30 French capital (5)
31 Mongrel dog (3)
32 Part of a stamen (6)
34 Rajah's wife (4)
35 Quarantine flag (10)

DOWN

1 Preference (6)
2 Peat moss (3)
3 Chirp (5)
4 Coarse tobacco (4)
5 Central US state (8)
6 Grow teeth (6)
8 Male child (3)
9 The Orient (4)
12 Nervous excitement (7)
14 Moan (5)
16 Salted, smoked pigmeat (5)
18 Eastern (8)
19 10th Hebrew letter (3)
20 Fireplace shelf (3)
22 Scrivener (6)
23 English river (4)
25 Distended (6)
27 Automobile (3)
28 Flipper (5)
30 South American money (4)
33 Lowest male rank in RAF (3)

ACROSS

1 Scar tissue (6)
4 Decrepit auto (6)
7 Accurately (9)
10 Roofing cover (4)
11 Bosom supporter (3)
12 Jump (4)
13 Christmas (4)
15 Canoe (5)
18 Threnody (5)
20 Thick slice (4)
21 Young salmon (4)
22 Takes paying guests (5)
24 NZ aboriginal (5)
26 Evaluation of skill (4)
29 Sisters (4)
31 Geological epoch (3)
32 Crack (4)
33 Rapt (9)
34 Rural (6)
35 Chant (6)

DOWN

1 Indonesian cigarette (6)
2 Musical instrument (4)
3 English town (5)
4 Mud hut (5)
5 Recline (4)
6 Joyful exclamation (6)
7 Argillite (9)
8 Observant Jews area (4)
9 Continuing through year (9)
14 Red wax coated cheese (4)
16 Fermented malt (3)
17 Mustard family plant (4)
19 Individual Retirement Account (acronym) (3)
22 Hamper (6)
23 Portuguese city (4)
25 Pierce (6)
27 Deficient in moisture (5)
28 African people (5)
30 Nasal phlegm (slang) (4)
32 Denomination (4)

210

ACROSS
1 Capital of Fiji (4)
3 A fold in rocks (8)
6 One who makes affidavit (7)
9 Pale bluish purple (5)
12 Deprived of sensation (4)
14 River in Thailand (3)
15 Digging machine (9)
17 Plunge head-first (4)
18 Drunkard (3)
19 Despised (5)
21 Narrow beam of light (3)
22 Mountain goat (4)
23 Behave badly (9)
27 Bird resembling the cassowary (3)
29 Jacob's twin (4)
30 Gum (5)
31 Roll (7)
33 Scorn (8)
34 Grove (4)

DOWN
1 Reptile (5)
2 The bird's name was Ian (anag.) (3)
3 Traditional Moslem law (5)
4 English university city (9)
5 Bright star (4)
7 Humorous (9)
8 Shorter Egyptian king (3)
10 Crafty (9)
11 Diplomatic agent (5)
13 Method (4)
16 Fury (9)
18 To swerve from a course (5)
20 Line about which an object rotates (4)
24 Posed (3)
25 Graduated glass tube (5)
26 Upright (5)
28 Written reminder (4)
32 Classic Japan drama (3)

ACROSS

1 Jovial (8)
5 Swell (4)
8 Malt beverage (3)
9 Make dull (8)
11 Sudden assault (4)
13 Agile (6)
15 Soft cheese (7)
16 Consign (6)
19 Exploit (3)
21 Grassland (3)
22 Added (6)
25 Chief (7)
26 Idle (6)
30 Rotate (4)
31 One-celled organisms (8)
32 Formerly known as (3)
33 Aggregate (4)
34 One of the twelve tribes of Israel (8)

DOWN

2 Conciliatory (6)
3 Loyalty (6)
4 Mortgage (4)
5 Moderate temperature (4)
6 USA state(7)
7 Face cover (4)
10 Conceit (6)
12 Divinity (5)
14 Image of a deity (4)
17 Interfere (6)
18 UK horse-racing town (5)
19 Referees (7)
20 Snake-like fish (4)
23 US railroad porter (6)
24 Pertaining to the races (6)
27 Large marine fish (4)
28 Singles (4)
29 Black (4)

212

ACROSS

1 Permanence (11)
8 Relating to palm of the hand (5)
10 Listens (5)
12 Golfer's tee (3)
14 Accomplish (7)
16 Upswept hairstyle (4)
18 Pronoun (3)
20 12th Jewish month (4)
21 Town in Kent (4)
22 Fahrenheit abbreviated (3)
24 Superlative form (3)
25 Ruined city of Iran (4)
26 Shrewd (4)
27 A can (3)
28 Mountains (4)
29 Eternal (7)
33 Incite (3)
35 Short surplice (5)
36 Boggy (5)
37 Crux (5-6)

DOWN

1 Boring annoying person (slang) (4)
2 Talk irrationally (4)
3 Rodent (4)
4 Unique (4)
5 Chinese instrument (4)
6 Most precipitous (8)
7 Firearm (6)
9 Pertaining to the axilla (8)
11 Musical study piece (5)
13 Thorough view (6)
15 Resembling a calyx (8)
17 Going out with(6)
19 Russian mystic (8)
23 Contraction of has not (5)
25 Intoxicated (6)
30 Slender missile (4)
31 Full of doubts (4)
32 Growl (4)
33 Little island in a river (4)
34 Between black and white (4)

ACROSS
1 Clearly stated (11)
6 Small portable house (7)
9 A blackjack (3)
12 Muchness (9)
14 Beard (6)
15 Placed a golf ball (4)
16 To yield (3)
17 TV award (4)
18 To dip lightly in water (3)
19 Beige (4)
20 Spoken Morse dash (3)
22 Standard (4)
24 Naked (6)
25 Poverty (9)
27 Yes (3)
28 Measuring device (5)
29 X-ray photography of a breast (11)

DOWN
2 Lumberjack (6)
3 Sand hill (4)
4 Silly (5)
5 Arrogant (10)
7 Asset easily converted (9)
8 Part of verb to be (3)
9 Simmer (4)
10 Pertaining to lice(9)
11 Stunningly surprising (10)
13 On the top (4)
16 Exclamation (3)
18 Ruin (4)
20 Fall in drops (4)
21 Part of the foot (6)
23 Music hall (5)
24 Employ (3)
26 Islamic chieftain (4)

214

ACROSS

2 Confidential (10)
7 Not much at all (4)
8 A wine store (6)
10 Sphere (3)
11 Radioactive gas (5)
13 Gave food (3)
15 A failure (3)
16 Yearn deeply (4)
17 Prince of India (5)
20 Part of small intestine (5)
21 Applicable in all cases (9)
22 Mooch (5)
24 Middle (5)
26 Therefore (4)
27 S. African word for hill (3)
29 Male sheep (3)
30 Sweetheart (5)
31 Banish (3)
32 Spain and Portugal (6)
34 A metrical foot (4)
35 Business activity (10)

DOWN

1 Nonbeliever in Islam (6)
2 Small domestic feline (3)
3 In front (5)
4 Picture (4)
5 Sheet of floating ice (8)
6 Crown (6)
8 A person (3)
9 Knee (4)
12 Duchy (7)
14 Mud from thermal springs (5)
16 Tartan (5)
18 Discernment (8)
19 Hasten (3)
20 Doctrine (3)
22 Moderate to deep red (6)
23 Bedouin (4)
25 Pulsates (6)
27 New Zealand parrot (3)
28 Verily (Fr.) (5)
30 One who tells lies (4)
33 Decease (3)

215

1			2		3	■	4		5			6

ACROSS

1 Translucent plastic (6)
4 Obdurate (6)
7 Drought resistant space (9)
10 Hold as an opinion (4)
11 Vehicle (3)
12 Formerly (4)
13 Stepped (4)
15 Dry red wine (5)
18 Warble (5)
20 Large burrowing rodent (4)
21 Persian fairy (4)
22 Red earth pigment (5)
24 Right (5)
26 Iranian Money (4)
29 Brass wind instrument (4)
31 Alkali (3)
32 Volcano which last erupted in 1961 (4)
33 Subject to excise (9)
34 Remnant (6)
35 One who sells lingerie (6)

DOWN

1 Climbing device (6)
2 Specific thing (4)
3 Decree (5)
4 Very large in scale (5)
5 Easy stride (4)
6 Inn (6)
7 One who is frightened of foreigners (9)
8 Reddish brown quartz (4)
9 Extirpate(9)
14 Famous Quaker martyr(4)
16 Glass container (3)
17 A tree with winged fruit (4)
19 Metal-bearing mineral (3)
22 Vent (6)
23 Puts down (4)
25 Catapult (6)
27 Greek epic poem (5)
28 Percolate (5)
30 Wheel shaft (4)
32 Old cloth measures (4)

216

ACROSS

1 Swagger (4)
3 Welsh native (8)
6 Make rough (7)
9 Full of news (5)
12 Ethereal (4)
14 Garden implement (3)
15 Homesickness (9)
17 Let it stand (4)
18 Indian dish (3)
19 Lawsuits (5)
21 Lion---, female (3)
22 Combustible matter (4)
23 In name only (9)
27 German river (3)
29 No longer living (4)
30 Religion founded in Iran (5)
31 Arsenic sulfide (7)
33 Growing underground (8)
34 Horses of a brownish grey colour (4)

DOWN

1 Member of the nobility (5)
2 Two-wheeled one-horse carriage (3)
3 Mosquito bite (5)
4 Chinese revolutionary leader (9)
5 Too (4)
7 Generous (9)
8 Negative (3)
10 Surrender flag (9)
11 Shouts (5)
13 Ascend (4)
16 Moving upward (9)
18 Nerd (5)
20 Drug yielding plant (4)
24 Impair (3)
25 Perfect (5)
26 Back gardens (US) (5)
28 Numerous (4)
32 Cover (3)

ACROSS

1 Suitable (8)
5 Placed a golf ball (4)
8 Chop (3)
9 Chat (8)
11 Minerals (4)
13 Spurt (6)
15 Situated on the side (7)
16 Heavy rope for mooring (6)
19 Apply (3)
21 Nevertheless (3)
22 Fur skins (6)
25 Rattling sound(7)
26 Joined by treaty (6)
30 Nipple (4)
31 Strengthen (8)
32 Consumed (3)
33 The objective *they* (4)
34 Staggered (8)

DOWN

2 Antelopes (6)
3 Foray (6)
4 Departs (4)
5 The addressee (anac.) (4)
6 Spookiest (7)
7 Jug (4)
10 Involving sexism (6)
12 Severe (5)
14 Wharf (4)
17 Veer toward the west (6)
18 Small fish (5)
19 Wail (7)
20 Bird, *Haliaeetus albicilla* (4)
23 Dodged (6)
24 Come to a conclusion (6)
27 Wife of Jacob (4)
28 Time (anag.) (4)
29 Couple (4)

218

ACROSS
1 Rascal (11)
8 Mingle (5)
10 Go into (5)
12 Unit of resistance (3)
14 Electric appliance (7)
16 Starchy food grain (4)
18 Spur on (3)
20 Torch (4)
21 Flesh of a calf (4)
22 Chatter (3)
24 Half-sized ems (3)
25 Trickery (4)
26 Unconvincing (4)
27 Peg used to hodl a ball (3)
28 Seaward (4)
29 Convent for nuns (7)
33 Very first number (3)
35 Spanish bagpipe (5)
36 Slap (5)
37 Without limit (11)

DOWN
1 Repeat (4)
2 Prissy (4)
3 Used to untangle hair (4)
4 Elegance (4)
5 Chilled (4)
6 Nourishing (8)
7 Light reddish brown (6)
9 Inference (8)
11 Impertinence (5)
13 Scottish pudding (6)
15 Turnip-shaped (8)
17 Garrison (6)
19 Galen's medical system (8)
23 Beautiful (slang) (5)
25 Move back and forth (6)
30 A grandmother (4)
31 Name from the Bible (4)
32 Lively (4)
33 Native of Oklahoma (inf.) (4)
34 Goddess of strife (4)

ACROSS

1 Act of deifying (11)
6 Masquerade ball (7)
9 By way of (3)
12 Alderman (archaic) (9)
14 Arrival (6)
15 Lubricates (4)
16 Used for resting (3)
17 Doing nothing (4)
18 And not (3)
19 Fast aircraft (4)
20 One who steers a ship (3)
22 ---- of Dogs (4)
24 Head garland (6)
25 Insipid (9)
27 Fruit of the hawthorn berry (3)
28 Amulet (5)
29 Jukebox (11)

DOWN

2 Purpose (6)
3 Image of a deity (4)
4 Whirl (5)
5 Originality (10)
7 Manta (9)
8 Make lace (3)
9 Empty (4)
10 Netherlands city (9)
11 Modest (10)
13 One who does (4)
16 A container (3)
18 Festive season (4)
20 Ball of yarn (4)
21 Demented (6)
23 Pile (5)
24 --- blonde, hair colouring (3)
26 Reflection (4)

220

ACROSS
2 Irregular heartbeat (10)
7 Voluntary contributions (4)
8 Pertaining to revenues (6)
10 Space (3)
11 Grey (5)
13 Gorged (3)
15 Haul (3)
16 Forage (4)
17 ----- mortis, muscular stiffening (5)
20 Run away with lover (5)
21 N. Ireland Protestant (9)
22 Puff up (5)
24 Offspring (5)
26 Helper (4)
27 id ---, i.e. (3)
29 Uncooked (3)
30 Alternative (5)
31 Edge (3)
32 Containing iridium (6)
34 Exhort (4)
35 Enrolment (10)

DOWN
1 Jackfish (6)
2 Request (3)
3 Heat excessively (5)
4 Lean (4)
5 Tubular pasta (8)
6 Assert (6)
8 Not many (3)
9 Overhead (4)
12 Gluttonous (7)
14 Goddess of seasons (5)
16 Position (5)
18 Benevolence (8)
19 --- race, survival of the fittest (3)
20 Picas (3)
22 Barium sulphate (6)
23 Fibber (4)
25 Inventor of logarithms (6)
27 And so on (abbrev.) (3)
28 Tantalize (5)
30 Anoints (4)
33 Nevertheless (3)

ACROSS

1 Compost (6)
4 Spanish port (6)
7 Stately (9)
10 Limericks (4)
11 Large parrot (NZ) (3)
12 Prima donna (4)
13 Pipe elbows (4)
15 Ooze out (5)
18 Feudal vassal (5)
20 N. American rail (4)
21 A rough edge (4)
22 Hindu religious teacher (5)
24 Woman's undergarment (5)
26 Large bag (4)
29 Elongated S (4)
31 First note of a music scale (3)
32 Flagon (4)
33 Inhabitant of Mycenae (9)
34 Method (6)
35 Form into fire (6)

DOWN

1 Resist (6)
2 Extinct wild ox (4)
3 Elicit (5)
4 Basic (5)
5 Extol (4)
6 A layperson (6)
7 Capital of Israel (9)
8 Electric ----, fish with powerful discharge (4)
9 Heavy quilt (9)
14 Loose woman (4)
16 Dominican (abbrev.) (3)
17 Goddess of chaos (4)
19 Wrath (3)
22 Chairs (6)
23 Image (4)
25 Lively (6)
27 Revoke a legacy (5)
28 Light olive brown (5)
30 Ait (4)
32 Acquire (4)

222

ACROSS

1 Team (4)
3 Cut short, crisply (music) (8)
6 Having an Oedipus complex (7)
9 Friend (5)
12 Bract (4)
14 Heckle (3)
15 Herb doctor (9)
17 Islet (4)
18 End of Data (acronym) (3)
19 Fatty part of milk (5)
21 Not (Scot) (3)
22 Chinese 2-stringed instrument (4)
23 Detach (9)
27 Travel on snow (3)
29 Storage space (4)
30 Purposeful (5)
31 Rot (7)
33 Trifling (8)
34 To put out (4)

DOWN

1 Laziness (5)
2 Biblical judge of Israel (3)
3 Dandruff (5)
4 Artisan (9)
5 Roman garment (4)
7 Recklessly bold (9)
8 Wreath of flowers (3)
10 Inanimate (9)
11 Pointed arch (5)
13 Continent (4)
16 Domain controlled by an archduke (9)
18 Excrete (5)
20 Spoil (4)
24 Taste (3)
25 Musical composition (5)
26 Country in NE Africa (5)
28 French military cap (4)
32 Dowel (3)

ACROSS

1 Venomous (8)
5 Black in colour (4)
8 Yonder (3)
9 Divide into pages (8)
11 Large stone (4)
13 Mythical sea monster (6)
15 Violinist (7)
16 Informal chat (6)
19 Pitcher (3)
21 Sheep in its 2nd year (3)
22 Protective coating (6)
25 Garden of fruit trees (7)
26 Wide stiff collar (6)
30 Retail store (4)
31 Scepticism (8)
32 East-Northeast (abbrev.) (3)
33 US stock exchange (4)
34 Native of Sudan (8)

DOWN

2 Slanting letter (6)
3 Medieval artillery (6)
4 Search (4)
5 Jaguarundi (4)
6 Engagement (7)
7 A single time (4)
10 Rare element (6)
12 Door handles (5)
14 Public disturbance (4)
17 Sanctuary (6)
18 Rips (5)
19 Mandible (7)
20 Notable adventure (4)
23 Poked (6)
24 Trousers (6)
27 Used to attract attention (4)
28 The vertex (4)
29 Belonging to us (4)

224

ACROSS

1 Young (11)
8 Fibre of the pineapple (5)
10 Dandy (5)
12 The sun (3)
14 Port on San Francisco Bay (7)
16 Sleeveless garment (4)
18 Mouthpiece of a bridle (3)
20 Mass of floating ice (4)
21 A flower (4)
22 Body of water (3)
24 Boundary (3)
25 Weaving apparatus (4)
26 Component (4)
27 Anhydrous (3)
28 Member of the Quechuan people (4)
29 Single (7)
33 Sorrowful (3)
35 Helmet-shaped structure (5)
36 Very small island (5)
37 An artist (11)

DOWN

1 Jowls (4)
2 Shroud (4)
3 International organization (4)
4 Look for (4)
5 Volcano (4)
6 Offered (8)
7 Chooses (6)
9 Gauzy-winged insect (8)
11 Blacksmith's block (5)
13 Prayer (6)
15 Woody (8)
17 Mountain range (6)
19 Aztec temple (8)
23 Astonish (5)
25 Lords (6)
30 Sailing vessel with 2 masts (4)
31 Greases (4)
32 Pronounce indistinctly (4)
33 Let it stand (4)
34 Expensive (4)

ACROSS

1 Capital of Argentina (6-5)
6 Mirror (7)
9 --- service, cups and saucers (3)
12 Outermost part of the brain (9)
14 Beat soundly (6)
15 Unwilling (4)
16 Sound of mild reproof (3)
17 Hitch (4)
18 Baby's garment (3)
19 Ruler (4)
20 Egg case (3)
22 Tickle (4)
24 Care for (6)
25 Worship (9)
27 Arrest (3)
28 Old French money (5)
29 State of a free person (7-4)

DOWN

2 Before this time (6)
3 Upon (4)
4 Lifeless (5)
5 Unrefined sweetener (5-5)
7 In leaf (9)
8 Porcino (3)
9 Hoot (4)
10 Godless (9)
11 Overstate (10)
13 Bludgeon (4)
16 Muscular contraction (3)
18 Thailand currency (4)
20 Incrustation (4)
21 Period of immaturity (6)
23 Pursue (5)
24 In place of (3)
26 Uncertain (4)

226

ACROSS

- **2** Irregularity in the rhythm of the heart (10)
- **7** Parched (4)
- **8** African republic (6)
- **10** Give a nickname (3)
- **11** Entreaties (5)
- **13** Lass (inf.) (3)
- **15** Termination (3)
- **16** More time in Italy (anag.) (4)
- **17** Burrowing animals (5)
- **20** Italian woman of rank (5)
- **21** Familiarize (9)
- **22** Nocturnal ungulate (5)
- **24** Lump of chewed food (5)
- **26** Curved moulding (4)
- **27** Woman's undergarment (3)
- **29** Generation (3)
- **30** Give up (5)
- **31** A wide sash (3)
- **32** Package (6)
- **34** Indolent (4)
- **35** Chiropodist (10)

DOWN

- **1** Without regularity (6)
- **2** Fuss (3)
- **3** Russian money (5)
- **4** Tugs (4)
- **5** Military stone-thrower (8)
- **6** Flowering shrub (6)
- **8** Far-out (inf.) (3)
- **9** Condemn (4)
- **12** Entrap (7)
- **14** Mysterious (5)
- **16** Spinning shaft (5)
- **18** Having drooping ears (8)
- **19** Knight's title (3)
- **20** A flatfish (3)
- **22** Metal tip on a shoe or boot (6)
- **23** Indian city (4)
- **25** Strikes (6)
- **27** Rubbish container (3)
- **28** Form of defence (5)
- **30** Exercise method (4)
- **33** Intelligence (3)

ACROSS

1 US State (6)
4 Like a zebra (6)
7 Cafeteria (9)
10 Noisy (4)
11 Large brownish-green parrot (3)
12 Baths (4)
13 Droops (4)
15 Kama ----- (5)
18 Strangely (5)
20 Charged particles (4)
21 Woody plant (4)
22 Official language of India (5)
24 Supernatural (5)
26 Delineate (4)
29 Thrust (4)
31 Along (3)
32 Nonsense (slang) (4)
33 Rebellious (9)
34 Approached (6)
35 Make less dangerous (6)

DOWN

1 Undeveloped seeds (6)
2 Showy trinket (4)
3 Notches (5)
4 Pit prop (5)
5 Civil disturbance (4)
6 Frothy (6)
7 Strength of constitution (9)
8 To make healthy (4)
9 Destructive (9)
14 Smarting (4)
16 Slender bar (3)
17 Indigo plant (4)
19 Scottish river (3)
22 Partial antigen (6)
23 Give off (4)
25 Erase (6)
27 Overgrown with climbers (5)
28 Aquatic plant (5)
30 Listen (4)
32 A wide gap (4)

228

ACROSS

1 Rascals (4)
3 Umbilicus (8)
6 Slid (7)
9 Drinking chocolate (5)
12 Take heed (4)
14 Elderly (3)
15 Ribbon worm (9)
17 Eager (4)
18 Amusement (3)
19 Church belonging to a monastery (5)
21 Boy's name (3)
22 Public exhibition (4)
23 Silent (9)
27 More of the same (abbrev.) (3)
29 Soup pasta (4)
30 In front (5)
31 Confine (7)
33 Separated (8)
34 Cartel (4)

DOWN

1 Norwegian dramatist (5)
2 A little taster (3)
3 Not concealed (5)
4 Trite (9)
5 Ancient Greek coin (4)
7 Inherence (9)
8 Jack ---, Brit. comedian (3)
10 Orange-flavoured liqueur (9)
11 Revoke a legacy (5)
13 Sponge dessert (4)
16 Ecstatic (9)
18 Small pit or depression (5)
20 Rude person (4)
24 Israeli submachine gun (3)
25 Wanderer (5)
26 Containing sodium (5)
28 Of thou (4)
32 Round object (3)

ACROSS

1 Osteoid (8)
5 To doff one's hat (4)
8 Past (3)
9 Fine sheep leather (8)
11 Supernatural force (4)
13 Listless (6)
15 Corrupt morally (7)
16 Midday nap (6)
19 Girl making her debut in society (inf.) (3)
21 Food grain (3)
22 Root vegetable (6)
25 Array (7)
26 Electrical unit (6)
30 Punctually (4)
31 Family tree (8)
32 Perceive (3)
33 Devices for fishing (4)
34 Chosen (8)

DOWN

2 A fast-running wild ass (6)
3 Whole (6)
4 A test (4)
5 Upper part of a boot (4)
6 Contrary to (7)
7 Groups of atoms (4)
10 A literate person (6)
12 Advanced (5)
14 Mixture or medley (4)
17 Relaxing (6)
18 Group of eight (5)
19 A tiny drip of liquid (7)
20 Wild pig (4)
23 Herb (6)
24 Electrical resistance (6)
27 Think (4)
28 Peepers (slang) (4)
29 Personalities (4)

230

ACROSS
1 An identifying name (11)
8 Conjunction (5)
10 Big cats (5)
12 Title of respect (3)
14 Proximate (7)
16 Sly look (4)
18 Roman goddess (3)
20 A shrub rose with grey-green leaves (4)
21 Grey eagle (4)
22 Deer (3)
24 Muscular contraction (3)
25 Notion (4)
26 Performs (4)
27 Pet (3)
28 Never (lit.) (4)
29 Costumed procession (7)
33 Seed of a legume (3)
35 Molars (5)
36 African hardwood, mahogany substitute (5)
37 Capsicum (5-6)

DOWN
1 High mountain meadows (4)
2 Superfuse (4)
3 Cut of meat (4)
4 Old Indian coin (4)
5 Indolent (4)
6 Modern (8)
7 Crave (6)
9 An amorous glance (8)
11 Tiles (anag.) (5)
13 Retard in movement (6)
15 Substance that undergoes change in an experiment (8)
17 Cover in a close fitting surround (6)
19 Railway ties (8)
23 Unit for measuring gold (5)
25 Set up (6)
30 Clarified butter (4)
31 Wife of one's uncle (4)
32 Roofing item (4)
33 Quick look (4)
34 Affirm (4)

231

ACROSS
1 Audio system (11)
6 Lubricated (7)
9 Employ (3)
12 Not limited by time (9)
14 Fibre for making mats (6)
15 Exclamation of mild dismay (4)
16 Metal container (3)
17 Narrow strip of land (4)
18 Large cask (3)
19 Sealed with a kiss (abbrev.) (4)
20 Electrical unit (3)
22 Part of a roof (4)
24 Hebrew tribe member (6)
25 Californian grape (9)
27 Sesame (3)
28 A tsarist decree (5)
29 Consequence (5-6)

DOWN
2 Not uttered (6)
3 Team (4)
4 Greek writer of fables (5)
5 Increase power of (10)
7 Competent (9)
8 Basque separatist movement (3)
9 Placed on top (4)
10 Of times past (9)
11 Bramble fruit (10)
13 Grumble (4)
16 Together with (prep.) (3)
18 At that time (4)
20 Elliptic (4)
21 Narrate (6)
23 Blazing (5)
24 Albanian currency (3)
26 False (informal) (4)

232

ACROSS

2 Cause to become hostile (10)
7 Snake-like fish (4)
8 Indian religious leader (6)
10 An so forth (3)
11 Relaxes (5)
13 Greek goddess of the dawn (3)
15 Pig enclosure (3)
16 Having the skill (4)
17 Favoured (5)
20 Measuring device(5)
21 Pluviometer (4-5)
22 Portion (5)
24 Dizzy (5)
26 Whip (4)
27 Command to a horse (3)
29 Emergency Medical Service (acronym) (3)
30 Markets (5)
31 Polite form of address (3)
32 Subsides (6)
34 Too (4)
35 Temple on the Acropolis (10)

DOWN

1 Assails (6)
2 A tree with hard, pale wood (3)
3 US State (5)
4 Responsibility (4)
5 Beholden (8)
6 Rubber (6)
8 Turkish ruler (3)
9 Gap (4)
12 Walk unsteadily (7)
14 Instruct (5)
16 Sponsorship (5)
18 Equine obedience (8)
19 Decease (3)
20 Drinking cup (3)
22 A polite request (6)
23 A metrical foot (4)
25 Composite plant (6)
27 Air-like fluid (3)
28 Short musical composition (5)
30 An interlaced structure (4)
33 Amateur actor (3)

1			2		3	■	4		5			6
	■	■		■		■		■		■	■	
	■	7				8				9	■	
10				■	11			■	12			
	■		■	■	13			14	■		■	
15			16	17	■		■	18	19			
■	■	20				■	21				■	■
22					■	23	■	24				25
	■		■	26	27		28	■	■		■	
29			30	■	31			■	32			
	■	33									■	
	■	■		■		■		■		■	■	
34						■	35					

ACROSS

1 Awkward (6)
4 Become a chrysalis (6)
7 Without knowing (9)
10 Wreath (4)
11 Spanish hero (3)
12 Catalogue (4)
13 Furniture wood (4)
15 Shouts (5)
18 Different (5)
20 Parental sibling (4)
21 Steps descending to a river (4)
22 Expenditure (5)
24 Automatic pistol (5)
26 Blink one eye (4)
29 Taverns (4)
31 Born (3)
32 Large mop (4)
33 Female African gamebird (9)
34 Stifled laugh (6)
35 Nun (6)

DOWN

1 Fashionable (dated) (6)
2 Fruit of the pine (4)
3 Vote for (5)
4 Chinese mammal (5)
5 A chess piece (4)
6 Person in charge of a newspaper (6)
7 Howling loudly (9)
8 Capital of the Ukraine (4)
9 Clothing worn in bed (9)
14 Eyeliner powder (4)
16 Pull laboriously (3)
17 Frozen water vapour (4)
19 19th letter of Greek alphabet (3)
22 Countries of the East (6)
23 Pivotal joint (4)
25 Thief (6)
27 Interior (5)
28 English poet (5)
30 Hard white fat used in cooking (4)
32 Hardens (4)

234

ACROSS

1 At what time (4)
3 Balletic (8)
6 Censure (7)
9 Dispute (5)
12 Makes last (4)
14 Take (3)
15 Callous (9)
17 So be it (4)
18 Aquatic salamander with permanent external gills (3)
19 Hawaiian tree (5)
21 Expression of surprise (3)
22 Glass ornament (4)
23 Street entertainment (5-4)
27 Gone by (3)
29 Flightless birds (4)
30 Wise man (5)
31 Marry (7)
33 Likely (8)
34 Supporter of the Conservative Party (4)

DOWN

1 Value (5)
2 And not (3)
3 Chairman's hammer (5)
4 School form peer (9)
5 Ox also known as the auroch (4)
7 Psalter (5-4)
8 Make last (3)
10 Formerly Canton, China (9)
11 Strange and mysterious (5)
13 Isaac's son (4)
16 Infectious disease of animals (US) (9)
18 Belief involving sorcery (5)
20 A round Dutch cheese (4)
24 Mourn (3)
25 A piece of writing (5)
26 Thin and puny (5)
28 Indian Ox (4)
32 Not in (3)

1	2				3		4 S		5	6	7	
							O		8			
9			10				F		11			12
							13 T	14 U	R	K	E	Y
15												
							16		17			
18		19 O	L	20 D				21				
22				I			23				24	
				E		25						
26	27		28	S	29							
30					31							
	32											
33					34							

ACROSS

1 Contenders (8)
5 Arab sailing vessel (4)
8 Synthetic garnet (3)
9 Faint reddish star (8)
11 Female sheep (4)
13 Christmas poultry (6) ✓
15 Light, golden lager with a strong hop flavour (7)
16 Precious stone (6)
19 Advanced in years (3) ✓
21 Hang down loosely (3)
22 The female organs of a flower (6)
25 Pert. to plants (7)
26 Crush (6)
30 A large enclosed shopping area (US) (4)
31 Augment (8)
32 Metric unit of volume equal to 10 litres (abbrev.) (3)
33 Very muddy or boggy (4)
34 Rice dish (8)

DOWN

2 Conciliatory (6)
3 Eluded (6)
4 Not hard (4) ✓
5 One who dyes (4)
6 Falconry (7)
7 Curve (4)
10 Desalinate (6)
12 Synthesizer (abbrev.) (5)
14 Tropical Asian tree (4)
17 Cause extensive damage to (6)
18 Sudden convulsion (5)
19 Relating to kissing (7)
20 Ceases living (4) ✓
23 Compelled through pressure or necessity (6)
24 Fine cloth (6)
27 Muslim judge (4)
28 Supporter (4)
29 Rube (4)

236

ACROSS
1 The act of saying farewell (11)
8 Part of the large intestine (5)
10 Model of perfection (5)
12 Some (3)
14 Lee side (7)
16 Earthen pot (4)
18 Primate (3)
20 Narrow strip of wood (4)
21 Flesh of a calf (4)
22 Small seed (3)
24 Eastern Standard Time (acronym) (3)
25 Sandy tract (4)
26 Continuous dull pain (4)
27 Feminine pronoun (3)
28 Scottish Gaelic (4)
29 Uppermost part of a tree (7)
33 Type of tree (3)
35 Poetry (5)
36 Once more (5)
37 Empty space (11)

DOWN
1 Acclamation (4)
2 Fine and delicate (4)
3 Vale (4)
4 Fruit of the pine (4)
5 Hip bones (4)
6 Unnecessary (8)
7 Befitting a son or daughter (6)
9 Amorous glance (8)
11 Herd (5)
13 Tool such as pincers or pliers (6)
15 Guard dog (8)
17 Workshop machinery (6)
19 German physicist (8)
23 Nobles (5)
25 Autocrat (6)
30 Ait (4)
31 Cab (4)
32 Sharp pain (4)
33 Poker stake (4)
34 Fruit of the rose (4)

237

ACROSS

1 Prophesy (11)
6 Immersing in liquid (7)
9 Move through the air (3)
12 Bland (9)
14 Pendant ornament (6)
15 Wimp (4)
16 Being at the middle (3)
17 Sour (4)
18 Cigarette (3)
19 Technician (abbrev.) (4)
20 Not new (3)
22 Distinctive quality (4)
24 Boundary (6)
25 Female mammal (5,4)
27 Burdensome charge (3)
28 In an inferior manner (5)
29 Betrothal (11)

DOWN

2 Gave a speech (6)
3 Garden tools(4)
4 Bellows (5)
5 Pertaining to parrots (10)
7 Person who attacks (9)
8 Girl or woman (3)
9 Land held in fee (4)
10 The day before today (9)
11 Of equal temperature (10)
13 Thin offshoot (4)
16 Deranged (3)
18 An iris or cattail (4)
20 Large African Antelope (4)
21 Frankfurter (3-3)
23 Not appropriate (5)
24 Bleat (3)
26 One sixth of a drachma (4)

238

ACROSS
2 Not developed (10)
7 Electronic Point of Sale (acronym) (4)
8 Copper-zinc alloy (6)
10 Frozen water (3)
11 Attack on all sides (5)
13 Bemoan (3)
15 Hot tub (3)
16 S. American monkey (4)
17 Scoop (5)
20 Stupefy with drink (5)
21 Choosing governments (9)
22 Castrated cockerel (5)
24 Trades (5)
26 Touching (4)
27 Musical performance (3)
29 Domesticated animal (3)
30 Captivated by (5)
31 Tit for --- (3)
32 Detestable (6)
34 Affirm with confidence (4)
35 Impartial (10)

DOWN
1 Average (6)
2 Application (3)
3 The British ----- (5)
4 Public disturbance (4)
5 Whisker of a cat (8)
6 Duplicity (6)
8 Light meal (3)
9 Motorcar (4)
12 Soviet satellite (7)
14 Set apart (5)
16 An opinion or doctrine (5)
18 Appoint as deputy (8)
19 Even (poet) (3)
20 A person (3)
22 Long cloak with a hood (6)
23 Not up (4)
25 Sixth planet (6)
27 Sparse fluid (3)
28 Icy (5)
30 Posterior (slang) (4)
33 Sorrowful (3)

ACROSS

1 Friends Society member (6)
4 Overland expedition (6)
7 Scattered droplets (9)
10 Tartan skirt (4)
11 Person inhabiting southeast Ghana (3)
12 Pitcher (4)
13 Trigonomic function (4)
15 Sea foam (5)
18 Queues (5)
20 Festive occasion (4)
21 Trudge (4)
22 Prime minister of India (5)
24 Sullen (5)
26 To be without (4)
29 Rind (4)
31 Lair (3)
32 ---- Pavlova, Russian ballerina (4)
33 Having recourse (9)
34 Crumble (6)
35 Affected with rheum (6)

DOWN

1 Trembles (6)
2 Retained (4)
3 Taxes (5)
4 Luster (5)
5 Gratis (4)
6 Hardens (6)
7 Massacre (9)
8 Thin offshoot (4)
9 Flagging (9)
14 Old form of measure (4)
16 Impair (3)
17 Twelth month in the Jewish calendar (4)
19 Note of debt (3)
22 An incendiary jelly (6)
23 A person that uses (4)
25 Once annually (6)
27 Scent (5)
28 Go into (5)
30 Metal (4)
32 Before (prefix) (4)

240

ACROSS	
1	Military vehicle (4)
3	Of necessity (8)
6	Stuffed doll (7)
9	Pale reddish purple (5)
12	To a smaller extent (4)
14	Tool for making holes (3)
15	Magnesium carbonate (9)
17	Ship's greeting (4)
18	Bristle of barley (3)
19	Midway state (5)
21	Knock vigorously (3)
22	Lean (4)
23	Made cheerful (9)
27	Plant with edible tubers (3)
29	Tree frog (4)
30	Dogma (5)
31	Ewer (7)
33	Vain shallow person (8)
34	Command to stop a horse (4)

DOWN	
1	Large drink container (5)
2	School of whales (3)
3	Tugs (5)
4	Lie (9)
5	Sharp nail as on a cat (4)
7	Gigantic (9)
8	Wreath of flowers (3)
10	Maze (9)
11	Small cluster (5)
13	Thrust with a knife (4)
16	Instruct (9)
18	Astir (5)
20	Literary inwardly (4)
24	Snow-capped mountain (3)
25	Flower (5)
26	Indian millet (5)
28	King mackerel (4)
32	Call of the crow (3)

ACROSS

1 Study of sexuality (8)
5 Strange person (4)
8 Sick (3)
9 Observing (8)
11 Domesticated Indian ox (4)
13 Likenesses (6)
15 An agenda (7)
16 One that gains (6)
19 Swallowed (3)
21 Nae (3)
22 Companionless (6)
25 Pertaining to sex organs (7)
26 Pig (6)
30 Fruit of the blackthorn (4)
31 Short opera (8)
32 Part of mouth (3)
33 Dry watercourse (4)
34 Weird (8)

DOWN

2 Adequate (6)
3 Detestable (6)
4 One who practices yoga (4)
5 Suburb of Ciaro (4)
6 Graceful in form (7)
7 A Czech river (4)
10 Inborn (6)
12 Consumers (5)
14 Grumble (4)
17 Inpregnate with Iodine (6)
18 Slides (5)
19 Using no fluid (7)
20 Otherwise (4)
23 Decapitate (6)
24 Pertaining to divination (6)
27 Earthen pot (4)
28 French cap (4)
29 Acting part (4)

242

ACROSS
1 Inappropriately optimistic (11)
8 Music hall (5)
10 Sheet of water flowing over a dam (5)
12 Wapiti (3)
14 Sluggishness (7)
16 A hodgepodge (4)
18 Upper limb (3)
20 Passes away (4)
21 Pre-Easter period (4)
22 Large container (3)
24 Doctrine (3)
25 Portfolio (4)
26 Taverns (4)
27 Epoch (3)
28 Grants (4)
29 Graceful (7)
33 Slum (3)
35 Pointed mass of ice (5)
36 Pile (5)
37 Remove oxygen from (11)

DOWN
1 Whimper (4)
2 Small recess (4)
3 Angolan money (4)
4 Design of delicate figures (4)
5 Contraction of is not (4)
6 Inhabitant of Nepal (8)
7 Spotted wildcat (6)
9 Indefatigable (8)
11 Garlic-flavoured mayonnaise (5)
13 Immature insects (6)
15 Resounding (8)
17 Most intimate (6)
19 Overcame (8)
23 Unit of magnetic induction (5)
25 Stylish (6)
30 Rebounding sound (4)
31 Wan (4)
32 Domesticated (4)
33 Gull-like bird (4)
34 Piece of harness (4)

ACROSS

1 A curse (11)
6 Illegal liquor (7)
9 Cover (3)
12 Repetition (9)
14 Port in S. Ukraine (6)
15 Ice creams (4)
16 Singular (3)
17 Large 3-toed bird (4)
18 Small boy (3)
19 Put tags on the deer (anag.) (4)
20 Arab market (3)
22 Damn (4)
24 Island in SE China (6)
25 Living things (9)
27 Expire (3)
28 Standard of perfection (5)
29 Goodwill (11)

DOWN

2 Rather light in colour (6)
3 Side (4)
4 Hackneyed (5)
5 Loathing (10)
7 Unrestricted (4-5)
8 7th letter of Greek alphabet (3)
9 Delicate fabric (4)
10 Cloth for drying dishes (9)
11 Hostility (10)
13 Outer covering (4)
16 Acorn-bearing tree (3)
18 Ballerina's skirt (4)
20 Surfeit (4)
21 Main protein present in milk (6)
23 Elevate (5)
24 Spread out for drying (3)
26 Cambodian money (4)

244

ACROSS

2 Method of betting (10)
7 Border on a shield (4)
8 Protection for plants (6)
10 Perception (3)
11 As a result (5)
13 Hill or mountain (3)
15 Very skilled person (3)
16 US coin (4)
17 Discards (5)
20 Ventures (5)
21 Familiarize (9)
22 Shades (5)
24 Contradict (5)
26 Plant used in cosmetics (4)
27 Bag or pouch (3)
29 Pinch (3)
30 Criminal (5)
31 Jolt (3)
32 Draw idly (6)
34 Snare (4)
35 Salad dressing (10)

DOWN

1 Stupefied (slang) (6)
2 Espy (3)
3 Contour feather (5)
4 Thatched Samoan house (4)
5 Young rooster (8)
6 Experts (6)
8 A prompt (3)
9 Sharpen (4)
12 Public disgrace (7)
14 Lively outing (5)
16 Provide food (5)
18 Board game (8)
19 Flesh and blood (inf.) (3)
20 Quick, light pat (3)
22 One behind the other (6)
23 Potpourri (4)
25 Moon of Jupiter (6)
27 Behold (3)
28 Raccoon-like mammal (5)
30 Open tart (4)
33 Ingested (3)

ACROSS

1 Female relations (6)
4 Roman poet (6)
7 State of sleep (9)
10 Towards the mouth (4)
11 Steep (3)
12 Hindu mother goddess (4)
13 Distinctive style (4)
15 Chemical reaction (5)
18 Belief involving sorcery (5)
20 Poach (4)
21 Entrance to a mine (4)
22 Light-coloured hair (5)
24 Rewrites (5)
26 Organs of sound (4)
29 Barbarous person (4)
31 Pass on (3)
32 Obstacle (4)
33 Delightfuul (9)
34 Vomiting (6)
35 Restaurant (6)

DOWN

1 Knotty (6)
2 Wool cleaning brush (4)
3 Apportion (5)
4 W. African river (5)
5 African monetary unit (4)
6 Princely (6)
7 Target used for darts (9)
8 Blend (4)
9 Erasures (9)
14 Protruberance (4)
16 Term (3)
17 Sit astride (4)
19 Tender (3)
22 Female shirt (6)
23 Found in urine (4)
25 Sweet (6)
27 Farewell (5)
28 Large fishing net (5)
30 Slippery creatures (4)
32 Set of clothing (4)

246

ACROSS
1 Divisions of a play (4)
3 Preen (8)
6 Affluent (7)
9 Antelope with twisted horns (5)
12 Another term for iambus (4)
14 Remuneration (3)
15 Infant (9)
17 Marry (4)
18 Vegetable (3)
19 Tenor violin (5)
21 Spawn (3)
22 Bound (4)
23 Pointing inwards (9)
27 Adult male (3)
29 Not one (4)
30 Brass wind instrument (5)
31 Make happy (7)
33 Republic in S. Asia (8)
34 Amphibian (4)

DOWN
1 Lack of tone (5)
2 The sun (3)
3 Capital of Tunisia (5)
4 Intoxicant (9)
5 A prong of fork (4)
7 Howling as a dog (9)
8 Make lace (3)
10 Subsequently (9)
11 Playing card with 2 spots (5)
13 Whimper (4)
16 Duenna (9)
18 Establish a true vertical (5)
20 Suggestion (4)
24 Unit of energy (3)
25 Plastic yarn (5)
26 Adjusted pitch (5)
28 Emanation (4)
32 Tiny round mark (3)

ACROSS

1 Insurrection (8)
5 Polish parliament (4)
8 Tint (3)
9 Ornamental candlestick (8)
11 Ancient Roman days (4)
13 Redirect (6)
15 Scorn (7)
16 Banker, moneychanger (6)
19 A quick knock (3)
21 Cardinal number (3)
22 Stirrup (6)
25 Stronghold (7)
26 Fit to be eaten (6)
30 Rectangular groove cut into a board (4)
31 Majesty (8)
32 Crafty (3)
33 Difficult questions (4)
34 Moving in a sudden sweep (8)

DOWN

2 Rostrum (6)
3 Promoting peace (6)
4 Ornamental trinket (4)
5 Switchblade (4)
6 Benevolent demon (7)
7 Taunt (4)
10 Rash (6)
12 Cram (5)
14 Prickle (4)
17 Send back to custody (6)
18 Inquired (5)
19 Quickly (7)
20 Sound of bells (4)
23 Shrew (6)
24 Refute (6)
27 Morse element (4)
28 Male children (4)
29 Psyche (4)

248

ACROSS

1 Vile or shameful action (11)
8 Surmise (5)
10 Excrete (5)
12 Young goat (3)
14 Conceded (7)
16 Major Roman waterway (4)
18 7th letter of the Greek alphabet (3)
20 Employs (4)
21 Authenticating mark (4)
22 Sphere (3)
24 System for developing potential (3)
25 Poker bet (4)
26 A foil (4)
27 Japanese money (3)
28 Lay wood on a ship (4)
29 To stumble (7)
33 Alimentary canal (3)
35 Move slowly (5)
36 Type of spinach (5)
37 Diaphanous (11)

DOWN

1 Crazed with frenzy (4)
2 Roman poet (4)
3 Dubious (4)
4 Land measure (4)
5 Decorated (4)
6 Unnecessary (8)
7 Seabird (6)
9 Famous for his theory of relativity (8)
11 Wildfowl (5)
13 Chant (6)
15 Auditor (8)
17 Flat-bottomed rowboat (6)
19 Archaeological object (8)
23 Beneath (5)
25 Spiny tree (6)
30 Bone (4)
31 Specks (4)
32 NZ forest tree (4)
33 Type of butter used in Indian cooking (4)
34 Udder (4)

249

ACROSS
1 Salad dressing (11)
6 Muscle pain (7)
9 Allow (3)
12 Petrify (9)
14 Alloy of copper and zinc (6)
15 Expel (4)
16 Small boy (3)
17 Lazily (4)
18 Resting place (3)
19 Meaningless talk (4)
20 My secret (3)
22 Exclamations of surprise (4)
24 Polite (6)
25 Stupefy (9)
27 Cry of pain (3)
28 Crest (7)
29 Mollusc protection (11)

DOWN
2 To carp (6)
3 8th month of Jewish calendar (4)
4 Levels (5)
5 Incarnation (10)
7 Consisting of hoops (9)
8 Promise to pay a debt (3)
9 Deafening (4)
10 To tickle (9)
11 Prosperous (4-6)
13 Coerce (4)
16 Guided (3)
18 Woman's breast (4)
20 Display (4)
21 Remove silt (6)
23 In a cocked position (5)
24 Police gun (3)
26 Vexes (4)

250

ACROSS
2 Leader of the Mongol Empire, 1260–1294 (6-4)
7 Award (4)
8 Condition (6)
10 Unit of weight for wool (3)
11 Brown tint (5)
13 Coal scuttle (3)
15 --- and feather (3)
16 Trunk of a tree (4)
17 Upright stone slab (5)
20 Conditional auxiliary verb (5)
21 Insatiable (9)
22 Lacking hue (5)
24 Defecate (5)
26 Pass tongue over(4)
27 Two-year-old sheep (3)
29 Atomic mass unit (acr.)(3)
30 Affectations (5)
31 Rocky pinnacle (3)
32 Fanatic (6)
34 Bails out (4)
35 Twisted hairstyle (10)

DOWN
1 Rich cakes (6)
2 Wingless, bloodsucking fly (3)
3 Glass tube (5)
4 Concept (4)
5 Greenhouse (8)
6 Wanted (6)
8 Evergreen tree (3)
9 Recline in a relaxed manner (4)
12 Mends (7)
14 Congregate (5)
16 Tree branch (5)
18 Leave empty (8)
19 Shelter or refuge (3)
20 Distress (3)
22 Flared (6)
23 Calcium compound (4)
25 Bird (6)
27 Small child (3)
28 Of a gene (5)
30 Body of water (4)
33 Vessel or duct (3)

ACROSS

1 Tightly curled (6)
4 Proverb (6)
7 Piece of furniture (9)
10 Metallic element (4)
11 Strong alkaline solution (3)
12 Compact ---- (4)
13 Writing table (4)
15 Seaport in SE Scotland (5)
18 Opposite of odds (5)
20 Stepped (4)
21 16th letter of the Hebrew alphabet (4)
22 Muslim woman's robe (5)
24 Long stories (5)
26 Depend (4)
29 Male parent (4)
31 Tibetan gazelle (3)
32 Unattractive (4)
33 In another place (9)
34 Barren place (6)
35 Wild ass (6)

DOWN

1 Ornamental roof part (6)
2 Corn powder (4)
3 Give up (5)
4 Footwear (5)
5 Linear measure (4)
6 Gentle slope (6)
7 Card game for one (9)
8 Side issues (4)
9 Detach (9)
14 Lock openers (4)
16 Score in rugby (3)
17 Frost (4)
19 Through (3)
22 Utterly senseless (6)
23 Sudden misfortune (4)
25 Someone who cuts hair (6)
27 Expel (5)
28 Lout (5)
30 Added (4)
32 A she-bear (4)

252

ACROSS

1 Pier (4)
3 Small piece of lean meat (8)
6 Opening of the nose (7)
9 Eject (5)
12 Bridal headwear (4)
14 Fuss (3)
15 Secret dungeon (9)
17 Sewing case (4)
18 Raincoat (inf.) (3)
19 Gimmick (5)
21 Call for help (3)
22 Manager (inf.) (4)
23 Essential (9)
27 Drunk (Scot.) (3)
29 Secondhand (4)
30 Japanese dish (5)
31 Resembling fish (7)
33 Nonsense (8)
34 Act (4)

DOWN

1 Wild dog of Australia (5)
2 Equipment (3)
3 Ingenuous (5)
4 Cadavers (9)
5 Fettered (4)
7 Greasy (9)
8 Permit (3)
10 Of Asian roots (9)
11 Steals (5)
13 Article (4)
16 Creative imagination (9)
18 Fur covers for the hands (5)
20 Frozen treats (4)
24 Large edible mushroom (3)
25 Decree (5)
26 Give up (5)
28 Liqueur of Greece (4)
32 El --- (3)

ACROSS
1 Perplex (8)
5 Native of Scotland (4)
8 Hill or mountain (South African) (3)
9 Slaughterhouse (8)
11 Roman days (4)
13 Scope (6)
15 Long journey (7)
16 Place in Eastern Egypt (6)
19 Cry plaintively (3)
21 Not (3)
22 Tiny (6)
25 Pertaining to Sweden (7)
26 Accident (6)
30 Pilaster (4)
31 Wingless (8)
32 Relatives (3)
33 Coloured (4)
34 Practise (8)

DOWN
2 Exemplify (6)
3 Damned (6)
4 Attenuate (4)
5 Parody (4)
6 Analgesic (7)
7 Unfastened (4)
10 Pertaining to Tuscany (6)
12 Post (5)
14 Capital of Shaanxi province, China (4)
17 Commando (6)
18 Mouthlike opening (5)
19 Small animal (7)
20 Continent (4)
23 Spasm (6)
24 Flows out (6)
27 Atramentous (4)
28 Clock pointer (4)
29 Two identical things (4)

254

ACROSS

1 Prolongation (11)
8 Long-term prisoner (5)
10 Express mirth (5)
12 Mark aimed at in quoits (3)
14 Molting (7)
16 Bristle (4)
18 Free (3)
20 Prefix meaning 'strange' (4)
21 Put down (4)
22 Kernel (3)
24 Ensign (abbrev.) (3)
25 Flat-bottomed boat (4)
26 Streetcar (4)
27 Definite article (3)
28 Ghanaian monetary unit (4)
29 Precisely (7)
33 Hide of a small beast (3)
35 Child's knickers (5)
36 Dog-like African mammal (5)
37 Virilize (11)

DOWN

1 Storyline (4)
2 Stare at (4)
3 Widespread (4)
4 Thin rope (4)
5 Evils (4)
6 Inducing vomiting (8)
7 Execute (6)
9 Wide-ranging (8)
11 Passageway (5)
13 Show clearly (6)
15 Rank of a yeoman (8)
17 First month of the Jewish calendar (6)
19 Part of the small intestine (8)
23 Amidst (5)
25 Ranges (6)
30 Affirmative votes (4)
31 'You' in Middle English (4)
32 Himalayan creature (4)
33 Shinto deity (4)
34 Heap (4)

		1		2		3			4			
5												
6		7			8			9		10		11
				12			13					
14							15					
						16						
17					18				19			
				20				21				
		22	23				24					
25						26						
		27				28						
29												

ACROSS

1 Fertilizes (11)
7 State in New England (7)
9 Amplifier (abbrev.) (3)
12 Resembling wine (9)
14 Craft (6)
15 Dry red wines (4)
16 Needlefish (3)
17 Cook (4)
18 Clumsy boat (3)
19 Catch sight of (4)
20 Posed (3)
22 Holly (4)
24 Birthplace of St. Francis (6)
25 To keep company as a friend (9)
27 Floor covering (3)
28 To cause confusion (5)
29 To be in disarray (11)

DOWN

2 Evergreen shrub (6)
3 Paradise (4)
4 Equipped (5)
5 Member of the armed forces (10)
7 Hypnotism (9)
8 Zero (3)
9 Shrub (4)
10 Owning (9)
11 Suffocate (10)
13 Bedouin (4)
16 Alimentary canal (3)
18 Hackney carriage (4)
20 Denomination (4)
21 Advantageous (6)
23 Slender freshwater fish (5)
24 Scoffed (3)
26 Adept (4)

256

ACROSS
2 Neglected (7-3)
7 Probability (4)
8 Anxiety (6)
10 Petroleum (3)
11 Stinking (5)
13 An old Saxon letter (3)
15 Viper (3)
16 Exhort (4)
17 Fur scarf (5)
20 Willow (5)
21 An urban shade tree (9)
22 Queried (5)
24 Muslim messiah (5)
26 Brought forth by birth (4)
27 --- Darya, Asian river (3)
29 Large-billed bird (3)
30 Intertwine (5)
31 Salted or smoked pork (3)
32 Derivative of cedar (6)
34 At any time (4)
35 Lottery (10)

DOWN
1 Machines capable of following instructions (6)
2 Utilize (3)
3 Capital of Crete (5)
4 Looked at (4)
5 Febrile (8)
6 Slice of bacon (6)
8 Bite (3)
9 Fringe (4)
12 Tidal wave (7)
14 Extraterrestrial (5)
16 Customary (5)
18 US atomic research centre (8)
19 Antiquity (arch.) (3)
20 Has the same symbol as Omega (3)
22 Calculating device (6)
23 A subjective unit of loudness (4)
25 Imprison(6)
27 Grass spike (3)
28 Mosslike lichen (5)
30 Snare (4)
33 Maiden name (3)

257

ACROSS

1 Blood vessel (6)
4 Planks (6)
7 Illuminate from behind (9)
10 Likeness (4)
11 Extension of time (3)
12 Poetical name for Ireland (4)
13 Hideout (4)
15 Nest (5)
18 Suspensoin of breathing (5)
20 Periods of history (4)
21 Personal bearings (4)
22 Rotates (5)
24 Water repellent cloth (5)
26 Foot of a horse (4)
29 Sea bird (4)
31 Form of transport (3)
32 Move off hastily (4)
33 Awkwardness (9)
34 Commemorating the resurrection of Jesus (6)
35 Hawaiian shaman (6)

DOWN

1 Movement (6)
2 Hyphen (4)
3 Country bumpkin (5)
4 Yeast-raised pancake (5)
5 Soreness (4)
6 Yellowish-brown pigment (6)
7 Adjoining (9)
8 Burden (4)
9 Convert (9)
14 Fixed horizontal bar (4)
16 Vase (3)
17 Satin band (4)
19 In favour of (3)
22 Triple (6)
23 Biblical character(4)
25 South American rodent (6)
27 Happen (5)
28 Anomaly (5)
30 Compass point (4)
32 Asian religion (4)

258

ACROSS

1 Low plant with many branches (4)
3 Control column of an aircraft (8)
6 Metallic element #45 (7)
9 Master (East Africa) (5)
12 Speech defect (4)
14 Taxi (3)
15 Centesimal (9)
17 Small parcel of land (4)
18 Dandy (3)
19 Speak in a slow manner (5)
21 Shaggy ox (3)
22 The goddess of youth (4)
23 Recalls (9)
27 North Indian teak like tree (3)
29 Where Adam and Eve lived (4)
30 Stadium (5)
31 Simplicity (7)
33 Contrite (8)
34 Behave badly (4)

DOWN

1 Shelflike sleeping space (5)
2 Brick carrier (3)
3 Unit of energy (5)
4 A zoological category (9)
5 Scene of first miracle (4)
7 Wine connoisseur (9)
8 Half way through (3)
10 Highly flammable gas (9)
11 Taken by surprise (5)
13 Simmer (4)
16 Robin (9)
18 Cavity (5)
20 Grass (4)
24 Adult males (3)
25 Play out (5)
26 Surround (5)
28 Behave stupidly (4)
32 Enthusiasm (3)

ACROSS
1 Punctuation mark (4-4)
5 Shift a sail from side to side (4)
8 Type of sorrel (3)
9 Person who rebuts (8)
11 Narrates (4)
13 Make possible (6)
15 End result (7)
16 Evening party (6)
19 Residue after burning (3)
21 Droop (3)
22 Rhythmic (6)
25 To straighten out (7)
26 Two seater bicycle (6)
30 One of the Great Lakes (4)
31 Bodily exertion (8)
32 Light brown (3)
33 Is not (4)
34 Cherish (8)

DOWN
2 Beneficial (6)
3 Traditional Japanese floor covering (6)
4 Ponder intently (4)
5 Spanish dance (4)
6 Floating mass of ice (7)
7 Sphere (4)
10 Air shaft in a mine (6)
12 Even (5)
14 Temple (4)
17 Medical (6)
18 Flood (5)
19 Eternal (7)
20 Shelter for honeybees (4)
23 Withdraw (6)
24 Minor (6)
27 ---- and crafts (4)
28 Depression in a surface (4)
29 Encounter (4)

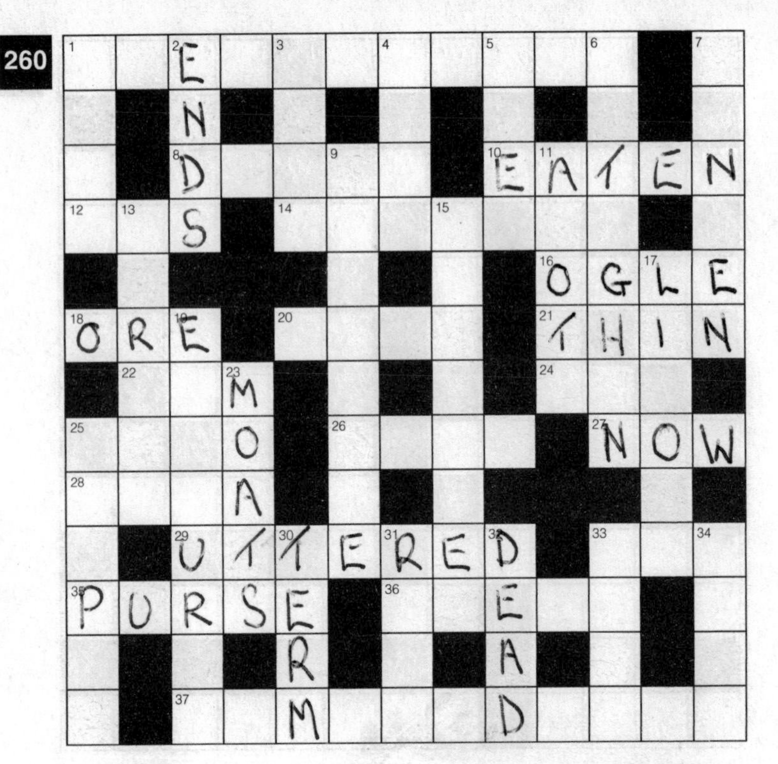

ACROSS
1 3D vision (11)
8 Compel (5)
10 Dined (5)
12 Tropical shrubs (3)
14 Showy solo passage (7)
16 Stare at lecherously (4)
18 Valued mineral (3)
20 Twining stem (4)
21 Lean (4)
22 13th letter of Hebrew alphabet(3)
24 Luck (3)
25 Tropical Asian plant (4)
26 Claw or talon (4)
27 At the present time (3)
28 South American Indian (4)
29 Spoke (7)
33 Weird (3)
35 Money bag (5)
36 Regions (5)
37 Abridged (11)

DOWN
1 Habitual drunkards (4)
2 Terminates (4)
3 Grandiose (4)
4 Storage shelter (4)
5 Augury (4)
6 Turkish sabre (8)
7 Lime tree (6)
9 Discrepancy (8)
11 Alchemist's mercury (5)
13 Deliverer of frozen water (6)
15 Cosmetic applied to the eyelids (8)
17 Fatty (6)
19 Containing mercury (8)
23 Castle water pits (5)
25 Scarf (6)
30 Division of a school year (4)
31 Tear down (4)
32 No longer living (4)
33 Norway's main port (4)
34 Stains (4)

ACROSS

1 Disastrous (11)
6 Italian dumplings (7)
9 Honey insect (3)
12 Foreigner (9)
14 Half the diameter (6)
15 Assistant (4)
16 Exclamation of contempt (3)
17 Tide (4)
18 Not good (3)
19 Angolan money (4)
20 Organ of the face (3)
22 Good fortune (4)
24 Refluent (6)
25 Seaport in Belgium (9)
27 Pronoun (3)
28 Leers (5)
29 Pollute (11)

DOWN

2 Space devoid of matter (6)
3 Parody (4)
4 Tendency (5)
5 Glorify (10)
7 Criminal court of London (3-6)
8 Belonging to him (3)
9 Enticement (4)
10 An alpine plant (9)
11 Speaking three languages fluently (10)
13 Extol (4)
16 Jack ---, sailor (3)
18 Capital of Azerbaijan (4)
20 Fawn coloured (4)
21 Type of honey suckle (6)
23 German submarine (1-4)
24 Cell (3)
26 Asian desert (4)

262

ACROSS
2 Australian lungfish (10)
7 Leak out slowly (4)
8 Extent (6)
10 Outer edge (3)
11 Nippon (5)
13 Tibetan gazelle (3)
15 Uncooked (3)
16 Act of despoliation (4)
17 Made a mistake (5)
20 Miscellany (5)
21 Who catches the worm (9)
22 Answer (5)
24 Greek writer (5)
26 Handles (4)
27 Nevertheless (3)
29 British Airport Authorities (acronym) (3)
30 Basic (5)
31 Curvature (3)
32 A gun cartridge (6)
34 Ancient water god (4)
35 Radar viewing screen (10)

DOWN
1 Unrefined (6)
2 Beseech (3)
3 Detection equipment (5)
4 Demeanour (4)
5 Misers (8)
6 Ancient Greek district (6)
8 Rule of conduct (3)
9 Pith helmet (4)
12 Bulrush (7)
14 Contracts (5)
16 Less common (5)
18 Revoked (8)
19 Arid (3)
20 By way of (3)
22 Eraser (6)
23 He sold birthright (4)
25 Outing (6)
27 Racket (3)
28 Set apart as sacred (5)
30 Endure (4)
33 Shelter (3)

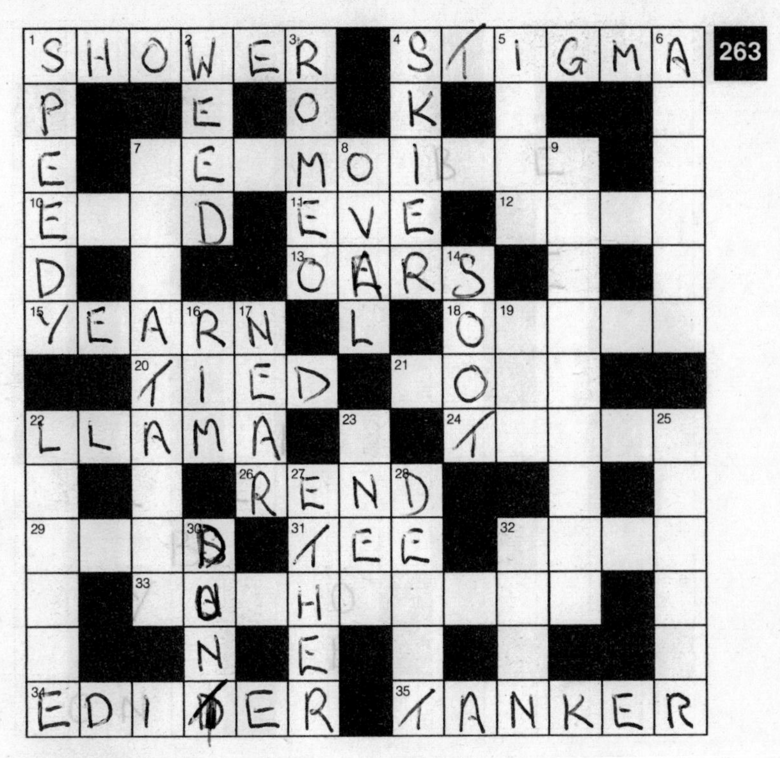

ACROSS

1 Fall of rain (6)
4 Stain (6)
7 Capital of Iowa (9)
10 Supplemented with effort (4)
11 First woman (3)
12 Russian parliament (4)
13 Soar through the water (anag.) (4)
15 Hanker (5)
18 Belief involving sorcery (5)
20 Bound (4)
21 Type of frost (4)
22 S American ruminant (5)
24 Reduce gradually (5)
26 Tear apart (4)
29 S African open country (4)
31 Starting point in golf (3)
32 Facing the sea (4)
33 Employ euphemism(9)
34 Journalist (6)
35 Transports liquids (6)

DOWN

1 Fast (6)
2 Undesirable plant (4)
3 Juliet's lover (5)
4 One who skis (5)
5 Chilled (4)
6 Join (6)
7 Open to question (9)
8 London cricket ground (4)
9 Place on something else (9)
14 Smoke deposit (4)
16 Outer part of wheel (3)
17 Close (4)
19 British Airports Authority (3)
22 Herb of parsley family (6)
23 ---- high, short (4)
25 Corrects printer's proofs (6)
27 Anaesthetic (5)
28 Relinquish (5)
30 Finely powdered earth (4)
32 Islamic call to prayer (4)

264

ACROSS

1 Head sculpture (4)
3 Occult doctrine (8)
6 Jewish articles (7)
9 Elude (5)
12 Single entity (4)
14 Excellent (slang) (3)
15 Undivided opinion (9)
17 Hint (4)
18 Steam room (3)
19 1st Greek letter (5)
21 North East England (3)
22 Cap of Scottish origin (4)
23 Offensive word (9)
27 Curve (3)
29 True (4)
30 Turkish military authority (5)
31 Large NZ reptile(7)
33 Domaine of a pasha (8)
34 Feathers (4)

DOWN

1 A jewel (5)
2 Scottish two (3)
3 Cavity open at one end (5)
4 Bring into an acetyl group (9)
5 Sodium carbonate (4)
7 Insincere behaviour (9)
8 Tropical American bird (3)
10 S American country (9)
11 Develop (5)
13 Chafe (4)
16 Female sweetheart (9)
18 Fragment (5)
20 Roundish projection (4)
24 Posed (3)
25 Hen cry (5)
26 Lust after (5)
28 Hindu music (4)
32 Former weight of wool (3)

ACROSS	DOWN
1 Insure again (8)	2 Eluded (6)
5 Complication (4)	3 Directed (6)
8 Craving (3)	4 Watched closely (4)
9 A small bundle (8)	5 Synchronise (4)
11 Ensnares (4)	6 Necessary(7)
13 Small African antelope (6)	7 Against (4)
15 One who plays cello (7)	10 Underground room (6)
16 Whisky (6)	12 Escarpment (5)
19 Cushion (3)	14 Hip bones (4)
21 To be unwell (3)	17 Albanian money (6)
22 Capital of Lebanon (6)	18 A deep chasm (5)
25 Conveyance on air (7)	19 Pathetic (7)
26 Sled (6)	20 Manure (4)
30 Unstable lepton (4)	23 Flag (6)
31 Unlearned (8)	24 African country (6)
32 Barrel (3)	27 Stringed instrument (4)
33 To a smaller extent (4)	28 Taverns (4)
34 European Asian mix (8)	29 Bee shelter (4)

266

ACROSS

1 Tumultuous (11)
8 Nickel-cadmium battery (5)
10 Destitute (5)
12 Ocean (3)
14 German biologist (7)
16 20th Hebrew letter (4)
18 Vitality (3)
20 Increases (4)
21 Component (4)
22 A coat or cloak (3)
24 Attention (3)
25 Implement (4)
26 Winged-fruit tree (4)
27 Laboratory (3)
28 European eagle (4)
29 Retrofit (7)
33 Even (3)
35 African mammal (5)
36 Pains (5)
37 Using one language (11)

DOWN

1 Makes brown (4)
2 Supernatural force (4)
3 Apiece (4)
4 Sea motion (4)
5 Hog sound (4)
6 Emaciated (8)
7 Beat (6)
9 African burrower (8)
11 Strange and mysterious (5)
13 Newspaper executive (6)
15 Skin preparation (8)
17 Mexican shawl (6)
19 Ray of night light (8)
23 Derive (5)
25 Tie up (6)
30 Son of Adam (4)
31 Drop (4)
32 At that time (4)
33 The first Edomite (4)
34 Lone time at Christmas (anag.) (4)

ACROSS

1 Laundress (11)
6 Keep out (7)
9 Statute (3)
12 In the natural state (2-7)
14 Musical effect (6)
15 Central part (4)
16 Vigour (3)
17 Askew (4)
18 Little sister (3)
19 Healed wound mark (4)
20 Small barrel (3)
22 Drug addict (4)
24 Split in two (6)
25 Arrives before others (9)
27 Greek goddess (3)
28 Pleasing (5)
29 Hotelier (11)

DOWN

2 Equal-sided rectangle (6)
3 Well-balanced (4)
4 Happen (5)
5 Outdoor tavern (10)
7 Concealment (9)
8 Invest with nickname (3)
9 Aloft (4)
10 Treason(9)
11 Festering (10)
13 Perfect serves (4)
16 Hog (3)
18 Serbian inhabitant (4)
20 Answers (4)
21 Abduct (6)
23 Seaweed (5)
24 Breast holder (3)
26 Gathering dust (4)

268

1			2		3			4		5		6
7												
							8				9	
10				11		12				13		
			14		15				16			
17		18		19				20				
		21										
22	23							24				25
26					27		28					
29				30						31		
32									33			
									34			
35												

ACROSS

2 Sleight of hand (5-5)
7 Reverberate (4)
8 Stingy (6)
10 Japanese vegetable (3)
11 Causing jolts (5)
13 Afghanistan money (3)
15 Extinct flightless bird (3)
16 Masculine (4)
17 Furnishings (5)
20 Sponsorship (5)
21 Irish Protestant (9)
22 Spearmint taste (5)
24 Factory (5)
26 Shrewd (4)
27 Hardened (3)
29 Oospore (3)
30 Alone (5)
31 Used to be (3)
32 Beast (6)
34 Swedish pop group (4)
35 Storyteller (10)

DOWN

1 Fruitful (6)
2 Shelf above a fire (3)
3 Blind gut (5)
4 Small and cramped (4)
5 Roman plain (8)
6 Fashions (6)
8 Gymnasium (3)
9 Type of dog (4)
12 Crossbreed (7)
14 Value (5)
16 Repasts (5)
18 Imagine (8)
19 Narrow beam of light (3)
20 Amplifier (Inf.) (3)
22 Gourd-shaped rattle (6)
23 Metallic element (4)
25 Dutch navigator (6)
27 Old French coin (3)
28 All (mus.) (5)
30 Stated (4)
33 Held meeting (3)

ACROSS

1 Generous gift (6)
4 Small ball of fabric (6)
7 Protection (9)
10 Sandy tract (4)
11 Grandmother (3)
12 Joint between thigh and ankle (4)
13 Lillian ----, US film actress (4)
15 Shining brightly (5)
18 Leers (5)
20 Horizontal passage (4)
21 Roman goddess (4)
22 Large jib for yachts (5)
24 Abounding in rushes (5)
26 Rich source (4)
29 Certify (4)
31 Soak (3)
32 Inside (4)
33 Extremely beautiful (9)
34 Maiden (6)
35 Abdicate (6)

DOWN

1 Load (6)
2 A number (4)
3 Youthful (5)
4 Seed vegetables (5)
5 Summon (4)
6 More than is necessary (6)
7 Without delay (9)
8 Sudden assault (4)
9 Shutting in (9)
14 Period of time (4)
16 Artificial language (3)
17 Clock face (4)
19 Wildebeest (3)
22 Pregnant (6)
23 ---- of March, date of Caesar's death (4)
25 A farmer (6)
27 Bay window (5)
28 Volatile liquid (5)
30 Torn clothing (4)
32 Hostels (4)

270

ACROSS

1 Book of the New Testament (4)
3 Defensive mounds (8)
6 Entrance (7)
9 Supply with new personnel (5)
12 Depression (4)
14 Beer (3)
15 Juvenile (9)
17 Strives for victory (4)
18 Sound of a dove (3)
19 Terminated (5)
21 Nocturnal bird (3)
22 Short letter (4)
23 Insipid (9)
27 Turkish headwear (3)
29 Chaplet (4)
30 Resin used as incense (5)
31 Veil worn by Muslim women (7)
33 Reduce (8)
34 A layer (4)

DOWN

1 Serrated (5)
2 Before (3)
3 Studies (5)
4 Game bird (9)
5 Small dabbling duck (4)
7 To make German (9)
8 Nevertheless (3)
10 Stately tomb (9)
11 Country in the Himalayas (5)
13 Top of a glacier (4)
16 To set apart (9)
18 Abrade (5)
20 Close (4)
24 Artful (3)
25 Instruct (5)
26 Eurasian falcon (5)
28 Dim, short-lived disc of light (4)
32 Crude shelter (3)

ACROSS

1 Newscast with another person (2-6)
5 Motion picture (4)
8 Definite (3)
9 Itinerant (8)
11 Existence (prefix) (4)
13 Synthetic (6)
15 Muted (7)
16 Abrupt (6)
19 Perform (3)
21 Greek goddess of dawn (3)
22 Put a bet on (6)
25 Bicker (7)
26 Emphasis (6)
30 Decanter (4)
31 Custody (8)
32 7th letter of Greek alphabet (3)
33 Professional charges (4)
34 Box for tea leaves (3-5)

DOWN

2 Hard metallic element (6)
3 Lifted with great effort (6)
4 Network of nerves (4)
5 Talks in murmurs (4)
6 Entrails (7)
7 After deductions (4)
10 Uncouple (6)
12 Colourless gas (5)
14 A rake (4)
17 Misgivings (6)
18 Corpulent (5)
19 Grow together (7)
20 Strives (4)
23 Coypu (6)
24 Joined by treaty (6)
27 Affectedly dainty (4)
28 Epochs (4)
29 Study hard (4)

272

ACROSS

1 Cluster together (11)
8 Tall (5)
10 Theme (5)
12 Prosecute (3)
14 Patronage (7)
16 Epic poetry (4)
18 Vast expanse of water (3)
20 To vote (4)
21 Serpents (4)
22 Pin used to separate rope (3)
24 --- in the bud (3)
25 Rough edge (4)
26 Enthusiastic (4)
27 Razor-billed --- (3)
28 Otherwise (4)
29 Small black beetle (7)
33 African antelope (3)
35 Destroy (5)
36 Desire (5)
37 Pegasus (6-5)

DOWN

1 Ratchets (4)
2 Egyptian river (4)
3 Porous limestone (4)
4 Puts down (4)
5 Against (4)
6 Good digestion (8)
7 Over-abundance (6)
9 Custody (8)
11 Pacific ----- (5)
13 Advantageous (6)
15 Thin membrane (8)
17 Dispute (6)
19 Propeller (8)
23 Fear greatly (5)
25 Bell tower (6)
30 Soft feathers (4)
31 Harplike instrument (4)
32 Apiece (4)
33 Snarl (4)
34 Beseech (4)

ACROSS
1 Coiffeur (11)
6 Envelope (7)
9 Decease (3)
12 Basic (9)
14 A mission (6)
15 Comply (4)
16 Butter measure (3)
17 Weeps (4)
18 High-pitched (3)
19 Not fearful (4)
20 Artful (3)
22 Braid (4)
24 Shady recess (6)
25 Cutting side of a blade (5-5)
27 Hero (3)
28 Prepared (5)
29 Abatement (11)

DOWN
2 Approach (6)
3 Dreadful (4)
4 Hog (5)
5 Lottery (10)
7 Vigorously active (9)
8 To grow old (arch.) (3)
9 Arrears (4)
10 World history (9)
11 Defamatory (10)
13 Foss (4)
16 Wield (3)
18 Frontward (4)
20 Raced (4)
21 Wrinkle (6)
23 Ablaze (5)
24 Existence (3)
26 Endure (4)

274

ACROSS

2 Lungfish (10)
7 Discharge (4)
8 Annul (6)
10 Engage in espionage (3)
11 Frenzied (5)
13 Small amount (3)
15 Showed the way (3)
16 Chapter of the Koran (4)
17 Norse god of winds (5)
20 Commotion (5)
21 Infringement (9)
22 Inferior wheat (5)
24 Very hard mineral (5)
26 Shoreline deposit (4)
27 Lair (3)
29 Part of phonetic alphabet (3)
30 Chinese language (5)
31 Leather punch (3)
32 ------ lights, type of window (6)
34 Public swimming pool (4)
35 N. Amer fresh-water fish (10)

DOWN

1 Alarm bell (6)
2 Honey insect (3)
3 Magnificent (5)
4 A meadow (arch.) (4)
5 Piano composition (8)
6 Daylong (3-3)
8 Criminal Investigation Department (3)
9 British nobleman (4)
12 Conducted oneself properly (7)
14 Bird-song (5)
16 Official language of Finland (5)
18 Repair (8)
19 Speck (3)
20 Happen (3)
22 Odorous (6)
23 Crown of the head (4)
25 A colour (6)
27 Father (3)
28 Nigerian money (5)
30 Game of chance (4)
33 Thickening of tissue (3)

ACROSS
1 A faint arc-shaped light (6)
4 Brawl (6)
7 Percussion instrument (9)
10 To fix (4)
11 Definite article (3)
12 Beloved (4)
13 Sharpen (4)
15 To produce (5)
18 Apple polisher (5)
20 Storyteller (4)
21 Swamp (4)
22 Foreign (5)
24 Bondage (5)
26 A church (4)
29 Regretted (4)
31 A digit (3)
32 Brooch (4)
33 Able to be healed (9)
34 Award (6)
35 Slag left after smelting (6)

DOWN
1 Hysteria (6)
2 Abscess (4)
3 Price (5)
4 Grey (5)
5 River crossing (4)
6 Annually (6)
7 That is, namely (9)
8 Used to attract attention (4)
9 Teacher (9)
14 Small case for sewing implements (4)
16 Be supine (3)
17 Unpleasantly moist (4)
19 Lever for rowing (3)
22 Nimble (6)
23 Horse's gait (4)
25 N. African desert (6)
27 European country (5)
28 English poet (5)
30 Fall in drops (4)
32 Paraphernalia (4)

276

ACROSS

1 Compassionate (4)
3 Charger (8)
6 Gasping (7)
9 Pass into disuse (5)
12 Wristband (4)
14 Venomous snake (3)
15 Fastened (9)
17 Annual herb with nutritious oil-rich seeds (4)
18 Become rigid (3)
19 Vigorous attack (5)
21 To feel regret (3)
22 Timber wolf (4)
23 One who brings order (9)
27 Possess (3)
29 Single entity (4)
30 Juridical (5)
31 Surging (7)
33 Handbill (8)
34 Merit (4)

DOWN

1 Ruined (5)
2 Short signal in Morse code (3)
3 Flinch (5)
4 Six (4, 5)
5 Solve (4)
7 Evening until morning (9)
8 Weapon (3)
10 Freelance photographer (9)
11 Part of a choral ode in classical Greek drama (5)
13 Gathering, for a special activity (4)
16 Middle Eastern salad (9)
18 Cylinder of wound thread (5)
20 Bereft (4)
24 Castrated male cat (3)
25 Inclined (5)
26 Semisynthetic textile (5)
28 Well-being (4)
32 Shelter (3)

ACROSS
1 Alienate (8)
5 Scrutinize (4)
8 Milk (3)
9 Volume of a solid (8)
11 Arm bone (4)
13 Body's communication system (6)
15 Incomplete (7)
16 Husky (6)
19 Amber brew (3)
21 Bashful (3)
22 Narrate (6)
25 Beg (7)
26 Cover to protect plants (6)
30 Fruit with sweet green pulp (4)
31 From the direction of a compass point (8)
32 Mesh (3)
33 Surrender (4)
34 Portrayed (8)

DOWN
2 Plucky (6)
3 Nothing (6)
4 Balanced (4)
5 Insult (4)
6 Place of crucifixion (7)
7 Skin eruption (4)
10 King of the Huns (6)
12 Cinders (5)
14 Number of poems (4)
17 On horseback (6)
18 Fissure (5)
19 Permited (7)
20 Imprint (4)
23 Complete agreement (6)
24 Dwarf Australian eucalyptus (6)
27 Thin continuous mark (4)
28 Quote (4)
29 Urn (4)

278

ACROSS

1 Well-mannered (11)
8 Cuban dance (5)
10 Seat (5)
12 Retreat (3)
14 Annoyance (7)
16 Hip bones (4)
18 Viper (3)
20 Spoken (4)
21 Trigonometric function (4)
22 Play on words (3)
24 Conclusion (3)
25 King mackerel (4)
26 Narrow strip of land (4)
27 Castrated male cat (3)
28 As previously given (4)
29 Tend (7)
33 Weep (3)
35 Sturdy (5)
36 Red pigment (5)
37 Consolidate (11)

DOWN

1 Spanish painter (4)
2 Small notch (4)
3 Loan (4)
4 Drink made from honey (4)
5 Charming (4)
6 Young goat (8)
7 Unhatched insects (6)
9 Pledge (8)
11 Hoist (5)
13 Uttered gratingly (6)
15 Promoting the flow of milk (8)
17 Blue dye (6)
19 Pedigree (8)
23 Vagabond (5)
25 Coded message (6)
30 Side issues (4)
31 Ballad (4)
32 Objective case of thou (4)
33 Plural of serum (4)
34 Remain (4)

279

ACROSS

1 Having both male and female characteristics (11)
6 Dwell in (7)
9 Law enforcement agency (abbrev.) (3)
12 Sickly (9)
14 Contract (6)
15 Exultation (4)
16 Comrade (3)
17 Depart (4)
18 Last letter of the alphabet (3)
19 Free from bias (4)
20 Prisoner of War (3)
22 Equipment (4)
24 Uncouth (6)
25 Intoxicant (9)
27 Fish eggs (3)
28 Get to know (5)
29 Analysis of chromosomes (11)

DOWN

2 Expose as being false (6)
3 Sworn declaration (4)
4 Aristocratic (5)
5 Extracted from flax seed (10)
7 Herald (9)
8 Writing fluid (3)
9 Autumn (4)
10 Repetition (9)
11 Difficulty in speech (10)
13 Mild exclamation (4)
16 Church seat (3)
18 Japanese sandal (4)
20 Peel (4)
21 Thick woven straw mat (6)
23 Deep, lustrous black (5)
24 First number (3)
26 An alcoholic (slang) (4)

280

ACROSS

2 Disparity (10)
7 Role model (4)
8 Wager (6)
10 Vital element (3)
11 Nucleus of a regiment (5)
13 Honey (3)
15 Casual affirmative reply (3)
16 Remain undecided (4)
17 Arm joint (5)
20 Locations (5)
21 Precipitation creator (9)
22 Evict (5)
24 Of Nordic stock (5)
26 Unwilling (4)
27 Petroleum (3)
29 Cinders (3)
30 Cow's mammary gland (5)
31 Secondary matter (3)
32 Saying (6)
34 Image of a deity (4)
35 Branching (10)

DOWN

1 Used to cut grain (6)
2 Public House (3)
3 Shelter (5)
4 Peak (4)
5 Equality of measure (8)
6 Cedes (6)
8 Individual Retirement Account (acronym) (3)
9 Hawaiian goose (4)
12 Skinlike (7)
14 Carriage (5)
16 Wharves (5)
18 Brothers (8)
19 Humour (3)
20 Jamaican popular music (3)
22 Venomous snake (6)
23 Good-natured banter (4)
25 Sewing instrument (6)
27 Lyric poem (3)
28 Slowly (mus.) (5)
30 ---- friendly (4)
33 Direct a gun (3)

ACROSS

1 Inducing fatigue (6)
4 Grinding implement (6)
7 Shapeless (9)
10 Grave (4)
11 Papa (3)
12 Rice and flour pancake (4)
13 Shrub (4)
15 Deprived (5)
18 Tolerate (5)
20 Gradient (4)
21 Land measure (4)
22 Raw fish dish (5)
24 Taken food (5)
26 Primitive wind instrument (4)
29 Spore-bearing parts of a moss capsule (4)
31 Denial (3)
32 Authenticating mark (4)
33 Regions (9)
34 Prefix, meaning 'past' (6)
35 Sprite (6)

DOWN

1 Scottish fabric (6)
2 Poetic meter (4)
3 Lake in northern Italy (5)
4 Muslim messiah (5)
5 Admire (4)
6 Give account (6)
7 Symbol for 'and' (9)
8 Part of a window (4)
9 Organizations (9)
14 Ornamental fabric (4)
16 Spoken representation of a dash in Morse code (3)
17 Mythical Norse giant (4)
19 Woman's undergarment (3)
22 Robust (6)
23 Cherished (4)
25 Wrestling hold (6)
27 Join (5)
28 Expiring (5)
30 Separate finely (4)
32 Puncture (4)

282

ACROSS

1 Prophet (4)
3 Concise (8)
6 Ancient capital of Assyria (7)
9 Roman goddess of the home (5)
12 Tranquillity (4)
14 Man's name (3)
15 Holiest Jewish holiday (3-6)
17 The highest volcano in Europe (4)
18 Drinking place (3)
19 Hidden (5)
21 Encountered (3)
22 An exclamation of sorrow (4)
23 Irresistible urge (9)
27 Girl (inf.) (3)
29 Piece of earth (4)
30 Used in varnish and inks (5)
31 As above (2,5)
33 Inhabitant of Bucharest (8)
34 Large N. African wrap (4)

DOWN

1 Bright (5)
2 Whisky grain (3)
3 Precipitous (5)
4 Concealment (9)
5 Pigeon coop (4)
7 Capable of being counted (9)
8 Luck or fortune (3)
10 Steamer (9)
11 Convert (5)
13 Made a court petition (4)
16 Collision (9)
18 Spree (5)
20 Eldest son of Isaac (4)
24 French wine producing region (3)
25 Many times (5)
26 Slap (5)
28 Too (4)
32 Exclamation of disgust (3)

ACROSS

1 The study of forces in motion (8)
5 Immerses(4)
8 Generation (3)
9 Lamentation (8)
11 River in northern England (4)
13 Owner (6)
15 Tend (7)
16 Old Portuguese money (6)
19 German physicist (3)
21 ---, Dick and Harry (3)
22 Old Macdonald was one (6)
25 Pillar in human form (7)
26 Capital of Canada (6)
30 A system of weights (4)
31 Small guitars (8)
32 Exasperation (3)
33 Playthings (4)
34 Dominate (8)

DOWN

2 One enlisted in the U.S. Navy (6)
3 Relating to the eye (6)
4 An audible exhalation (4)
5 Distribute cards (4)
6 Whitish yellow metal (7)
7 To peel (4)
10 Beat (6)
12 Fungus infecting cereals (5)
14 Defeat (4)
17 Tufted (6)
18 Astir (5)
19 Art of public speaking (7)
20 Sound of a cat (4)
23 Deceive (6)
24 A wineshop (6)
27 Group of three (4)
28 Votes in favour (4)
29 Vehicle (abrev.) (4)

284

ACROSS
1 Plant of the buttercup family (4,2,1,4)
8 Slender piece of wood (5)
10 Bay window (5)
12 An ode to the deer (anag.) (3)
14 Collection of weaponry (7)
16 Wild mountain goat (4)
18 Atomic mass unit (3)
20 Baby powder (4)
21 Flat-fish (4)
22 Not young (3)
24 Conclusion (3)
25 Low female singing voice (4)
26 To the inside of (4)
27 Even (poet) (3)
28 Seaport in NE Egypt (4)
29 Name for fox-trickster (7)
33 Theory (3)
35 Odd-toed ungulate (5)
36 Monument (5)
37 USA's smallest state (5, 6)

DOWN
1 Obscene (4)
2 Save the flowers (anag.) (4)
3 Hip bones (4)
4 Questions (4)
5 Metallic element (4)
6 Coccyx (8)
7 Of special elegance (6)
9 Act of invention (8)
11 Bring up (5)
13 Copper and zinc alloy (6)
15 And so forth (8)
17 Flowering shrubs (6)
19 Intentionally kept concealed (8)
23 Group of twelve (5)
25 Stellar (6)
30 Bobbin-like toy (4)
31 Plot (4)
32 Immerses(4)
33 Person from Peru (4)
34 Intellectual faculty (4)

ACROSS
1 Intractable (11)
6 God of love (5)
8 Judge of Israel (3)
11 Pen name (9)
13 Head garland (6)
14 Unskilled labour (4)
15 No or not (prefix) (3)
16 Autographs (4)
17 Devoted follower (3)
18 Amount of space (4)
19 Fractional monetary unit of Japan (3)
21 Very small amount (4)
23 Songbird (6)
24 Mandarin (9)
26 Pile driver (3)
27 Animal (5)
28 Young (11)

DOWN
2 Cup-shaped (6)
3 Method (4)
4 Eskimo dwelling (5)
5 Aptitude (10)
6 Skin of roast pork (9)
7 Doctrine (3)
8 Garden of ---- (4)
9 Deepest (9)
10 Shady (10)
10 On top of (4)
15 River in Thailand (3)
17 Anxiety (4)
19 Type of gun (4)
20 Wrinkle (6)
22 Pointed arch (5)
23 First number (3)
25 Large wading bird (4)

286

ACROSS
2 Sentimental movie (4,6)
7 Fencing sword (4)
8 German composer (6)
10 Sesame plant (3)
11 E. Indian pepper plant (5)
13 Wreath of flower (3)
15 Portable bed (3)
16 Small nail (4)
17 Bunches (5)
20 Slatted wooden box (5)
21 Military uniform colour (9)
22 Fragment (5)
24 Conjunction (5)
26 Weapons (4)
27 Equal scores in a contest (3)
29 Nothing (3)
30 Not fully developed (5)
31 Foot of an animal (3)
32 Spain and Portugal (6)
34 Deeds (4)
35 During the recent past (10)

DOWN
1 Group of six (6)
2 --- Commandments (3)
3 A native of 16th C. Mexico (5)
4 Lord (4)
5 Cultivated cabbage (8)
6 Stay (6)
8 Stake (3)
9 Flesh (4)
12 Blood poisoning (7)
14 Collection of maps (5)
16 Stigma (5)
18 Shapeless (8)
19 Little drink (3)
20 Clinical Research Unit (acronym) (3)
22 Soundness of judgement (6)
23 Child's bed (4)
25 Almost in original state (6)
27 Hot drink (3)
28 Overjoy (5)
30 Immoral habit (4)
33 Glass container (3)

1			2		3		4		5			6

ACROSS

1 Capital of Mali (6)
4 Legless fly larva (6)
7 Shutting in (9)
10 Use a keyboard (4)
11 Baseball term (acr) (3)
12 11th Hebrew letter (4)
13 Platform (4)
15 Of necessity (5)
18 Murders (5)
20 Mackerel shark(4)
21 Serum (pl) (4)
22 Fragrant resin (5)
24 Swindler (5)
26 Requirement (4)
29 Wading bird (4)
31 Oxlike African antelope (3)
32 A flower (4)
33 Rid of the mystery (9)
34 Talisman (6)
35 Tomboy (6)

DOWN

1 Overfeed (6)
2 Facial pimples (4)
3 Greased (5)
4 African pastoral people (5)
5 Greasy residue (4)
6 Skintight knit hose (6)
7 Mayfly (9)
8 The road led to the mouth (anag.) (4)
9 Heroic bravery (9)
14 Timber attached to the stern of a boat (4)
16 Block up (3)
17 Pelt (4)
19 A militant organization (3)
22 Riddle (6)
23 Recognizes (scot) (4)
25 Attach firmly (6)
27 Country in NE Africa (5)
28 From the Netherlands (5)
30 Exchange for money (4)
32 Questionable (4)

288

ACROSS
1 Hollow (4)
3 Perceptible (8)
6 Stupidity (7)
9 Highly successful (slang) (5)
12 Stem (4)
14 Scarlet (3)
15 Extending into future (4-5)
17 Broad smile (4)
18 Tenure (3)
19 Convulsion (5)
21 Equipment (3)
22 Mark on skin (4)
23 Defamatory (9)
27 Handwoven Scandinavian rug (3)
29 Indian city (4)
30 Demobilization (abbrev.) (5)
31 Judge (7)
33 Establish firmly (8)
34 Glimpse (4)

DOWN
1 A hand tool (5)
2 Unit of weight (3)
3 Scriptural narrative (Buddhism) (5)
4 Subcutaneous (9)
5 Animate existence (4)
7 To a sickening degree (2-7)
8 Craving (3)
10 Capital of Kentucky (9)
11 Writer of poems (5)
13 Embryos (4)
16 Able to be remerchandized (9)
18 Long narrow inlet of sea (5)
20 A prude (4)
24 Underwear for support (3)
25 Planet (5)
26 Grieved (5)
28 Bear young (4)
32 Rage (3)

ACROSS

1 Gleaming (8)
5 Partial dark (4)
8 Expression of repugnance (3)
9 Heavenly (8)
11 Wooden shoe (4)
13 Liniment (6)
15 Towards the land (7)
16 A coarse-toothed saw (6)
19 Ball (3)
21 Tabby (3)
22 Plant with colourful leaves (6)
25 Stream of electrons (7)
26 Assails (6)
30 Sore (4)
31 Melt (8)
32 Weeding tool (3)
33 Mixed education system (4)
34 Any unnamed object (8)

DOWN

2 Area of high elevation (6)
3 Type of laced shoe (6)
4 Trade in (4)
5 Conduit (4)
6 Most unsightly (7)
7 Used to frighten away (4)
10 Round body (6)
12 Chews (5)
14 Auricular (4)
17 Stately dance (6)
18 Diving apparatus (5)
19 Comfortably familiar (7)
20 Push with horns (4)
23 Bell tower (6)
24 Man raised by apes (6)
27 Elucidation (4)
28 Watched (4)
29 Chapter of the Koran (4)

290

ACROSS
1 Useful (11)
8 Fear greatly (5)
10 Battery terminal (5)
12 River (3)
14 To go out of trajectory (7)
16 Change direction (4)
18 One that commands (3)
20 Overruns (4)
21 Artillery (4)
22 Rock (3)
24 Edge (3)
25 Cajole (4)
26 To press clothes (4)
27 Brown-capped mushroom (3)
28 Ornamental ladies' bag (4)
29 Sparkle (7)
33 Incidentally (3)
35 Pallid (5)
36 Willow (5)
37 Defraud (5-6)

DOWN
1 Raced (4)
2 Travelled on (4)
3 Frozen (4)
4 Taro root (4)
5 Reveal indiscreetly (4)
6 External (8)
7 Scoffs (6)
9 Vigorous exercises (8)
11 Growing in snow (5)
13 Implant deeply (6)
15 Meatballs (8)
17 Sovereignty (6)
19 Game of chequers (8)
23 Banish (5)
25 Made of a certain wood (6)
30 Inside of (4)
31 Wrongful act (4)
32 Almost (4)
33 Outer layers of cereal (4)
34 Contentment (4)

ACROSS

1 Presides over a meeting (11)
6 Milky (7)
9 Wide sash (3)
12 Not limited by time (9)
14 Middle (6)
15 Motor vehicle (abbrev.) (4)
16 A nun (abbrev.) (3)
17 Make beer (4)
18 Electrically charged atom (3)
19 Butter used in Indian cooking (4)
20 Entirely (3)
22 Songbird (4)
24 Scarcity (6)
25 Pertaining to arthritis (9)
27 Parched (3)
28 Rework (5)
29 Substitute (11)

DOWN

2 Scared (6)
3 Jurisdiction (4)
4 Automaton (5)
5 Fruit of the bramble (10)
7 Hidden (9)
8 Banqueted (3)
9 Masterpiece (4)
10 Early term for a train (9)
11 Brass instrument (10)
13 Principal (4)
16 5th tone of the diatonic scale (3)
18 Every (Scots) (4)
20 Military force (4)
21 Disqualify (6)
23 Listening (5)
24 Abate (3)
26 Reliable (4)

292

ACROSS

2 Particularly (10)
7 Dry (4)
8 Misgivings (6)
10 Tureen (3)
11 Ghostly (5)
13 Direct a gun (3)
15 Momentarily go off course (3)
16 A volcano (4)
17 To be (5)
20 Extraterrestrial (5)
21 A martial art (9)
22 Phase (5)
24 Dogma (5)
26 Robust (4)
27 Scandinavian currency (3)
29 Biblical high priest (3)
30 Leather with soft napped surface (5)
31 In the capacity of (3)
32 Venomous snake (6)
34 Redundant (4)
35 Yore (10)

DOWN

1 Matching set of jewels (6)
2 Symbol in phoenic alphabet (3)
3 Scapegoat (5)
4 Ferrous (4)
5 Pouring of liquid (8)
6 Sycophant (6)
8 Condensed moisture (3)
9 Branch of deer's antlers (4)
12 Out of control (7)
14 Long-continued practise (5)
16 Senior (5)
18 European race (8)
19 Golfer's mound (3)
20 Small insect (3)
22 Lustrous (6)
23 High (4)
25 River in S. England (6)
27 Musical instrument (3)
28 Develop (5)
30 Team (4)
33 Affectation (3)

ACROSS

1 Figure of speech (6)
4 Arouse (6)
7 Robin (9)
10 Side (4)
11 Period (3)
12 Exclamation of mild dismay (4)
13 Clock face (4)
15 Go into (5)
18 Last letter of Greek alphabet (5)
20 Mountain range (4)
21 Size of space (4)
22 Seraglio (5)
24 Expired (5)
26 Drama (4)
29 A debauched man (4)
31 Fury (3)
32 Small nail (4)
33 Baking soda (9)
34 Venerate (6)
35 Located beneath (6)

DOWN

1 Carved image (6)
2 An account (4)
3 Declined (5)
4 Stadium (5)
5 Additionally (4)
6 Biliousness (6)
7 Blissfully happy (9)
8 Irritate (4)
9 Bullfighters (9)
14 Traditional knowledge (4)
16 Aforetime (3)
17 Inclination (4)
19 Homo sapiens (3)
22 A man who tends livestock (6)
23 Catherine ----, last wife of Henry VIII (4)
25 Totter (6)
27 Lord (5)
28 Long for (5)
30 Comfort (4)
32 Head and shoulders sculpture (4)

294

ACROSS

1 Ambitions (4)
3 Zig-zag stitch (8)
6 Farewell (7)
9 Paddled (5)
12 Limits (4)
14 Stratosphere (3)
15 Canis Minor (6-3)
17 Pluck (4)
18 The letter 's' (3)
19 Cavity (5)
21 Circles or ovals (3)
22 Boat timber (4)
23 Washing (9)
27 Bill and --- (3)
29 Marks aimed at in quoits (4)
30 Native of India (5)
31 Bites gently (7)
33 Soft green felt hat with a feather (8)
34 Badgers (4)

DOWN

1 Celestial being (5)
2 Unhappy (3)
3 Purchaser (5)
4 A silk or silklike fabric with crosswise ribs (9)
5 Angolan money (4)
7 Persistent desire (9)
8 Terminus (3)
10 Predatory (9)
11 Apparel (5)
13 Canines (4)
16 Adequate (9)
18 Historical period (5)
20 Flirtatious look (4)
24 Even (poet.) (3)
25 Of Eastern descent (5)
26 Fights for breath (5)
28 Greasy (4)
32 Storage container (3)

ACROSS
1 Regulating water valve (8)
5 Anger (4)
8 Don't lie to the judge (anag.) (3)
9 Commonplace (8)
11 English river (4)
13 Cured ham (6)
15 Disposed to love (7)
16 Full assembly (6)
19 Man's name (3)
21 Ultimately (3)
22 Hang around (6)
25 A Protestant (7)
26 Hammer (6)
30 Soft cheese (4)
31 Frozen dessert (8)
32 Dark fluid ejected from an octopus or squid (3)
33 Wise man (4)
34 Devouring (8)

DOWN
2 Poise (6)
3 Detestable (6)
4 Monarch (4)
5 Quantity of paper (4)
6 Nutriment (7)
7 Unemployment cheque (4)
10 Sharply hooked (6)
12 Foe (5)
14 Friendly nation (4)
17 More spooky (6)
18 Seal with lead (5)
19 Murdering (7)
20 Wild goose (4)
23 Exclamation of triumph (6)
24 Place of contentment (6)
27 A melody (4)
28 Albanian currency (4)
29 Fork prong (4)

296

ACROSS

1 Carbon 14 (11)
8 Skinflint (5)
10 Visual (5)
12 A small peg (3)
14 Molasses (7)
16 Supporter (4)
18 Rondure (3)
20 End of prayer (4)
21 Ardour (4)
22 Branch (3)
24 Viper (3)
25 Portico (4)
26 Right-angled bends (4)
27 Secret agent (3)
28 Agreement (4)
29 Article of personal property (7)
33 Hovel (3)
35 Glaze (5)
36 Proverb (5)
37 Lack of desire (11)

DOWN

1 Floating platform (4)
2 Matron (4)
3 Kiln for drying hops (4)
4 Plot of land (4)
5 Cartel (4)
6 Unnoticed (8)
7 Finger (6)
9 Bursting forth (8)
11 Public square (5)
13 List of errors (6)
15 Abolished (8)
17 Decorative flap (6)
19 Green flower vegetable (8)
23 Mathematics (abbrev.) (5)
25 Faucet (6)
30 Supermarket chain (4)
31 Compact by pounding (4)
32 Ultimate (4)
33 Spotted (4)
34 Period extending from Dec. 24 to Jan. 6 (4)

297

ACROSS
1 Not resolute (11)
6 Mystery (7)
9 Unit of electric current (3)
12 Narratives (9)
14 Spiritually revived (6)
15 Method (4)
16 Fruit seed (3)
17 Have regard (4)
18 A failure (3)
19 As previously given (4)
20 Debutante (inf.) (3)
22 Capital of W. Samoa (4)
24 Specified year of a monarch's reign (6)
25 Canis Minor (6-4)
27 Adolescent (3)
28 Concert hall (5)
29 Impetuous (11)

DOWN
2 Against (6)
3 Fabric with metallic threads (4)
4 Shy (5)
5 Type of cheese (10)
7 Broadcast by cable (9)
8 Vessel (3)
9 On high (4)
10 Pen name (9)
11 Large gathering (10)
13 Among (4)
16 Hostelry (3)
18 Darling (4)
20 Expired (4)
21 Fable (6)
23 Sacred song (5)
24 Bar (3)
26 Dead as a ---- (4)

298

ACROSS

2 Art of handwriting (10)
7 Steady easy gait (4)
8 Equine sounds (6)
10 Conflict (3)
11 Fear (5)
13 Humble dwelling (3)
15 Intention (3)
16 Angolan money (4)
17 Cheerful (5)
20 Discontinue (5)
21 Study of the nervous system (9)
22 Avowed (5)
24 Aromatic herb (5)
26 Skin growth (4)
27 Dip in liquid (3)
29 Embelish (3)
30 More delicate (5)
31 Public transport (3)
32 On the right side (6)
34 Small box hung from a Kimono sash (4)
35 Atomic physics (10)

DOWN

1 Blossom (6)
2 Fastener (3)
3 Nigerian currency (5)
4 Requirement (4)
5 Main roads (8)
6 Adhesive-backed label (6)
8 Vietnam (abbrev.) (3)
9 Colours (4)
12 Phantom (7)
14 Inactive (5)
16 Lawful (5)
18 Suffering from an eating disorder (8)
19 Large cask (3)
20 Male swan (3)
22 Country in N. Europe (6)
23 Rouse from sleep (4)
25 Capital of Portugal (6)
27 Male address (3)
28 Woman's slip (5)
30 Companion (4)
33 Sloth (3)

299

ACROSS

1 Extreme distress (6)
4 Decorative (6)
7 Without one's knowledge (9)
10 Garden tool (4)
11 Sum charged (3)
12 Human spirit (4)
13 Web-footed aquatic bird (4)
15 Hillsides (5)
18 Caper (5)
20 Formerly Persia (4)
21 Capital of Western Samoa (4)
22 Suspends (5)
24 Spread out (5)
26 Mess (4)
29 Peruse (4)
31 Honey insect (3)
32 Helper (4)
33 Capital of Tonga (9)
34 Agile (6)
35 Sequence (6)

DOWN

1 Beetle, revered in Egypt (6)
2 Grape-producing plant (4)
3 Robbery (5)
4 Holder (5)
5 Information (4)
6 Of a period of expulsion (6)
7 Slavic language (9)
8 Bottom of a ship's hull (4)
9 Sentimental yearning (9)
14 Sleeps briefly (4)
16 Centimeter-gram-second unit of energy (3)
17 Ribbon around the waist (4)
19 Pinch (3)
22 In this (6)
23 Facing the sea (4)
25 Gives up (6)
27 Misuse (5)
28 Aids (5)
30 Stupid (4)
32 Remote (4)

300

ACROSS

1 Social standing (4)
3 Excited (8)
6 Make insane (7)
9 Golf clubs (5)
12 Person of Islamic religion (4)
14 Corded cloth (3)
15 Dryness of the skin (9)
17 Flair (4)
18 Bring civil action against (3)
19 Type of pancake (5)
21 Needlefish (3)
22 Foretell (4)
23 Data transmission (9)
27 Bother (3)
29 Tune (4)
30 Governor in Mogul India (5)
31 Spirit (7)
33 Interfered with (8)
34 Trampled (4)

DOWN

1 Brought back (5)
2 Hawaiian acacia (3)
3 Pond scum (5)
4 Loyalty to one's group (9)
5 Old poetic form of eyes (4)
7 Peepshow (9)
8 Sin (3)
10 Long-armed ape (9)
11 Weapon (5)
13 So be it (4)
16 Open to question (9)
18 Closed automobile (5)
20 Sly look (4)
24 Falsehood (3)
25 Relaxed (5)
26 Production (5)
28 Facts (4)
32 Newt (3)

ACROSS

1 Break-in (8)
5 Narrow ledge (4)
8 Period of time (3)
9 Starlike symbol (8)
11 Short message (4)
13 Saturated (6)
15 To obtain by persuasion (7)
16 Subtle difference (6)
19 Spout (3)
21 Special Operations Group (Acronym) (3)
22 Gourmet (6)
25 Blind alley (4, 3)
26 Raved (6)
30 Cutlass (4)
31 Old World pigeon (8)
32 Displeasure (3)
33 Poses (4)
34 Credulous (8)

DOWN

2 Conclusion (6)
3 Acetose (6)
4 Tibetan oxen (4)
5 Curve (4)
6 Wearing (7)
7 Charge per unit (4)
10 Banished (6)
12 Finished (5)
14 The burden of responsibility (4)
17 Barbary sheep (6)
18 Burning (5)
19 Fine woodwork (7)
20 Pave (4)
23 Herb (6)
24 Bellyache (6)
27 Capital of Samoa (4)
28 Starts off (4)
29 Haul (4)

302

ACROSS
1 Separate into parts (11)
8 Happen (5)
10 Log in (5)
12 Woolen cap, Scottish (3)
14 Ecclesiastical floor cushion (7)
16 Tantrum (4)
18 *Haliaeetus albicilla* (3)
20 Khaki (4)
21 Competes (4)
22 Play it by --- (3)
24 Letter 'L' (3)
25 Leaf of a book (4)
26 Pick out (4)
27 Fluid in a plant (3)
28 Fine breed of horse (4)
29 Chooses (7)
33 Move from side to side (3)
35 Manila hemp (5)
36 Dog-like African mammal (5)
37 Birthright (11)

DOWN
1 Level (4)
2 Smallest component (4)
3 Check (4)
4 Giant (4)
5 A jump in figure skating (4)
6 Intestines (8)
7 Chisels (6)
9 Vehicle with one wheel (8)
11 Impertinence (5)
13 Debt that remains unpaid (6)
15 Evenness (8)
17 Ethiopian baboon (6)
19 Target of WWII atomic bomb (8)
23 Medieval string instrument (5)
25 Procession (6)
30 Whip (4)
31 River in central France (4)
32 Chair (4)
33 Large, open farm wagon (4)
34 Adhesive(4)

ACROSS

1 Impaired working (11)
6 Dissenter (7)
9 Suffering (3)
12 Locomotive (inf.) (9)
14 Volcanic material (6)
15 Exclamation of accident (4)
16 Silent (fam.) (3)
17 Object of scorn (4)
18 Ballet step (3)
19 Jar (4)
20 Jazz-style dance (3)
22 Go solo to Norway (anag.) (4)
24 Observation (6)
25 Uselessness (9)
27 Drain (3)
28 Dark-coloured rock, derived from alteration of basalt (5)
29 Small light boat (11)

DOWN

2 Literary ridicule (6)
3 Remarkable (4)
4 Band (5)
5 Luminiferous (10)
7 Aggressive (9)
8 Militant Irish group (3)
9 Objective case of 'who' (4)
10 Of times past (9)
11 Bring under one control (10)
13 Intellect (4)
16 Chart (3)
18 Small body of still water (4)
20 Bleep (4)
21 Human mind (6)
23 Pyramid (5)
24 Seventh letter of the Greek alphabet (3)
26 Assuredly (archaic) (4)

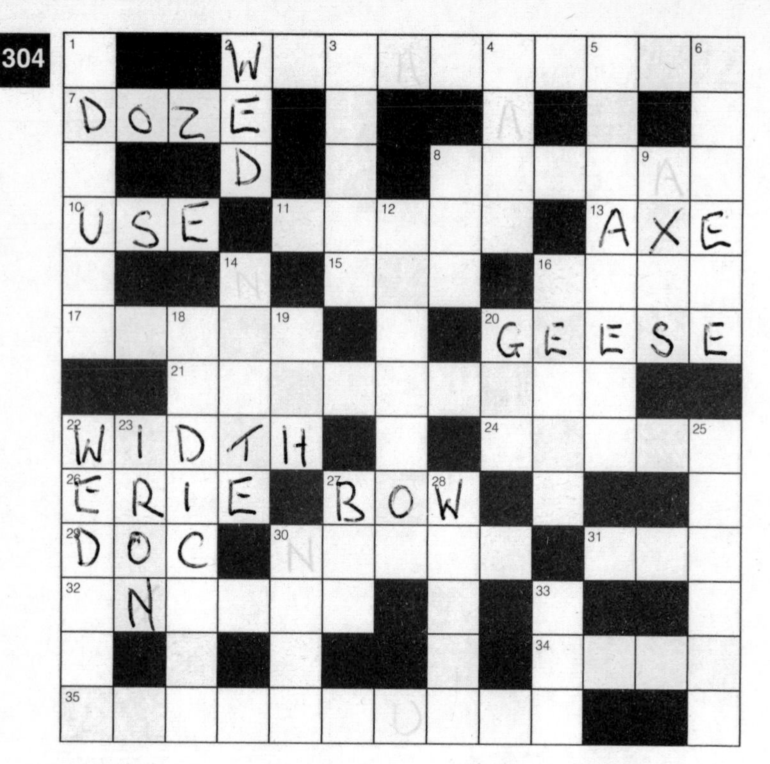

ACROSS
2 Pleasingly shaped (10)
7 Sleep lightly (4)
8 One year of a reign (6)
10 Employ (3)
11 Blanched (5)
13 Chopping tool (3)
15 Ingest (3)
16 Dust (4)
17 An instant (5)
20 Large water birds (5)
21 Nourishment (9)
22 Breadth (5)
24 Reddish dye (5)
26 Lake ---- (4)
27 A low curtsey (3)
29 What's Up ---? (3)
30 Famous (5)
31 Muscle spasm (3)
32 Knotted (6)
34 Gathering dust (4)
35 Raffle (10)

DOWN
1 Acclimatize (6)
2 Marry (3)
3 Unconstrained (5)
4 Augury (4)
5 Mosque towers (8)
6 Erase (6)
8 Submerge (3)
9 Pivotal shaft (4)
12 Holy place (7)
14 Sharp (5)
16 Jib for yachts (5)
18 Betoken (8)
19 Old English letter (3)
20 Correspond (3)
22 Jams tight (6)
23 Ferrous metal (4)
25 A silvery metal (6)
27 24-hour period (3)
28 Contour feather (5)
30 Flutter (4)
33 Cruise (3)

ACROSS
1 Coax (6)
4 Cone-shaped (6)
7 Having two branches (9)
10 Idiot (slang) (4)
11 To observe (3)
12 Patchy in colour (4)
13 Aristocrat (4)
15 Blade (5)
18 Involving the ileum (5)
20 Tints (4)
21 Entreaty (4)
22 Grasps (5)
24 Teacher (5)
26 A bumpkin (4)
29 Specks (4)
31 Exclamation of surprise (3)
32 A vagrant (4)
33 Chief magistrate of a shire (9)
34 Originating in the mind (6)
35 Made invalid (6)

DOWN
1 Bowl-shaped depression (6)
2 Leave out (4)
3 Eliminate (5)
4 Gaiety (5)
5 Tongue or pole of a cart (4)
6 Twofold (6)
7 Competitor in a biathlon (9)
8 A meadow (4)
9 An outline (9)
14 Light, happy song (4)
16 African lute (3)
17 20th letter of Hebrew alphabet (4)
19 Leucine (abbrev.) (3)
22 A bricklayer's tender (6)
23 Resound (4)
25 Firmly implanted (6)
27 Containing iodine (5)
28 Sacred Islamic writings (5)
30 Preservative (4)
32 Greet (4)

ACROSS
1 Ripped (4)
3 Bishop's throne (8)
6 Panacea (7)
9 Yugoslavian seaport (5)
12 Adriatic wind (4)
14 Before (3)
15 Child (9)
17 Edible starchy root (4)
18 Cleaning implement (3)
19 A burning itch (5)
21 Socialize (3)
22 Carry (4)
23 Disqualify (9)
27 Pronoun (3)
29 Festive season (4)
30 Stenographer (inf.) (5)
31 Closest (7)
33 Capital of Syria (8)
34 Always (4)

DOWN
1 Aromatic herb (5)
2 In no way (3)
3 Bludgeons (5)
4 Perilous (9)
5 Bellow (4)
7 Art of carving (9)
8 Witty remark (3)
10 Putrefy (9)
11 To recombine (5)
13 Tall perennial grass (4)
16 Viscid (9)
18 Methylated spirits (abbrev.) (5)
20 City in W. Nevada (4)
24 Lair (3)
25 Intestinal obstruction (5)
26 Gain entrance (5)
28 The neat volcano (anag.) (4)
32 Weep over (3)

307

ACROSS

1 Torpid (8)
5 At what time (4)
8 Paddle (3)
9 Folk instrument (8)
11 Girl's name (4)
13 Inclined head (6)
15 Sensation of dizziness (7)
16 Leave hastily (6)
19 Ruddy (3)
21 Synthetic garnet (3)
22 Accept as true (6)
25 A plague (7)
26 Pay as due (6)
30 Skirmish (4)
31 Vehicle with one wheel (8)
32 Fluid ejected by octopus (3)
33 Allot (4)
34 A building (8)

DOWN

2 Undeveloped seeds (6)
3 Electrical resistance (6)
4 Deserve (4)
5 Plant of the mustard family (4)
6 Pocketbook (7)
7 Type of eagle (4)
10 Having a city (6)
12 Take as one's own (5)
14 Comply (4)
17 Awning (6)
18 Neck warmer (5)
19 Fragment (7)
20 Gaming cubes (4)
23 Ineffective (6)
24 Theatre district (6)
27 Native American people (4)
28 A ditch or channel (4)
29 A mysterious poem (4)

308

ACROSS

1 Summarize (11)
8 Rob (5)
10 Coniferous evergreen forest (5)
12 Apex (3)
14 Wandering (7)
16 Alcoholic drink (4)
18 Silk filaments (3)
20 Corona (4)
21 Relaxation (4)
22 Rodent (3)
24 Rotational speed (abbrev.) (3)
25 Decree — (4)
26 Mountain goat (4)
27 To go quickly (3)
28 Kiln for hops (4)
29 Area around an altar (7)
33 Electron microscopes (abbrev.) (3)
35 Greek physician (5)
36 Decree (5)
37 Separate into component parts (11)

DOWN

1 Compass point (4)
2 Complain unreasonably (4)
3 Fruit (4)
4 Middle layer of the eye (4)
5 Opposed to (4)
6 Statue inscription (8)
7 Alter (6)
9 Calling (8)
11 Vexation (5)
13 Ancient region of Transcaucasia (6)
15 Wide-eyed (8)
17 Metallic element (6)
19 Music symbol (8)
23 A tenth part (5)
25 Small mug (6)
30 Rectangular pier (4)
31 US coin (4)
32 Swimming pool (4)
33 Sicilian volcano (4)
34 Underside of the foot (4)

ACROSS

1 Degree of response (11)
6 Cover surface (7)
9 Smidgen (3)
12 Adroitness (9)
14 North American lynx (6)
15 Incline from the vertical (4)
16 The sun (3)
17 Lazily (4)
18 To plant (3)
19 Cherished (4)
20 Mountain meadow (3)
22 Pelvic bones (4)
24 Vinegar (6)
25 Said with no forethought (9)
27 Short dashes (3)
28 Male voice (5)
29 Under the tongue (11)

DOWN

2 Dorsal (6)
3 A tiny amount (4)
4 A delicious dish (5)
5 Fringed (10)
7 Mineral used in ceramics (9)
8 Become firm (3)
9 Make a phone call (4)
10 Yeoman of the Guard (9)
11 Long, steep slope (10)
13 Sailing vessel (4)
16 Drench (3)
18 Spank (4)
20 Intentions (4)
21 Views (6)
23 Slow (music.) (5)
24 Exist (3)
26 ---- von Bismark (4)

310

ACROSS

2 Build-up of calcium (10)
7 Make new (4)
8 Hike (6)
10 Type of deer (3)
11 Girl's name (5)
13 Strive (3)
15 Recent (3)
16 A pile (4)
17 Goes over (5)
20 Hairy (5)
21 Notwithstanding (archaic) (9)
22 Coldly (5)
24 Straw beehive (5)
26 Pigeon coop (4)
27 Flower wreath (3)
29 --- Wallach, US actor (3)
30 Boat spines (5)
31 Besides (3)
32 Slowly (music) (6)
34 Pagan symbol (4)
35 Mechanical (10)

DOWN

1 Glaciate (6)
2 Child's bed (3)
3 Long, narrow lagoon (5)
4 Ark builder (4)
5 Destroy (8)
6 Weary (6)
8 Uncooked (3)
9 Trickster (4)
12 Arbitrator (7)
14 Stagnant (5)
16 Outer shells of seeds (5)
18 Begin (8)
19 Pig's home (3)
20 Moroccan city (3)
22 Time of the great freeze (3-3)
23 Chilled (4)
25 Bicycle seat (6)
27 Star sign (3)
28 Pertaining to the ileum (5)
30 Tartan skirt (4)
33 Nothing (3)

311

ACROSS

1 Wintry (6)
4 Rude (6)
7 Kidnapping (9)
10 Digits (4)
11 An old French coin (3)
12 Collard (4)
13 Supplements with great effort (4)
15 Remains (5)
18 Immature egg (5)
20 Black-and-white diving birds (4)
21 Growl (4)
22 Italian physicist who invented the battery (5)
24 Tidbit (5)
26 Lash (4)
29 Deep wound (4)
31 Singular (3)
32 Heavily spiced stew (4)
33 Process of fossilization (9)
34 Respect (6)
35 Without friends (6)

DOWN

1 Playful conversation (6)
2 Jostles (4)
3 Parasite (5)
4 Pineapple fibre (5)
5 Prepare food (4)
6 Cylindrical (6)
7 Trapeze artist (9)
8 Half burnt coal (4)
9 Inherently (9)
14 Male descendants (4)
16 Kernel (3)
17 A cape on the northernmost tip of Jutland (4)
19 Covered vehicle (3)
22 Able to move freely (6)
23 Wine (4)
25 Tangled (6)
27 Boring and dull (2-3)
28 Subject to punishment (5)
30 Execrate (4)
32 Sign (4)

312

ACROSS

1 Gloomy (4)
3 Rashness (8)
6 Lift up (7)
9 Bird (5)
12 Type of eagle (4)
14 Some (3)
15 Woman who works with cows (9)
17 Sets of tools (4)
18 Premier ---, fine wine (3)
19 Embankment (5)
21 Target area in quoits (3)
22 Small rivulet (4)
23 Artefact (9)
27 Reggae (3)
29 Well-being (4)
30 Mountain on which the 10 Commandments were received (5)
31 Tedium (7)
33 Ancestral line (8)
34 Flying mammals (4)

DOWN

1 Fear greatly (5)
2 Reverend (abbrev.) (3)
3 Emblem (5)
4 Advantageous (9)
5 Lean (4)
7 Having expensive taste (9)
8 Term of time (3)
10 Cummerbund (9)
11 A levy of one tenth (5)
13 Greek goddess of victory (4)
16 Becoming faded (9)
18 Category (5)
20 Czech river (4)
24 Punch (3)
25 Abscond (5)
26 Domesticates (5)
28 Light flying framework (4)
32 Backflow (3)

ACROSS
1 Cut across (8)
5 Similar (4)
8 Single item (3)
9 Holiday (8)
11 Operates (4)
13 Pledge (6)
15 Earthshaking (7)
16 Repressed (4-2)
19 Estimated Time of Arrival (acronym) (3)
21 Three-toed sloth (3)
22 Place in bondage (6)
25 Light spear (7)
26 Foray (6)
30 Bound (4)
31 Basic principles (8)
32 Father (3)
33 Obtains (4)
34 Water line on the shore (8)

DOWN
2 One who studies literary works (6)
3 Draw out (6)
4 Converts into leather (4)
5 Set lower (4)
6 Six-legged creatures (7)
7 Young guinea fowl (4)
10 Having a handle (6)
12 Slender, graceful woman (5)
14 Compound excreted in urine (4)
17 ------ Creed, statement of Christian belief (6)
18 Record of sum owed (5)
19 Copy of court records (7)
20 Part of a town, city etc. (4)
23 The last remaining part (3-3)
24 Irregular movement (6)
27 Brood of pheasants (4)
28 Probability (4)
29 Neatly skilful (4)

314

ACROSS

1 Ordinary (11)
8 Entrails (5)
10 Swampy coniferous forest tree of Siberia (5)
12 Rent out (3)
14 Leaking (7)
16 Plant with showy flowers (4)
18 Acquire (3)
20 Flat-fish (4)
21 Club-like weapon (4)
22 As being (3)
24 Mimic (3)
25 Irrational (4)
26 Food grain (4)
27 A witch (3)
28 Narrow lane (4)
29 Plunge (7)
33 Gave food (3)
35 Layers (5)
36 Mountain ridge (5)
37 Pottery of hardened clay (11)

DOWN

1 Slaughter (4)
2 Subject to debate (4)
3 Clumsy people (4)
4 Long, cylindrical piece of wood (4)
5 Opposed to (4)
6 A short quotation (8)
7 Commendation (6)
9 Airmail letter (8)
11 Soul (5)
13 Funeral ceremony (6)
15 Minister (8)
17 Time of extensive freezing (3-3)
19 Tollgate (8)
23 To confuse (5)
25 Sweeping blows (6)
30 One who utilizes something (4)
31 Soft pulpy mass (4)
32 Web-footed bird (4)
33 Type of cheese (4)
34 Completed (4)

ACROSS

1 Polite refusal (11)
6 Innocently charming (7)
9 Kimono sash (3)
12 A strict teacher (9)
14 Concealed (6)
15 Capital of Switzerland (4)
16 Maiden name (3)
17 Slimy dirt (4)
18 Wager (3)
19 A bone (4)
20 Original state (3)
22 Is indebted (4)
24 Small yellow moth (6)
25 Memory (9)
27 Headgear (3)
28 Little (5)
29 Perplexing situation (11)

DOWN

2 Barrel maker (6)
3 Frozen over (4)
4 Small drum (5)
5 Vatican bodyguard (5-5)
7 Cravat (9)
8 Came across (3)
9 S-bend (4)
10 Bursting into flame (9)
11 To put at risk (10)
13 Encourage in wrongdoing (4)
16 Not old (3)
18 Strong woody fibre (4)
20 Lease out (4)
21 End (6)
23 Woodland (5)
24 Forepart of a hoof (3)
26 Bones (4)

316

ACROSS

2 Joint pain (10)
7 By mouth (4)
8 Oval-shaped nut (6)
10 Female member of a religious group (3)
11 Scoop (5)
13 Large antelope (3)
15 Recent (3)
16 Flutter (4)
17 Sleeveless garment (5)
20 Dark grey roofing tile (5)
21 Worship (9)
22 Earnings (5)
24 Radio waves (5)
26 Winged (4)
27 Type of tree (3)
29 International distress signal (acronym) (3)
30 Boat spines (5)
31 T'ai ---, form of exercise (3)
32 Frontal (4-2)
34 Strong desire (4)
35 The clergy (10)

DOWN

1 Straw hat (6)
2 A priest's robe (3)
3 Experiment (5)
4 Deep valley (4)
5 Criminal underworld (8)
6 Sagacious (6)
8 Number of threads (3)
9 Single thing (4)
12 Information (7)
14 Drink made from apples (5)
16 Decorated parade vehicle (5)
18 Seaport hit by an atom bomb (8)
19 Long-leaved lettuce (3)
20 Title of respect (3)
22 To clean dishes (4-2)
23 Evergreen plant with thick pointed leaves (4)
25 Commando (6)
27 Cycle (3)
28 French underground railway (5)
30 Records (4)
33 Of no value (3)

ACROSS
1 Bother (6)
4 Ineffective (6)
7 Written sign or symbol (9)
10 Charming (4)
11 And not (3)
12 Make less painful (4)
13 Child's toy (4)
15 Roost (5)
18 Noblemen (5)
20 Wild goat (4)
21 Wood tool (4)
22 Waterlily (5)
24 Seductive woman (5)
26 Listen to (4)
29 Relocate (4)
31 Used to indicate maiden name (3)
32 To snarl (4)
33 Impression (9)
34 Type of oil (6)
35 Chiselled (6)

DOWN
1 Diaphragm spasm (6)
2 Team (4)
3 Very dark wood (5)
4 Like a teddy bear (5)
5 Drink to excess (4)
6 Goes into a particular place (6)
7 Repetitious (9)
8 Make a silly mistake (4)
9 Longing (9)
14 Likelihood that something will happen (4)
16 Grade of wine (3)
17 Shambles (4)
19 Type of machine gun (3)
22 Scottish loch (6)
23 Greek goddess of the earth (4)
25 Tended to the sick (6)
27 To register (5)
28 Make merry (5)
30 Stops (4)
32 Midge (4)

318

ACROSS
1 Small spots (4)
3 Attaining (8)
6 Traveller (7)
9 Beastly (5)
12 Flower (4)
14 Capitalize (3)
15 Retire for the winter (9)
17 Outermost points (4)
18 Fifth tone of the diatonic scale (3)
19 Packs tightly (5)
21 To brown in the sun (3)
22 Tropical Jamaican fruit (4)
23 Small ball of ice (9)
27 Etcetera (abbrev.) (3)
29 Earthware pot (4)
30 Clip wool (5)
31 Dormer window (7)
33 Hand down (8)
34 Sewing bag (4)

DOWN
1 Get rid of (5)
2 Honorific title (3)
3 Sticky substance (5)
4 Generally accepted opinion (9)
5 Dry fruit with hard shells (4)
7 Disorientation (9)
8 Tax Reform Act (acronym) (3)
10 Insolation (9)
11 Be passionate (5)
13 One thing on a list (4)
16 Steeplechaser (9)
18 Auctions (5)
20 Free of pretence (4)
24 Sickly (3)
25 Express mirth (5)
26 Listlessness (5)
28 Objective case of thou (4)
32 To go quickly (3)

ACROSS

1 Remove knots from (8)
5 French clergyman (4)
8 Extinct flightless bird (3)
9 Japanese dish (8)
11 Each, every (Scots) (4)
13 Boredom (6)
15 Fleshy part of the ear (7)
16 An idyllic place (6)
19 Small evil spirit (3)
21 To spoil (3)
22 Screech (6)
25 Natural environment (7)
26 Make amends (6)
30 Two identical things (4)
31 Beget (8)
32 Small carpet (3)
33 Donations to the poor (4)
34 Stretched out (8)

DOWN

2 Chewy confectionery (6)
3 Grasping (6)
4 Doorway (4)
5 Amongst (4)
6 Venezuelan mountain (7)
7 Capital of Azerbaijan (4)
10 To light up (6)
12 Love affair (5)
14 Dutch cheese (4)
17 A country (6)
18 Encroach (5)
19 Brittle metallic element (7)
20 Bellboy (4)
23 Nothingness (6)
24 Sheer fabric (6)
27 British peer (4)
28 Energy units (4)
29 Allot (4)

320

ACROSS

1 Censorship (11)
8 Smelling -----, sniffed as a stimulant (5)
10 Derange (5)
12 Expression of annoyance (3)
14 Room for cooking food (7)
16 Low female singing voice (4)
18 Be beholden (3)
20 To swear (4)
21 Landscape (4)
22 Curve (3)
24 Finale (3)
25 Family ----, genealogical chart (4)
26 Hotels (4)
27 Alcoholic beverage (3)
28 Christian song (4)
29 Make a list (7)
33 Amplifier (inf.) (3)
35 Fidgety (slang) (5)
36 Pardon (5)
37 Sudden disaster (11)

DOWN

1 Throw a fishing line (4)
2 Thin fog (4)
3 Chatter (4)
4 Price (4)
5 Engrave (4)
6 Young sheep or goat (8)
7 Before this time (6)
9 Lustrous white metallic element (8)
11 Pillage (5)
13 Not alert to danger (6)
15 Declare to be a saint (8)
17 State of being bored (6)
19 Living like a hermit (8)
23 Monetary units (5)
25 Deliver a hard blow (6)
30 Small island in a lake (4)
31 Part of the eye (4)
32 Islamic chieftain (4)
33 At the peak (4)
34 Heap (4)

321

ACROSS

1 Accountable (11)
6 Two-wheel vehicle (7)
9 Surrounds the tooth (3)
12 Chronicler (9)
14 Caffeine drink (6)
15 Misfortunes (4)
16 Rubbish container (3)
17 Satisfy to excess (4)
18 Devoted follower (3)
19 Rip (4)
20 Old plural of 'eye' (3)
22 Wrinkle (4)
24 Resembling salt (6)
25 Combine with oxygen (9)
27 Find the sum of (3)
28 Strike (5)
29 Chill (11)

DOWN

2 Small bag (6)
3 Singles (4)
4 Accustom (5)
5 Cutting off (10)
7 Lunchroom (9)
8 Recline (3)
9 Thug (4)
10 Be unsuitable (9)
11 Not shortened (10)
13 One of a matching pair (4)
16 Forbid (3)
18 Noteworthy achievement (4)
20 Mild exclamation (4)
21 Capital of the Philippines (6)
23 Cow's mammary gland (5)
24 In what way (3)
26 Haven (4)

322

ACROSS

2 Bone-forming cell (10)
7 Medium-sized pasta tubes (4)
8 Variant (6)
10 Worthless piece of cloth (3)
11 Titles (5)
13 Soft food for infants (3)
15 Not of the clergy (3)
16 A further (4)
17 Urges (5)
20 1st letter in Hebrew alphabet (5)
21 Outermost part of the brain (9)
22 Southpaw (5)
24 Home of the pyramids (5)
26 Sword for fencing (4)
27 Third person singular (3)
29 Rotter (slang) (3)
30 Away (5)
31 Mongrel dog (3)
32 Thespians (6)
34 Augury (4)
35 Irish parliament (10)

DOWN

1 Islands in N. Atlantic (6)
2 Petroleum (3)
3 Subject to sea movement (5)
4 Inlets (4)
5 Fit of extreme anger (8)
6 Fermented soybean cake (6)
8 Governor in the Ottoman Empire (3)
9 Grate (4)
12 Virgin Mary (7)
14 Mountain spur (5)
16 Mournful poem (5)
18 Liberate (8)
19 Asian condiment (3)
20 Had food (3)
22 Smooth (6)
23 Heroic (4)
25 Sovereign's seat (6)
27 Roman goddess of plenty (3)
28 Upright (5)
30 Extent of space (4)
33 Long-leaved lettuce (3)

323

ACROSS
1 Marvel (6)
4 33rd president of the US (6)
7 Excess fat at hips (9)
10 Frozen (4)
11 Action (suffix) (3)
12 Pulls with difficulty (4)
13 Ostracize (4)
15 Naming words (5)
18 Cylindrical larva (5)
20 Singly (4)
21 Spouse (4)
22 Book of the Bible (5)
24 Material made from pulp (5)
26 Stupid person (slang) (4)
29 Stinging insects (4)
31 Loud noise (3)
32 Employs (4)
33 One who gets something (9)
34 Absent without permission (6)
35 Non-resident doctor (6)

DOWN
1 Curse (6)
2 Couple (4)
3 Wireless (5)
4 Adolescence (5)
5 Mountain range (4)
6 Sickness (6)
7 Withdraw into solitude (9)
8 Clamorous (4)
9 Signboard (9)
14 Snare (4)
16 Not (3)
17 Disfigure (4)
19 Ate a letter (anag.) (3)
22 Capital of Tasmania (6)
23 Clench (4)
25 Hand in notice (6)
27 Commandment (5)
28 Cutting implement (5)
30 Bristle (4)
32 Single entity (4)

324

ACROSS

1 Matures (4)
3 State of drowsiness (8)
6 Similarly not (7)
9 Bunches (5)
12 Surrender possession of (4)
14 Type of tree (3)
15 Constellation (6-3)
17 Expresses accident (4)
18 Ban (3)
19 Scour (5)
21 Unwell (3)
22 Factual information (4)
23 Anointment (9)
27 Curved line (3)
29 Rabbit-like mammal (4)
30 As before (5)
31 Ingenuousness (7)
33 Roman emperor (8)
34 Strikes suddenly (4)

DOWN

1 Invalidate (5)
2 Perch (3)
3 Sibling's daughter (5)
4 Absolute (9)
5 Very small quantity (4)
7 Forbid (9)
8 Colour (3)
10 Antiquate (9)
11 Drinking toast (5)
13 Entrance (4)
16 Vigour of body (9)
18 General (5)
20 Japanese syllabic script (4)
24 Metal vessel with spigot (3)
25 Approaches (5)
26 Of necessity (5)
28 Iranian currency (4)
32 Namely (3)

ACROSS
1 Newcomer (8)
5 Barbarous person (4)
8 Go round (3)
9 Submission to destiny (8)
11 Energy units (4)
13 Infuriate (6)
15 Wanted (7)
16 A sideboard for china (6)
19 Criminal Investigation Dept. (acronym) (3)
21 Formerly known as (3)
22 Forming the apex (6)
25 Drunk (inf.) (7)
26 Peevish (6)
30 Camouflage (4)
31 Improving the mind (8)
32 Domesticated animal (3)
33 The sheatfish (4)
34 Adjustable resistor (8)

DOWN
2 Joined (6)
3 Unpowered aircraft (6)
4 Coating of ice (4)
5 Above (4)
6 Long-necked animal (7)
7 Called (4)
10 Caustic (6)
12 Places (5)
14 Part of speech (4)
17 Spirited (6)
18 Bring forth from the egg (5)
19 Stronghold (7)
20 Paint unskillfully (4)
23 Drink (6)
24 Rupture (6)
27 Matured (4)
28 Wagers (4)
29 365 days (4)

326

ACROSS
1 Beaten by the elements (11)
8 Hearth (5)
10 Register (5)
12 Conclusion (3)
14 Marked by pleasure (7)
16 Sticky wet substance (4)
18 Achievement (3)
20 Floating platform (4)
21 Detect (4)
22 A wee lamb (anag.) (3)
24 Edge (3)
25 Colonnade (4)
26 TV award (4)
27 Weep convulsively (3)
28 Opposite of nays (4)
29 Die (7)
33 Not many (3)
35 Fish (5)
36 Electronic message (5)
37 Remove oxygen from (11)

DOWN
1 Swell (4)
2 Sour(4)
3 Lofty (4)
4 Bewailed (4)
5 Not closed (4)
6 State of drowsiness (8)
7 Decrepit automobile (6)
9 Technical vocabulary of law (8)
11 Man's name (5)
13 Subtlety (6)
15 Expecting the best (8)
17 Resist (6)
19 Double meaning (3, 5)
23 Artist's support (5)
25 Adventurous expedition (6)
30 King mackerel (4)
31 Ethereal (4)
32 Supinity (4)
33 Parasitic insect (4)
34 Broad (4)

ACROSS

1 Sexploitation (11)
6 Release from slavery (7)
9 Fastening (3)
12 Train (inf.) (9)
14 Bitter conflict (6)
15 State or condition (suffix) (4)
16 Fever (3)
17 Carbamide (4)
18 Emolument (3)
19 Hit sharply (4)
20 Earth or land (3)
22 Move carefully (4)
24 Rather wide (6)
25 Extended discussion (9)
27 Monetary unit of Romania (3)
28 Edict of the czar (5)
29 Promotion in rank (11)

DOWN

2 To branch out (6)
3 Upon (4)
4 Negatively charged ion (5)
5 Castrate (10)
7 Neuron (9)
8 Indignation (3)
9 Used to indicate the one being addressed (4)
10 Of times past (9)
11 Sweetheart (10)
13 Egypt's river (4)
16 Nourished (3)
18 Worry (4)
20 Name from the Bible (4)
21 End (6)
23 Pack leader (5)
24 Large bowl-shaped pan (3)
26 Enormous (4)

328

ACROSS

2 Found fault (10)
7 Oxen harness (4)
8 Bladder (6)
10 Tuxedo (abbrev.) (3)
11 Intense light beam (5)
13 Not good (3)
15 Unit of illumination (3)
16 Mottled yarn or fabric (4)
17 Sleight of hand (5)
20 Kitten (5)
21 Study of sound (9)
22 Lover of Juliet (5)
24 Celtic priest (5)
26 Avouch (4)
27 Printer's measure (3)
29 Passenger vehicle (3)
30 Cocked (5)
31 Pronoun (3)
32 Simple life form (6)
34 Water (4)
35 Exceed in importance (10)

DOWN

1 Method (6)
2 The letter 'c' (3)
3 Absolute (5)
4 French river (4)
5 Large Japanese business conglomerate (8)
6 Lethal (6)
8 Annoy (3)
9 Wagon (4)
12 Subjoin (7)
14 Gambler (5)
16 Extremely small (5)
18 Playful (8)
19 Talk fondly (3)
20 Bamboozle (3)
22 Wired stiff collar (6)
23 Oospore (4)
25 Seaport in Natal (6)
27 Cycle (3)
28 Injure with hot liquid (5)
30 Recedes (4)
33 Grope (3)

ACROSS
1 Telltale (6)
4 Building material (6)
7 Extract obtained by decocting (9)
10 Wicked (4)
11 Kernel (3)
12 Early Russian parliament (4)
13 Yes (4)
15 Give up (5)
18 Choose (5)
20 Tides at their lowest (4)
21 Steep high cliff (4)
22 Pilsner (5)
24 Dull yellowish brown (5)
26 Strong taste (4)
29 Almost (4)
31 Seed of a legume (3)
32 ---- vera, plant (4)
33 Employ euphemism (9)
34 Apprehensive (6)
35 Federal soldier (inf.) (6)

DOWN
1 Indefinite portion (6)
2 Rind (4)
3 Black wood (5)
4 Short surplice (5)
5 Emotional state (4)
6 Occupant (6)
7 Detach (9)
8 Struck with a cue (4)
9 Capable of being counted (9)
14 Used as a mild oath (4)
16 Shelter (3)
17 Slender missile (4)
19 Sixth note in a musical scale (3)
22 Finch (6)
23 Joint (4)
25 Glacial epoch (3-3)
27 Plant louse (5)
28 Dry red wine (5)
30 Rounded protuberance (4)
32 Islamic call to prayer (4)

330

ACROSS

1 Pillar (4)
3 Frankly (8)
6 Slander (7)
9 Ivory (5)
12 Additionally (4)
14 Cardinal number (3)
15 Unreserved in speech (9)
17 Sharp to the taste (4)
18 Blackguard (3)
19 Fold (5)
21 Application (3)
22 Fermented paste made from cooked soy beans (4)
23 Of the second degree (9)
27 System for developing potential (3)
29 Hairstyle (4)
30 Red earth pigment (5)
31 Petroleum well (7)
33 Earthenware (8)
34 Close (4)

DOWN

1 Courtyard (5)
2 To free from (3)
3 Source of cocoa (5)
4 Device for triggering explosion (9)
5 Similar (4)
7 Consequence (9)
8 Moose (3)
10 Small statue (9)
11 Trap (5)
13 A stiff hair (4)
16 An insignificant person (9)
18 Carved gemstone (5)
20 An iron lump (4)
24 Commotion (3)
25 Lace mat (5)
26 Mass of broken oyster shells (5)
28 Rock outcrop (4)
32 Succeeded (3)

ACROSS

1 Pertaining to the zenith (8)
5 Agitate (4)
8 Shoddy articles (3)
9 Collection of rabbits (8)
11 Spots or pips on a domino (4)
13 Small crustacean (6)
15 Flesh of a deer (7)
16 Old Monetary unit of Portugal (6)
19 At a great distance (3)
21 Greek goddess (3)
22 Lighted by twilight (6)
25 Small wing or fin (7)
26 Ready for cultivation (6)
30 Subjective unit of loudness (4)
31 Not crying (8)
32 Playing card (3)
33 Capital of Yemen (4)
34 Careless (8)

DOWN

2 Overjoyed (6)
3 Egyptian goddess of love (6)
4 Produces eggs (4)
5 An outstanding person (4)
6 Roman historian (7)
7 Single component (4)
10 For a bride (6)
12 Ghost (5)
14 Flexible tube (4)
17 Dogwood (6)
18 Book of maps (5)
19 Monetary resources (7)
20 Iran money (4)
23 Borne in pairs (6)
24 Explosions (6)
27 Highway (4)
28 Part of verb to be (4)
29 Engrave with acid (4)

332

ACROSS
1 Pretentious display (11)
8 Governed (5)
10 Shocking (5)
12 Tree (3)
14 Least difficult (7)
16 A river of northeast France (4)
18 A wet-nurse (3)
20 Procurer (4)
21 Metric unit of mass (4)
22 12th letter of the alphabet (3)
24 Even (poet.) (3)
25 To pay up (4)
26 Greek god of love (4)
27 Transgression (3)
28 Stalk (4)
29 Revel noisily (7)
33 Unit of electrical resistance (3)
35 Rephrase (5)
36 Scent (5)
37 Lookout (11)

DOWN
1 Musical instrument (4)
2 Duration (4)
3 Longest river (4)
4 Calculates (4)
5 ---- of Skye (4)
6 Nourishes (8)
7 Make amends (6)
9 Ease of manner (8)
11 Long-continued practice (5)
13 Bewail (6)
15 Beseeched (8)
17 Expel (6)
19 Inseparable friend (5-3)
23 Yellow citrus fruit (5)
25 Teeming (6)
30 ---- of March (4)
31 A unit of pressure (4)
32 Roster (4)
33 Ricelike grains of pasta (4)
34 Numerous (4)

ACROSS
1 Identical in pronunciation (11)
6 Capital of Georgia (7)
9 More of the same (3)
12 Tasmanian wolf (9)
14 Seat for more than one person (6)
15 Not fake (4)
16 Exclamation of contempt (3)
17 Wool cleaning brush (4)
18 Stick (3)
19 Islamic call to prayer (4)
20 Brine (3)
22 Stringed instrument (4)
24 Citrus fruit (6)
25 Unlucky (9)
27 Teenage lout (3)
28 Not hesitant (5)
29 Negligence (11)

DOWN
2 Construction framing a fireplace (6)
3 Engage in prayer (4)
4 Of course (inf.) (5)
5 Series of interconnected things (10)
7 In the strict sense (9)
8 Definite article (3)
9 Any (4)
10 Citizens collectively (9)
11 Reliance (10)
13 Metal (4)
16 Snake (3)
18 Musical instrument (4)
20 Broken branch or stump (4)
21 Wild sheep of Asia (6)
23 Submarine (1-4)
24 Half of two (3)
26 Metallic element (4)

334

ACROSS

2 Swimming cap (10)
7 Thought (4)
8 Spray of hot water (6)
10 Plant (3)
11 Flat-bottomed fishing boat (5)
13 Cereal grass (3)
15 Governor (3)
16 A woman's breasts (4)
17 Birthplace of Muhammad (5)
20 Pulpy (5)
21 Turn towards the east (9)
22 Ancient region of S. Mesopotamia (5)
24 Protuberance (5)
26 Venomous snakes (4)
27 Racket (3)
29 Star sign (3)
30 Tool for boring holes (5)
31 Carrier for bricks (3)
32 Become inflexible (6)
34 Lecherous look (4)
35 Fruit (10)

DOWN

1 Supple (6)
2 Body of water (3)
3 Palpitate (5)
4 Back of the neck (4)
5 Merry-go-round (8)
6 Attractive (6)
8 Conniving (3)
9 Incision (4)
12 Cloth bag filled with beans (7)
14 Land measures (5)
16 Unit of currency in the Yemen (5)
18 Serene (8)
19 Atmosphere (3)
20 Fairy queen (3)
22 Biblical dancing girl (6)
23 Works with (4)
25 Endows with quality (6)
27 Purchase (3)
28 Male voice (5)
30 Doll (3)

335

ACROSS

1 Pyramid at Giza (6)
4 Feeling nauseous (6)
7 Drowsy (9)
10 Art of fencing (4)
11 Buddhist temple (3)
12 Torch (4)
13 Nasal phlegm (slang) (4)
15 Sound of a horse (5)
18 Cave (5)
20 Stead (4)
21 Independent ruler (4)
22 Sweatbox (5)
24 Fold (5)
26 Hoist (4)
29 Examination (4)
31 Not (Scot.) (3)
32 Ancient (4)
33 Recurved (9)
34 Jewish fraternity (6)
35 Male cat (6)

DOWN

1 Collapse (4-2)
2 Slender woodwind instrument (4)
3 Reduces speed (5)
4 Capital of Ecuador (5)
5 Heinous (4)
6 Exclamation to express joy (6)
7 Crescent (9)
8 Wife of rajah (4)
9 A case (9)
14 Compact by pounding (4)
16 Alcoholic liquor (3)
17 Make healthy (4)
19 Nullity (3)
22 Arm cover (6)
23 A long way (4)
25 Fervent (6)
27 Accustom (5)
28 4th month of the Jewish calendar (5)
30 Administer (4)
32 Tomcat (1-3)

336

ACROSS
1 Harvest (4)
3 Place for hatching eggs (8)
6 Portend (7)
9 Prohibit (5)
12 Extent (4)
14 Furore (3)
15 Lustihood (9)
17 Iota (4)
18 Bring civil action against (3)
19 Thighbone (5)
21 Assize (3)
22 Laugh loudly (4)
23 Tsunami (5-4)
27 Unit of energy (3)
29 Single thing (4)
30 Prescribed doctrine (5)
31 Endless (7)
33 Seasickness (3-2-3)
34 To put out (4)

DOWN
1 Drive back (5)
2 Thick liquid from infected tissue (3)
3 Navajo hut (5)
4 Pertaining to a cadastre (9)
5 Decipher (4)
7 Easter gift (9)
8 Before (3)
10 Loose-fitting overcoat (9)
11 Automaton (5)
13 Biblical twin (4)
16 Affect with folly (9)
18 Horse (5)
20 Ancient Gaelic name for Ireland (4)
24 Abate (3)
25 Fragrant oil (5)
26 Brilliant display (5)
28 Register (4)
32 Abolish (3)

ACROSS

1 Putting right (8)
5 Son of Jacob and Leah (4)
8 Frozen water (3)
9 Dining hall (4-4)
11 Lunge (4)
13 Governess (6)
15 Dominican friar (7)
16 Relating to universe (6)
19 Indisposed (3)
21 Denial (3)
22 Washed with clean water (6)
25 Author of an elegy (7)
26 Monetary unit of USA (6)
30 Theatre award (4)
31 Indefatigable (8)
32 Alone (3)
33 Taunt (4)
34 Imperil (8)

DOWN

2 Female follower of Bacchus (6)
3 Sloping letter (6)
4 Precious yellow metal (4)
5 Animate existence (4)
6 Thrifty management (7)
7 Blood vessel (4)
10 Mars (6)
12 Effeminate male (5)
14 Above (4)
17 Jackfish (6)
18 Hives (5)
19 Slant (7)
20 Russian river (4)
23 Overjoyed (6)
24 Interest paid on borrowed money (6)
27 Double-reed instrument (4)
28 Ogle (4)
29 Ancient Scandinavian poem (4)

338

ACROSS
1 Projecting parapets (11)
8 Mineral (5)
10 Shelter (5)
12 A dynasty in China (3)
14 Neither male or female (7)
16 At that time (4)
18 Doze (3)
20 Something lent (4)
21 Ornamental fabric (4)
22 Classical drama of Japan (3)
24 A letter in old Saxon (3)
25 Thin sheets of pastry (4)
26 Evils (4)
27 Epoch (3)
28 Sets in position for use (4)
29 Denoting part of bone around inner ear (7)
33 Unspecified system (3)
35 Echo-location (5)
36 City in Nebraska (5)
37 Considerable (11)

DOWN
1 Great in quantity (4)
2 City in NW France (4)
3 Mainly eaten in summer (4)
4 Large African antelope (4)
5 An abbot or cleric (4)
6 Visor to shield the eyes (8)
7 Halogen element (6)
9 N. American dogwood (8)
11 Pineapple fibre (5)
13 Republic of South Africa (6)
15 Floor covering (8)
17 Resounds (6)
19 Rapid breathing (8)
23 Book of the Bible (5)
25 Like floss (6)
30 Journey (4)
31 Exude slowly (4)
32 A Japanese liquor made from fermented rice (4)
33 Pattern of speech (4)
34 Hybrid (4)

ACROSS

1 Not healthy (11)
6 Belly (7)
9 --- picking, fussy (3)
12 Resident of Boston (9)
14 Debase (6)
15 Weeded with a hoe (4)
16 Convert into leather (3)
17 Amount of loudness (4)
18 Shoot a marble (3)
19 Bone in the arm (4)
20 Outlying (3)
22 Metal fastener (4)
24 Mammal related to the llama (6)
25 Make compatible (9)
27 Piece of earth (3)
28 Interlace (5)
29 Increasing in heat (11)

DOWN

2 Burrowing marsupial (6)
3 Possesses (4)
4 Fishing net (5)
5 Larva of a caddisfly (10)
7 Ascendancy (9)
8 Era (3)
9 Midday (4)
10 Overwhelming manifestation (5-5)
11 Intolerable (10)
13 Become liquid (4)
16 Road surface (3)
18 Fine powder (4)
20 Discover (4)
21 Give pleasure to (6)
23 Main artery (5)
24 Stout (3)
26 For sure (4)

340

ACROSS

2 Stereoscopic vision (10)
7 ---- vitae (4)
8 Scatter (6)
10 Definite article (3)
11 Epileptic seizure (5)
13 Slender metal fastener (3)
15 Part of verb to be (3)
16 Curve (4)
17 Grass-like (5)
20 Religious recluses (5)
21 Recompense (9)
22 Famous (5)
24 Projecting teeth (5)
26 At any time (4)
27 Understanding (3)
29 Lettuce (3)
30 A large, pointed mass of ice (5)
31 Type of gun (3)
32 Uncounted (6)
34 Arctic (4)
35 Type of tea (10)

DOWN

1 Seller of hats (6)
2 Sorrowful (3)
3 Type of heather (5)
4 Exclamation of mild dismay (4)
5 Snakes (8)
6 Uses money (6)
8 Issue a summons (3)
9 A foolish man (slang) (4)
12 A travelling performer (7)
14 Inhabitant of Cambodia (5)
16 Additional pay (5)
18 Academic session (8)
19 10th letter of Hebrew alphabet (3)
20 Bumped into (3)
22 Fruitful (6)
23 River in central England (4)
25 Tending to skid (6)
27 Sheep ..., a wingless bloodsucking fly (3)
28 Girl's name (5)
30 Fruit of the blackthorn (4)
33 Horse carriage (3)

ACROSS

1 Depart (2-4)
4 Hidden from view (6)
7 Device for triggering explosion (9)
10 Ripped (4)
11 First note of music scale (3)
12 Skin (4)
13 Cheese (4)
15 Antelope (5)
18 Of Nordic stock (5)
20 Repast (4)
21 Accelerated (4)
22 Tough (5)
24 Prop (5)
26 Complacent (4)
29 Lower layer of earth's crust (4)
31 Israeli gun (3)
32 ---- bomb (4)
33 Typify (9)
34 Hoisted (6)
35 Finch (6)

DOWN

1 Cockroach (6)
2 Ajar (4)
3 Lyric poem (5)
4 City on the Missouri river (5)
5 Hew (4)
6 Plaid (6)
7 Ancient time of the Aborigines (9)
8 Protuberance (4)
9 Restore moisture (9)
14 Charts (4)
16 Open mesh fabric (3)
17 24 hour periods (4)
19 Representative (abbrev.) (3)
22 Flowing oil well (6)
23 Greek Liqueur (4)
25 Ploy (6)
27 Subdued (5)
28 3rd letter of Hebrew alphabet (5)
30 Copies (4)
32 Summons to prayer (4)

342

ACROSS

1 Glass ornament (4)
3 Jumble (8)
6 Bristle (7)
9 One of the two equal sections of a cone (5)
12 Scottish Gaelic (4)
14 Established (abbrev.) (3)
15 Clearly (9)
17 Leave out (4)
18 Ten decibels (3)
19 Latin-American dance (5)
21 Fury (3)
22 Plebeian (4)
23 Detersive (9)
27 Winged mammal (3)
29 Pull or rip apart (4)
30 Oily resin (5)
31 Most wealthy (7)
33 Discern (8)
34 Prying (4)

DOWN

1 Plait (5)
2 Physician (inf.) (3)
3 Confused hand-to-hand fight (5)
4 Period of blissful harmony (9)
5 Drinks slowly (4)
7 Incriminate (9)
8 Biblical grandson of Benjamin (3)
10 Biocide (9)
11 Musical study piece (5)
13 Long, laborious work (4)
16 Sleuth (9)
18 Mordida (5)
20 Showing unusual talent (4)
24 Head of maize (3)
25 Come into being (5)
26 Courageous (5)
28 Winglike structures (4)
32 Female chicken (3)

ACROSS

1 Republic in central South America (8)
5 10 cents US (4)
8 Bother (3)
9 Reserve between people (8)
11 Structure for storing grain (4)
13 Reverberated (6)
15 Full of envy (7)
16 Large white stork (6)
19 Loud noise (3)
21 Fabled bird (3)
22 Supported (6)
25 Haunt (7)
26 Spatter (6)
30 God of love (4)
31 Bid lower than another (8)
32 Writing fluid (3)
33 Ova (4)
34 Emaciated (8)

DOWN

2 Unmitigated (6)
3 Of practical use (6)
4 Long ago (4)
5 Morse element (4)
6 Stupid (7)
7 Underground mammal (4)
10 Pertaining to ammonia (6)
12 Intense hatred (5)
14 Burn slightly (4)
17 Hot water tank (6)
18 Humiliate (5)
19 Lasting all day (7)
20 Promontory (4)
23 Tipple (6)
24 Bladder (6)
27 A conceited dandy (4)
28 Inquires (4)
29 Rude dwellings (4)

344

ACROSS

1 Anticipation (11)
8 Throw (5)
10 Ruffle (5)
12 Mineral spring (3)
14 Not solid or liquid (7)
16 Saucy (4)
18 Part of verb to be (3)
20 Hearing organs (4)
21 Sewing case (4)
22 Frozen water (3)
24 And so on (3)
25 Ashy substance (4)
26 Rowing implements (4)
27 Supplement (3)
28 Ostrich-like bird (4)
29 Curdled milk (7)
33 Doctrine (3)
35 Tawdry (5)
36 A poplar (5)
37 Meditate (11)

DOWN

1 Energy units (4)
2 Size of type (4)
3 A dull explosive sound (4)
4 Inquires (4)
5 Information (abbrev.) (4)
6 Small piece of lean meat (8)
7 Ice cream made with eggs (6)
9 Underground cemetery (8)
11 Monetary unit of India (5)
13 Outcast (6)
15 Bewitch (8)
17 Rumpus (6)
19 Choosing from various sources (8)
23 Elevate (5)
25 Faultfinder (6)
30 16th letter of Hebrew alphabet (4)
31 Harden by heat (4)
32 Coarse file (4)
33 Very small quantity (4)
34 Bring to existence (4)

ACROSS
1 Co-operation (4-3-4)
6 Patella (7)
9 System for developing potential (3)
12 Unharmed (9)
14 Fine cloth (6)
15 Above (4)
16 Not (3)
17 Posterior (4)
18 Speck (3)
19 Ink spot (4)
20 Sixth note in a musical scale (3)
22 Image (4)
24 Red dye or plant pigment (6)
25 Protestant of Northern Ireland (9)
27 Falsehood (3)
28 Disarm (5)
29 Confine (11)

DOWN
2 Space devoid of matter (6)
3 Serpents (4)
4 Flavour (5)
5 Book of literary drawings (10)
7 Indispensable (9)
8 One (Scots) (3)
9 Overhanging lower edge of roof (4)
10 Servitude (9)
11 Substance that adulterates (10)
13 Outer garment (4)
16 Classical drama of Japan (3)
18 Inhabitant of Denmark (4)
20 Booth (4)
21 Tropical fruit (6)
23 Nematocyst (5)
24 Adult male (3)
26 Silent (4)

346

ACROSS

2 Paralysis of one extremity (10)
7 Fit of shivering (4)
8 Ring of colour (6)
10 Mouthpiece of a bridle (3)
11 Task (5)
13 Rodent (3)
15 Id ---, that is (3)
16 Flightless bird (4)
17 Upright tripod (5)
20 Centre of insect's face (5)
21 Gradually (9)
22 Armistice (5)
24 Affairs of honour (5)
26 Rent (4)
27 Beneath (prefix) (3)
29 High priest (3)
30 Fundamental (5)
31 Blemish (3)
32 Inclined (6)
34 To tip the hat (4)
35 State of being a sister (10)

DOWN

1 Bet (6)
2 Came across (3)
3 Recess in a wall (5)
4 Decoy (4)
5 Halo (8)
6 Fortification made of tree branches (6)
8 Illustrative craft (3)
9 Mown grass (4)
12 Bony (7)
14 Free of ice (5)
16 Sauerkraut (5)
18 Counterfeit (8)
19 Edge (3)
20 Provided food (3)
22 Academic themes (6)
23 Brook (4)
25 Moneychanger (6)
27 Dejected (3)
28 Inept person (5)
30 English monk (4)
33 Find the sum of (3)

347

ACROSS

1 Woman's close-fitting hat (6)
4 Monetary unit of Albania (6)
7 German composer (9)
10 Cross ---- (4)
11 Moisten (3)
12 Jump (4)
13 Native of Arabia (4)
15 Captivated by (5)
18 Many times (5)
20 12th month of the Jewish calendar (4)
21 Covered walk (4)
22 Cleft (5)
24 Groups of animals (5)
26 Tart (4)
29 Adjoin (4)
31 Grade of wine (3)
32 Relating to the anus (4)
33 Arrange according to a method (9)
34 Seat for two people (6)
35 Soldier in the Civil War (6)

DOWN

1 Concrete (6)
2 Struck a billiard ball (4)
3 Beyond what is usual (5)
4 Allotted quantity (5)
5 Winter holiday (4)
6 Start again (6)
7 Transuranic element (9)
8 Illustrious warrior (4)
9 Variety of peach (9)
14 Two together (4)
16 Biblical name (3)
17 Kernels (4)
19 Enemy (3)
22 Phases (6)
23 Former coin of Spain (4)
25 Comfort in misfortune (6)
27 Yellow earth pigment (5)
28 Reddish (5)
30 Mammilla (4)
32 Call to the mosque (4)

348

1 E	A	S	2 Y		3			4			5	

ACROSS

1 Simple (4)
3 One of the 12 tribes of Israel (8)
6 Tingling (7)
9 Daughter of one's brother or sister (5)
12 Mislay something (4)
14 Penpoint (3)
15 Explicitly (9)
17 Harbinger (4)
18 Curve (3)
19 Cowboy display (5)
21 Bounder (3)
22 Tailless amphibian (4)
23 Consisting of money (9)
27 Gone by (3)
29 Move briskly (4)
30 Adherent of Hinduism (5)
31 Hole drilled for extracting oil (7)
33 Game of chance (8)
34 Infectious tropical disease (4)

DOWN

1 To rub out (5)
2 --- and yang (3)
3 Negates (5)
4 Holiday taken by newly married couple (9)
5 Positions (4)
7 State of being impacted (9)
8 Greek goddess (3)
10 Proclaim (9)
11 Grew less (5)
13 Bluish-black fruit of the blackthorn (4)
16 Delight beyond measure (9)
18 Supreme being (5)
20 River in central Europe (4)
24 Murmur in delight (3)
25 Useful (5)
26 Shouts (5)
28 Unemployment cheque (4)
32 For what (3)

ACROSS

1 Changing (8)
5 Nonsense (4)
8 Chemistry suffix, i.e. meth--- (3)
9 Disconnect (8)
11 Bloodsucking insect (4)
13 Envelop (6)
15 Height (7)
16 Inhabitant of Yemen (6)
19 Along with (conjunction) (3)
21 Part of verb to do (3)
22 Move about restlessly (6)
25 Sea north of Australia (7)
26 On board (6)
30 Noisy (4)
31 Incessant (8)
32 --- Fheis, Irish party political conference (3)
33 Tureens (4)
34 Someone who remains loyal (8)

DOWN

2 Lenient act (6)
3 Not pure (6)
4 Exultation (4)
5 Iron hook with a handle (4)
6 Loveless (7)
7 Examine by touch (4)
10 Picnic (6)
12 Freely (2-3)
14 Hanker after (4)
17 Ticked (6)
18 Garbage (5)
19 Postpone (7)
20 Animal (4)
23 Avaricious (6)
24 General tendencies (6)
27 Male swine (4)
28 Increases (4)
29 Blunt (4)

350

ACROSS

1 Involving two molecules (11)
8 Land measures (5)
10 Source of cocoa (5)
12 Domesticated animal (3)
14 Held in high esteem (3-4)
16 Little devils (4)
18 Videlicet (3)
20 Repast (4)
21 Apparatus for weaving (4)
22 Sparse fluid (3)
24 Abstract being (3)
25 Leave out (4)
26 Pronoun (4)
27 Tap gently (3)
28 Small yeast cake (4)
29 Cornbread baked in hot ashes (7)
33 Taxi (3)
35 Supple (5)
36 More pleasant (5)
37 Unpleasant to the taste (11)

DOWN

1 High-pitched tone (4)
2 Foss (4)
3 Old monetary unit of Italy (4)
4 Portfolio (4)
5 Positions (4)
6 Capital of Virginia (8)
7 Conceit (6)
9 Choosing from various sources (8)
11 Nimble (5)
13 Riddle (6)
15 Capital of Finland (8)
17 Inn (6)
19 Financial combination of Japan (8)
23 Hiding place (5)
25 Colonial marine hydrozoan (6)
30 Assist (4)
31 To do with the anus (4)
32 Authentic (4)
33 Crustacean (4)
34 Sever with the teeth (4)

ACROSS

1 Closing hymn (11)
6 Endeavours (7)
9 Colour (3)
12 Achieving (9)
14 French painter (6)
15 Singles (4)
16 10th letter of the Hebrew alphabet (3)
17 Skullcap for women (4)
18 To fish with bobbing bait (3)
19 Fencing sword (4)
20 Explosive sound (3)
22 Matures (4)
24 Take into custody (6)
25 Indefensible (9)
27 Consume (3)
28 Enthusiastic (5)
29 Following in time (11)

DOWN

2 High-altitude cloud (6)
3 Ruined city in W. Iran (4)
4 Corpulent (5)
5 Extraordinary; remarkable (10)
7 Construct (9)
8 Cardinal number (3)
9 Tough outer covering (4)
10 Vanish (9)
11 Self-centered (10)
13 Coil (4)
16 Shrill bark (3)
18 Indian stuffed pancake (4)
20 Closely confined (4)
21 State in the NW United States (6)
23 Toothed wheels (5)
24 Wing-like structure of a living organism (3)
26 Sweeheart (4)

352

ACROSS

2 Pertaining to the eye (10)
7 Having wings (4)
8 Small spots (6)
10 Equipment (3)
11 Trials (5)
13 Small wingless insect (3)
15 Asian condiment (3)
16 Spoken (4)
17 Mistake (5)
20 Tusks (5)
21 Member of the Orange Order (9)
22 Nervous and tense (5)
24 Dress for show (5)
26 Ditch around castle (4)
27 Tavern (3)
29 Not in (3)
30 Shouts (5)
31 Child's plaything (3)
32 Mysterious or puzzling person (6)
34 Bone of forearm (4)
35 Mental lapse (10)

DOWN

1 ------ Doodle, US song (6)
2 Sphere (3)
3 The world of the dead (5)
4 Snakes (4)
5 Tubular pasta (8)
6 Having a high price (6)
8 Pigpen (3)
9 Knot in wood (4)
12 Melodious (7)
14 Most unfavourable (5)
16 Female reproductive organ (5)
18 Turning, as a wheel (8)
19 Moonbeam (3)
20 Mischievous child (3)
22 Single-celled animal (6)
23 Part of speech (4)
25 Buttons for operating an electrical device (6)
27 Podded vegetable (3)
28 Small yeast pancake (5)
30 Primordial Norse giant (4)
33 Flee (3)

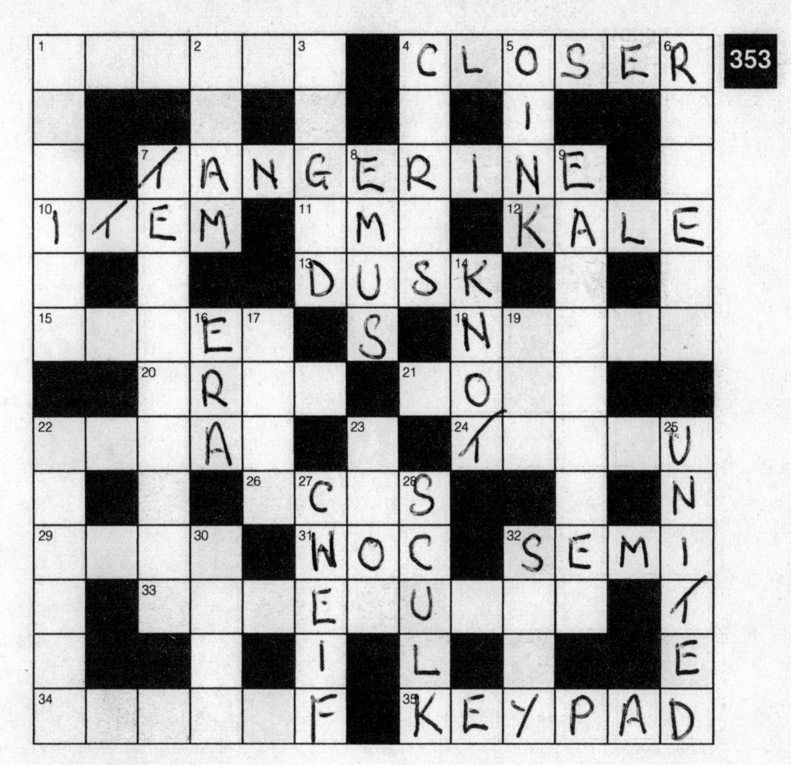

ACROSS

1 Arctic skua (6)
4 Nearer (6)
7 Mandarin (9)
10 Seperate article (4)
11 Small evil spirit (3)
12 Curley-leafed cabbage (4)
13 Partial darkness (4)
15 Much less common (5)
18 Lowest point (5)
20 Ring-shaped membrane behind the cornea (4)
21 System of electronic credit transfer (4)
22 Waste parts (5)
24 Highland area of moon or planet (5)
26 Declines (4)
29 Flat (4)
31 Large bowl-shaped pan (3)
32 Let sink (4)
33 Strong, lightweight alloy (9)
34 Conceptual framework (6)
35 Device with push-button controls (6)

DOWN

1 Relating to younger people (6)
2 Metric unit of mass (4)
3 Stiff (5)
4 Army unit (5)
5 Hog sound (4)
6 Try court case anew (6)
7 To be deeply afraid (9)
8 Large flightless birds (4)
9 Magistrate of a shire (9)
14 Tie or link together (4)
16 Period of time (3)
17 Vex (4)
19 Part of verb to be (3)
22 A mark used in ancient manuscripts (6)
23 Ancient Greek coin (4)
25 Joined by treaty (6)
27 Master (in Africa) (5)
28 Slink (5)
30 Unclothed (4)
32 Resembling vines (4)

354

ACROSS

1 English court (4)
3 Excessive flow of saliva (8)
6 Joined in matrimony (7)
9 Jewelled head band for women (5)
12 Member of Indian sect (4)
14 A thousand dollars (inf.) (3)
15 Fledgling (9)
17 Taking effect at a specified date (4)
18 Used to connect words (3)
19 Little (5)
21 Thick yellow liquid from infected body (3)
22 Hem or fringe (4)
23 Person promoting disorder (9)
27 Make a mistake (3)
29 Title (4)
30 Celestial body (5)
31 Pleated (7)
33 Narrow passageway (8)
34 Yellow metallic element (4)

DOWN

1 Not smooth (5)
2 Rocky pinnacle (3)
3 Squeeze (5)
4 Pertaining to arthritis (9)
5 Male parent (4)
7 Nematode (9)
8 Morse code sound (3)
10 Mother of Caligula (9)
11 Sponsorship (5)
13 Recognizes (Scot.) (4)
16 Heroic bravery (9)
18 Indian of Mexico (5)
20 Highest volcano in Europe (4)
24 Ampere (3)
25 Pass on (5)
26 Walk (5)
28 Irritate (4)
32 Gear tooth (3)

ACROSS

1 Olympic games (8)
5 A command (archaic) (4)
8 Choose (3)
9 Climbing shrub (8)
11 Monetary unit of Cambodia (4)
13 Extent (6)
15 Not religious (7)
16 Military decorations (6)
19 Bleat (3)
21 Total (3)
22 Republic in central Africa (6)
25 Peculiarity (7)
26 Deficiency in pigmentation (6)
30 Stupid person (4)
31 Modern (8)
32 To urinate (slang) (3)
33 Descriptive phrase (4)
34 Synical fold (8)

DOWN

2 Linger aimlessly (6)
3 Illusory (6)
4 Clock face (4)
5 Wind instrument (4)
6 Witty saying (7)
7 Let it stand (4)
10 Bird having a very large bill (6)
12 Capital of Tibet (5)
14 Uses something slowly and carefully (4)
17 Irresistable charm (6)
18 A mountain nymph (5)
19 Utters meaningless sounds (7)
20 Port at the mouth of the Red Sea (4)
23 To be next to (6)
24 Allot (6)
27 Slow pace of running (4)
28 Valued object (4)
29 Responsibility (4)

356

ACROSS

1 Origin (11)
8 Representative (5)
10 Enclosed automobile (5)
12 Letter of the alphabet (3)
14 Holiday resort (7)
16 Challenge (4)
18 Vessel built by Noah (3)
20 Ancient covered walkway (4)
21 Days before an event (4)
22 Vessel or duct (3)
24 Dominican (abbrev.) (3)
25 Boy or man (4)
26 Sprites (4)
27 Do away with (3)
28 Leap ----, occurring every 4 years (4)
29 Jewish literature (7)
33 Sibling (abbrev.) (3)
35 Step (5)
36 Pertaining to the Veda (5)
37 Baggage carried by soldiers (11)

DOWN

1 Folio (4)
2 Gemstone (4)
3 Gets with great effort (4)
4 Very small amount (4)
5 Decree ----, marriage annulment (4)
6 Strive (8)
7 Sacred river of India (6)
9 Young bird (8)
11 Having an edge (5)
13 Immature insects (6)
15 Frenzied rush (8)
17 Third sign of the zodiac (6)
19 Desert in SW Africa (8)
23 Caravansary (5)
25 Contractile protein of muscle (6)
30 Clench (4)
31 Enthusiastic (4)
32 Man's name (4)
33 Examine intensely (4)
34 Style of Caribbean music (4)

ACROSS

1 Domineering (11)
6 Comfortable chair (7)
9 Gymnasium (3)
12 Located near the navel (9)
14 Abilities (6)
15 Extinct flightless bird (4)
16 --- up, to urge forward (3)
17 Collector's piece (4)
18 Owns (3)
19 ---- of Wight (4)
20 Unit of tone of pitch (3)
22 Person who sees visions of the future (4)
24 Joined by treaty (6)
25 Ornate (9)
27 Not high (3)
28 Congenital anomaly of the skin (5)
29 Pun (4-2-5)

DOWN

2 Overwhelm (6)
3 A hurtful remark (4)
4 Swift (5)
5 Confidential (10)
7 Applicable in all cases (9)
8 Measures used in printing (3)
9 ---- gin (4)
10 Study of sound (9)
11 Breed of draught horse (10)
13 Ancient Roman days (4)
16 Girl or woman (3)
18 German Mister (4)
20 Sound of a cat (4)
21 Quick to understand (6)
23 A heavy, blackish wood (5)
24 Dined (3)
26 In a different way (4)

ACROSS
2 Frank and open (10)
7 Long fishes (4)
8 Roman poet (6)
10 Child's bed (3)
11 One of superior rank (5)
13 Classical poem (3)
15 Undercooked (3)
16 Step lively (4)
17 Prescribed amounts (5)
20 Wild Asian dog (5)
21 Island in the Indian Ocean (9)
22 Pelvic bone (5)
24 Destroy by immersion (5)
26 Remaining after all deductions (4)
27 Piece of work (3)
29 Dash in Morse code (3)
30 Having curls (5)
31 Drinking vessel (3)
32 Archetypes (6)
34 Stationary (4)
35 Dressing (10)

DOWN
1 Used to express disapproval (6)
2 Operate (3)
3 Reinforcement rod (5)
4 Muslim title (4)
5 Full of energy (8)
6 Erase (6)
8 Pledge (3)
9 Image of a deity (4)
12 Caretaker (7)
14 Something outstanding (slang) (5)
16 Long adit in a coalmine (5)
18 Workshop of a smith (8)
19 Total (3)
20 Part of verb to do (3)
22 Rare metallic element (6)
23 Metal (4)
25 Tool such as pincers or pliers (6)
27 A thin gravy (3)
28 Small pancake (5)
30 Family (4)
33 Hurry (3)

ACROSS

1 Sealed (6)
4 One of its kind (6)
7 Perspex (9)
10 Metallic element (4)
11 Member of a Pygmy people (3)
12 Test (abbrev.) (4)
13 Bristle (4)
15 Dolt (5)
18 Fish basket (5)
20 Mistress (4)
21 Festive season (abbrev.) (4)
22 Literary device (5)
24 Exalt (5)
26 Wristband (4)
29 Half burnt coal (4)
31 Disfigure (3)
32 The vascular middle layer of the eye (4)
33 Skywalk (9)
34 Bodily organ (6)
35 Adult mayfly (6)

DOWN

1 Occupied by a city (6)
2 Scrutinize (4)
3 Sums owing (5)
4 Submarine (1-4)
5 Avoiding work (4)
6 Nail polish (6)
7 Remote rural area (9)
8 Is indebted (4)
9 Inordinate (9)
14 Peak (4)
16 Policeman (3)
17 Executive officer (abbrev.) (4)
19 Hurried (3)
22 Trumpet fanfare (6)
23 By itself (4)
25 Once each year (6)
27 A flat-topped flower cluster (5)
28 Cooked by frying (5)
30 Makes something last longer (4)
32 Ill-favoured (4)

360

ACROSS
1 A sum of money saved (4)
3 Outmoded (8)
6 To recover (7)
9 Interior (5)
12 Fly (4)
14 Bird of the cuckoo family (3)
15 Surgical removal of stones from an organ (9)
17 Mischievous children (4)
18 An arithmetical problem (3)
19 Rope with running noose (5)
21 Perceive with the eyes (3)
22 Malarial fever (4)
23 Pen name (9)
27 Room within a harem (3)
29 Requests (4)
30 Russian revolutionary leader (5)
31 Weirdest (7)
33 Resolution into simple elements (8)
34 Eyeliner powder (4)

DOWN
1 Ferocious (5)
2 Unit equal to 10 litres (3)
3 Writer of lyric poetry (5)
4 Milkmaid (9)
5 Unwavering (4)
7 Sailboat with twin hulls (9)
8 Sound of a cow (3)
10 Birth (Fr.) (9)
11 Crest (5)
13 Throughout (4)
16 Possession of a property (9)
18 Abode of the dead (5)
20 Promontory (4)
24 To eat frugally (3)
25 Consumers (5)
26 Dense element (5)
28 Faculty head (4)
32 Class (3)

ACROSS
1 Relating to birds (8)
5 Green citrus fruit (4)
8 Poem (3)
9 Careless (8)
11 Call to mind (4)
13 Repeats someone's words (6)
15 Southern (7)
16 Russian sleigh (6)
19 Action (suffix) (3)
21 And the rest (3)
22 As a result of this (6)
25 Opposes (7)
26 An addition to a building (6)
30 Cut of meat (4)
31 Kilo (8)
32 Small amount (3)
33 Lairs (4)
34 Cut into two equal parts (8)

DOWN
2 Expressing regret (6)
3 Wintry (6)
4 Baggage (4)
5 Lake (4)
6 Stupid (7)
7 Dispense justice (4)
10 Monosaccharide (6)
12 Convocation of witches (5)
14 Cover with wax (4)
17 Not these (6)
18 Vial (5)
19 Inhabitant of Iran (7)
20 Pertaining to the Isle of Man (4)
23 Flowering (6)
24 Not accented (6)
27 Brief written record (4)
28 Terminates (4)
29 Draw with acid (4)

362

ACROSS

2 Completely (10)
7 Ancestor of domestic cattle (4)
8 Inflammation of the tonsils (6)
10 Cleaning implement (3)
11 Division of a blood vessel (5)
13 Speck (3)
15 Parrot (3)
16 Housemaid (4)
17 Percentage (5)
20 Warning bell (5)
21 Pointed (9)
22 Greek epic poem (5)
24 Upright (5)
26 Yellow metal (4)
27 Estimated time of arrival (acronym) (3)
29 And not (3)
30 Filch (5)
31 Man's name (3)
32 Carbon copies (6)
34 Gemstone (4)
35 Impartial (4-6)

DOWN

1 Mutter (6)
2 Tree (3)
3 Pinch (5)
4 Large flightless birds (4)
5 Not manufactured (8)
6 Beat (6)
8 In the capacity of (3)
9 Fly (4)
12 Souvenir (7)
14 Rechargeable battery (5)
16 Perceptive (5)
18 Watercourse leading away from a mill (8)
19 Musical instrument (3)
20 Fed (3)
22 Set on fire (6)
23 Apparatus for weaving (4)
25 Uproar (6)
27 Winged goddess (3)
28 Bitterly pungent (5)
30 Network (4)
33 Seed vessel (3)

SECTION TWO

SOLUTIONS

1

S	T	U	N	N	I	N	G		B	A	C	K
	A				N		A		O	U	R	
A	B	R	I	D	G	E	D		A	R	E	A
	A		N		O		S	T	R	E	W	N
E	R	U	D	I	T	E		E		O		G
	D		O		S		T	A	L	L	E	R
S		P	O	D				L	I	E		Y
T	U	R	R	E	T		D		M		F	
O		E		N		D	I	M	P	L	E	S
R	E	F	U	T	E		N		E		R	
E	R	A	S		T	I	N	C	T	U	R	E
	I	C	E		C		E				E	
L	E	E	S		H	E	R	E	W	I	T	H

4

J			D	R	E	A	D	L	O	C	K	S
A	N	T	A		N			U		A		E
E			M		T		E	X	E	M	P	T
G	A	T		S	E	N	T	E		P	A	T
E			R		R	O	C		B	O	N	E
R	E	P	E	L		X		B	A	R	G	E
		I	N	A	N	I	M	A	T	E		
R	U	T	T	Y		O		A	H	E	A	D
A	R	T	S		O	U	R		E			E
I	D	A		U	P	S	E	T		B	A	N
D	U	N	A	N	T		B		E			O
E		C		C			E		L	A	S	T
R	H	E	T	O	R	I	C	A	L			E

2

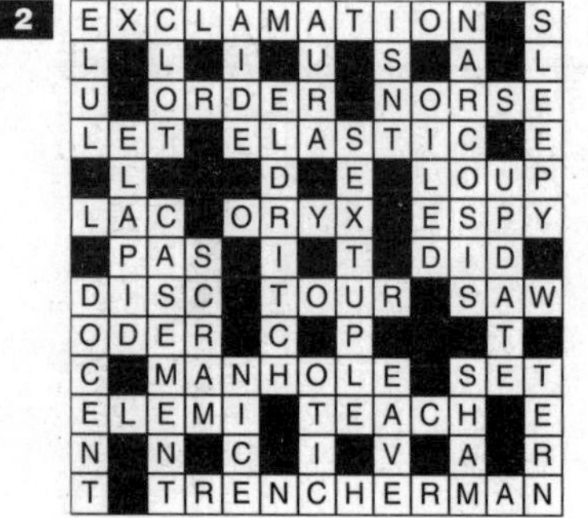

5

3 **6**

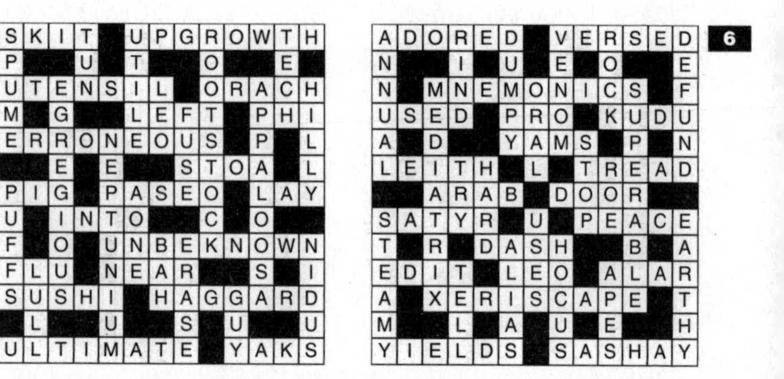

7

HOSTELRY COOP
D O E RUB
LITTORAL ATOM
O A D PIMPLE
LUCKILY N A D
S E Y ACACIA
A JIB ALE L
CHANEL L I E
O I R VARYING
CRANNY T A S
KILO OVERHAUL
CAR L N E
SKIM KATMANDU

10

A OPPRESSIVE
BASH A C M L
A M P HOOPLA
TEN TACET LOP
I O LUX GOBI
SELLS R EARED
ADAPTABLE
EBBED A BADGE
BOON TIL H V
BAR VILLA HIE
IRIDIC A H N
N T N N AUNT
GREGARIOUS S

8

HOROLOGICAL C
E O O A E I H
R OUTER DUNCE
SUM SIBLING O
R N I SEEP
GAM ISNT ARMS
NAG T E YIP
MINI EARL EEL
ACTS I A R
Y EMANATE GYM
FELON GECKO O
L E N E H Y T
Y TRANSLOCATE

11

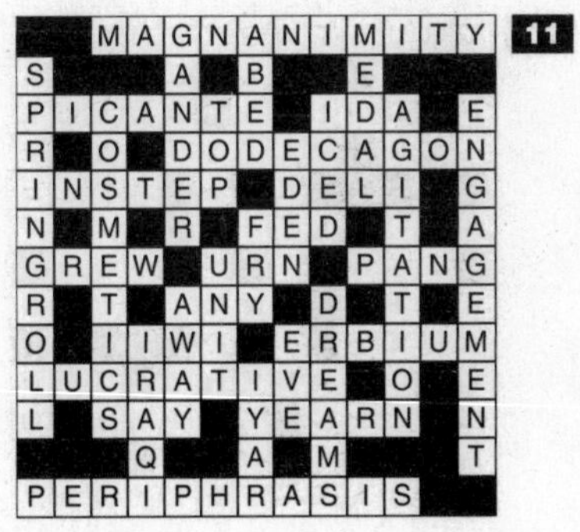
MAGNANIMITY
S A B E
PICANTE IDA E
R O DODECAGON
INSTEP DELI G
N M R FED T A
GREW URN PANG
R T ANY D T E
O IIWI ERBIUM
LUCRATIVE O E
L SAY YEARN N
Q A M T
PERIPHRASIS

9

FLOP STUDIOUS
O A I W G
RAYLESS IMPLY
K A AKIN RYA
SCRUBLAND O R
D I CLOP D
SIS BAHAI EMS
K TILE N L
U I IRREGULAR
LAC COOL E A
KUKRI EAGERLY
N S N L O
STARTLED LIMN

12

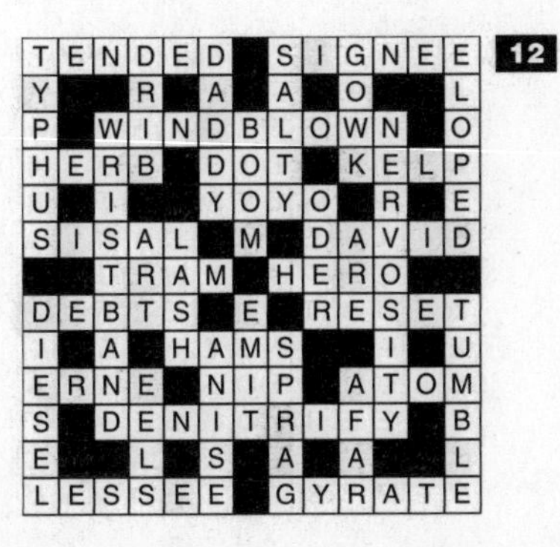
TENDED SIGNEE
Y R A A O L
P WINDBLOWN O
HERB DOT KELP
U I YOYO R E
SISAL M DAVID
TRAM HERO
DEBTS E RESET
I A HAMS I U
ERNE NIP ATOM
S DENITRIFY B
E L S A A L
LESSEE GYRATE

13

H	A	N	D	M	A	D	E		Y	A	R	N
	S				U		D		O	B	I	
T	W	O	S	I	D	E	D		G	A	M	E
	A		Y		I		O	R	A	T	E	D
A	R	M	L	O	A	D		I		I		G
	M		V		L		A	V	E	N	G	E
B		G	A	B				E	G	G		R
R	E	I	N	E	D		C		R		M	
A		R		C		S	A	V	E	L	O	Y
S	P	A	R	K	Y		R		S		R	
H	I	F	I		E	U	R	A	S	I	A	N
	E	F	T		A		O				L	
T	R	E	E		H	O	T	E	L	I	E	R

16

E			M	E	T	R	O	P	O	L	I	S
F	O	R	E		R			E		A		H
F			T		O		G	A	U	C	H	O
A	S	H		R	O	W	E	L		R	I	G
C			F		P	A	L		T	O	F	U
E	S	B	A	T		N		B	A	S	I	N
		E	R	R	O	N	E	O	U	S		
F	A	N	C	Y		A		A	N	E	N	T
L	U	N	E		E	B	B		T			I
O	R	E		F	L	E	E	T		M	A	N
S	A	V	A	I	I		I		W			D
S		I		F			G		A	X	L	E
Y	E	S	T	E	R	Y	E	A	R			R

14

T	R	U	S	T	W	O	R	T	H	Y		O
O		P		A		A		E		E		A
P		O	G	L	E	S		C	L	A	C	K
I	N	N		K	I	T	C	H	E	N		L
	E				N		L		A	L	E	E
A	R	C		A	S	E	A		V	I	N	Y
	E	A	R		T		Y		E	N	D	
P	I	T	A		E	M	M	Y		G	I	N
A	D	A	M		I		O				N	
L		C	A	N	N	E	R	Y		U	G	H
M	O	O	L	A		T	E	A	M	S		O
A		M		B		U		W		E		L
R		B	A	S	T	I	L	L	E	D	A	Y

17

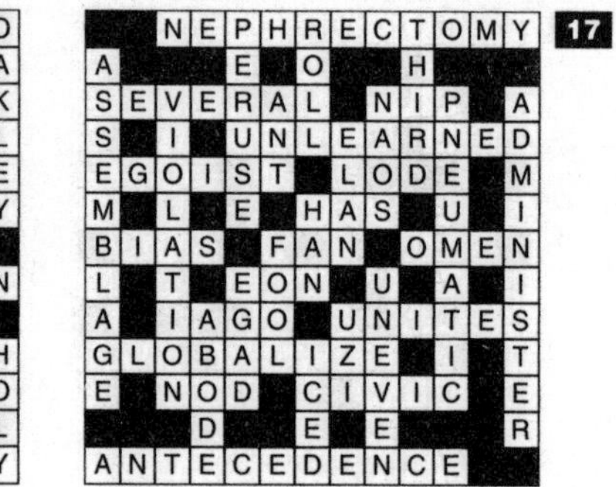

		N	E	P	H	R	E	C	T	O	M	Y
A				E		O			H			
S	E	V	E	R	A	L		N	I	P		A
S		I		U	N	L	E	A	R	N	E	D
E	G	O	I	S	T		L	O	D	E		M
M		L		E		H	A	S		U		I
B	I	A	S		F	A	N		O	M	E	N
L		T		E	O	N		U		A		I
A		I	A	G	O		U	N	I	T	E	S
G	L	O	B	A	L	I	Z	E		I		T
E		N	O	D		C	I	V	I	C		E
			D			E		E				R
A	N	T	E	C	E	D	E	N	C	E		

15

F	L	O	E		T	O	M	T	H	U	M	B
A			K		U			A			E	
I	N	S	E	C	T	S		X	H	O	S	A
N		Y			T	U	B	E		U	S	A
T	A	N	T	M	I	E	U	X		T		R
		A		Y			Y	E	A	N		O
S	A	G		C	H	A	S	M		U	R	N
H		O	B	O	E			P		M		
E		G		V	E	G	E	T	A	B	L	E
L	E	U		I	D	O	L			E		A
F	L	E	E	R		D	E	M	E	R	I	T
	S			U			C		N			E
H	E	M	I	S	E	C	T		D	O	W	N

18

R	A	N	C	O	R		C	L	O	S	E	T
O			H		I		O		V			A
T		M	A	R	S	U	P	I	U	M		C
A	T	O	P		E	N	S		M	A	L	T
T		R			R	I	E	L		T		I
E	N	T	E	R		T		I	L	E	A	C
		I	R	A	N		O	D	E	R		
D	E	C	A	F		S		O	U	N	C	E
E		I		T	R	O	T			I		T
C	H	A	R		A	L	E		P	T	A	H
E		N	E	W	J	E	R	S	E	Y		I
I			N		A		R		A			C
T	W	I	T	C	H		A	C	T	O	R	S

19

R	E	M	E	D	I	A	L		D	U	L	L
	N				C		U		U	S	A	
L	O	W	L	Y	I	N	G		C	H	I	P
	U		I		C		E	A	T	E	R	S
I	G	N	O	B	L	E		E		R		A
	H		N		E		O	R	D	E	A	L
S		B	E	D				O	U	D		M
C	A	R	T	E	L		M		G		L	
I		O		E		W	A	G	O	N	E	R
O	C	C	U	P	Y		R		N		S	
N	E	A	P		E	U	L	O	G	I	S	T
	I	D	O		A		I				E	
G	L	E	N		N	O	N	E	V	E	N	T

22

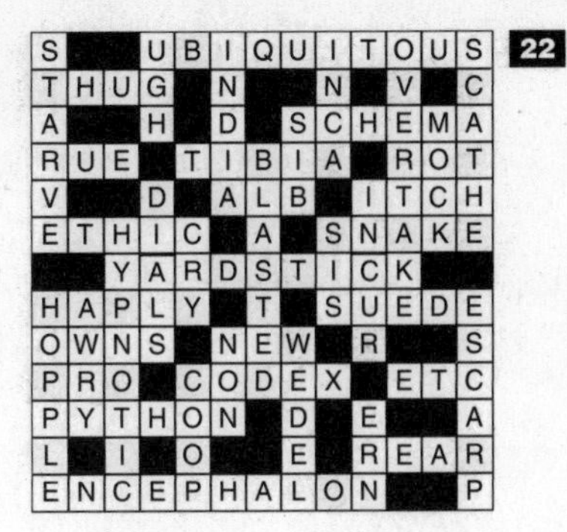

20

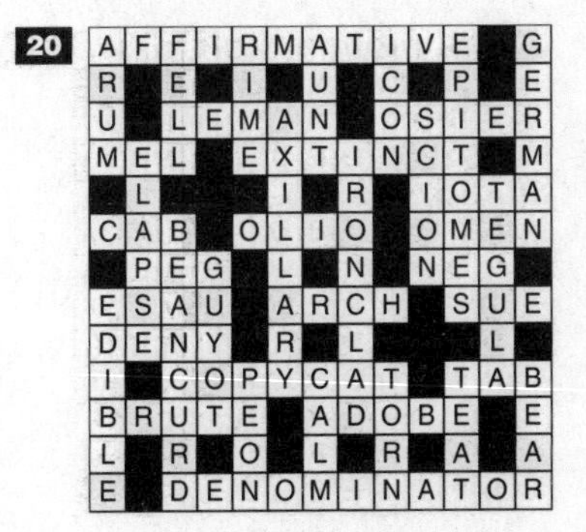

23

21

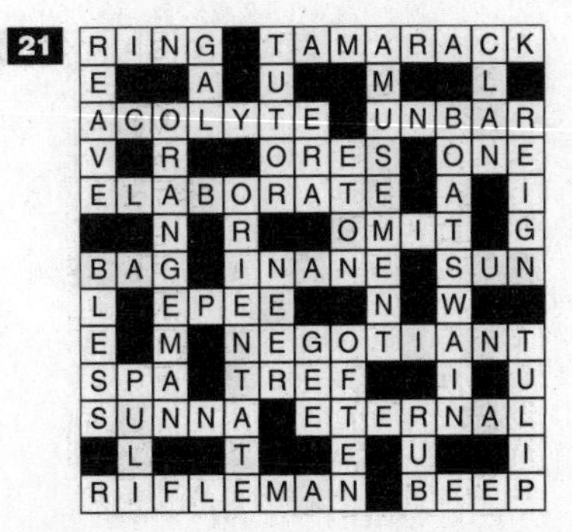

24

25

M	A	G	E	L	L	A	N		D	A	C	E
	V				E		I		A	L	E	
F	O	O	T	B	A	L	L		R	I	D	E
	U		O		D		E	S	T	E	E	M
O	C	T	O	B	E	R		H		N		B
	H		T		D		T	O	P	E	K	A
U		A	L	B				E	R	E		Y
L	A	B	E	L	S		P		O		D	
P		U		O		B	L	U	F	F	E	D
A	T	T	A	C	H		A		I		L	
N	O	T	E		O	R	N	I	T	H	I	C
	T	A	R		B		E				C	
R	E	L	Y		O	B	T	U	R	A	T	E

28

E			P	R	E	J	U	D	I	C	E	D
S	A	G	E		V			U		H		I
C			A		E		B	E	S	E	T	S
O	B	I		E	N	R	O	L		R	I	P
R			S		S	E	W		L	O	D	E
T	E	S	T	A		B		Y	O	K	E	L
		U	R	C	E	O	L	A	T	E		
O	R	B	I	T		A		P	I	E	T	Y
B	O	T	A		G	N	U		C			E
T	O	O		P	A	T	T	Y		Z	O	O
U	T	T	E	R	S		I		B			M
S		A		O			L		E	T	N	A
E	N	L	I	S	T	M	E	N	T			N

31

S	A	T	A	N	I	S	M		G	U	S	H
	D				R		I		A	N	T	
I	N	T	E	R	I	O	R		U	R	A	L
	A		U		T		E	N	R	A	G	E
O	T	A	L	G	I	A		I		V		E
	E		O		S		S	C	R	E	E	D
U		U	G	H				E	E	L		S
B	A	N	Y	A	N		R		S		T	
O		C		I		H	E	L	I	C	A	L
A	W	H	I	L	E		A		D		G	
T	H	A	N		W	A	L	L	E	Y	E	D
	O	I	L		E		I				N	
Z	A	N	Y		R	H	A	P	S	O	D	Y

32

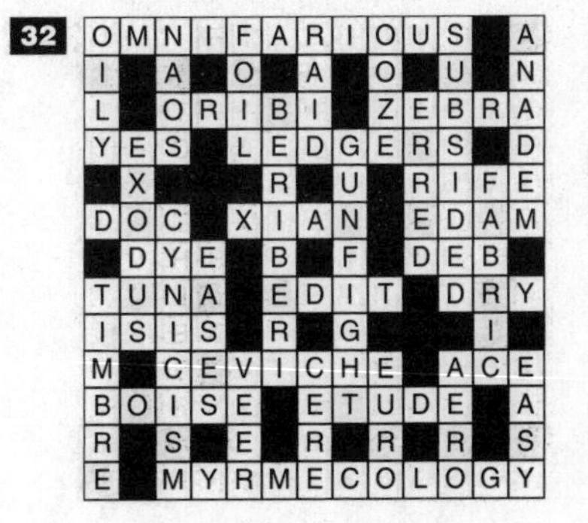

O	M	N	I	F	A	R	I	O	U	S		A
I		A		O		A		O		U		N
L		O	R	I	B	I		Z	E	B	R	A
Y	E	S		L	E	D	G	E	R	S		D
	X				R		U		R	I	F	E
D	O	C		X	I	A	N		E	D	A	M
	D	Y	E		B		F		D	E	B	
T	U	N	A		E	D	I	T		D	R	Y
I	S	I	S		R		G				I	
M		C	E	V	I	C	H	E		A	C	E
B	O	I	S	E		E	T	U	D	E		A
R		S		E		R		R		R		S
E		M	Y	R	M	E	C	O	L	O	G	Y

33

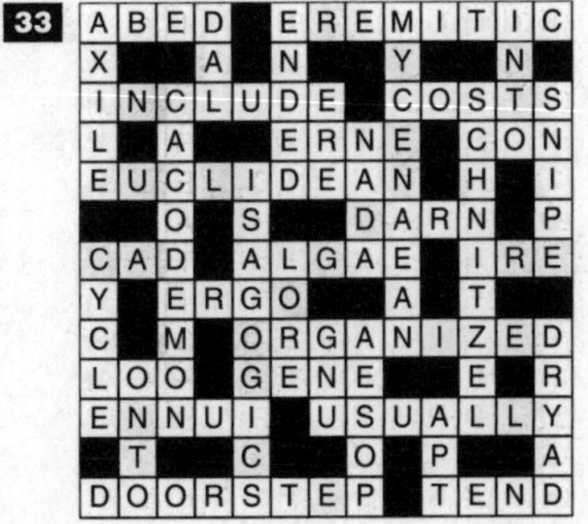

A	B	E	D		E	R	E	M	I	T	I	C
X			A		N		Y			N		
I	N	C	L	U	D	E		C	O	S	T	S
L		A			E	R	N	E		C	O	N
E	U	C	L	I	D	E	A	N		H		I
		O		S			D	A	R	N		P
C	A	D		A	L	G	A	E		I	R	E
Y		E	R	G	O			A		T		
C		M		O	R	G	A	N	I	Z	E	D
L	O	O		G	E	N	E			E		R
E	N	N	U	I		U	S	U	A	L	L	Y
	T			C			O		P			A
D	O	O	R	S	T	E	P		T	E	N	D

34

B			C	H	A	T	T	E	R	B	O	X
L	I	E	U		D			C		A		I
E			D		I		D	H	A	R	M	A
A	R	T		D	E	P	O	T		R	I	M
R			R		U	R	N		V	A	N	E
Y	A	P	O	K		O		R	I	C	I	N
		R	O	O	T	S	T	O	C	K		
E	D	E	M	A		A		B	A	S	A	L
L	A	C	Y		P	I	N		R			E
E	R	E		C	A	C	A	O		A	S	S
C	E	D	A	R	N		C		O			I
T		E		O			R		B	R	I	O
S	E	D	U	C	T	R	E	S	S			N

35

		R	E	P	E	T	I	T	I	O	U	S
S				L		E			N			
C	U	N	E	A	T	E		F	L	U		F
U		E		C	U	M	B	R	A	N	C	E
L	I	G	N	I	N		L	O	W	N		L
P		L		D		A	I	M		A		I
T	O	I	L		Z	I	P		O	T	I	C
R		G		C	I	D		H		U		I
E		E	T	O	N		G	A	R	R	E	T
S	E	N	E	S	C	E	N	T		A		O
S		T	A	T		A	U	R	A	L		U
			C			S		E				S
L	I	G	H	T	H	E	A	D	E	D		

36

F	L	I	T	C	H		O	U	T	A	G	E
O			H		O		F		O			F
O		Z	E	B	R	A	F	I	S	H		F
D	R	E	E		S	E	A		H	O	B	O
I		B			Y	O	L	K		U		R
E	E	R	I	E		N		E	G	R	E	T
		A	C	N	E		S	N	A	G		
V	O	W	E	D		S		O	R	L	O	P
I		O		S	A	T	E			A		A
S	L	O	T		D	A	D		O	S	A	R
H		D	E	L	I	R	I	O	U	S		D
N			R		O		C		S			O
U	R	A	N	U	S		T	I	T	I	A	N

37

C	A	P	A	C	I	T	Y		T	E	R	M
	E				R		O		O	B	I	
G	R	A	N	D	E	U	R		O	B	E	Y
	A		O		N		K	I	T	T	L	E
S	T	A	N	N	I	C		D		I		A
	E		A		C		B	L	A	D	E	S
M	U	G	H					E	R	E		T
E	S	T	E	E	M		W		I		Q	
L		E		A		C	H	A	G	R	I	N
E	U	R	O	P	A		O		H		N	
E	R	I	N		W	E	L	L	T	O	D	O
	A	N	Y		E		L				A	
F	L	E	X		S	A	Y	O	N	A	R	A

40

G			F	R	E	Q	U	E	N	T	L	Y
R	U	L	E		Q			C		H		I
A			D		U		T	H	R	E	A	P
V	E	X		P	A	S	E	O		R	I	P
E			R		L	E	A		T	I	M	E
R	I	S	E	S		G		E	R	A	S	E
		A	S	T	H	M	A	T	I	C		
A	G	L	E	Y		E		A	B	A	S	E
P	I	E	T		A	N	T		E			L
O	B	S		E	X	T	R	A		O	D	D
D	E	M	O	T	E		E		W			E
A		A		C			A		E	R	O	S
L	O	N	G	H	E	A	D	E	D			T

38

41

39

43

U	P	R	I	S	I	N	G		R	I	V	E
	R				B		R		O	N	E	
B	E	R	I	B	E	R	I		O	H	I	O
	A		L		R		M	U	T	A	N	T
A	C	C	L	A	I	M		R		B		H
	H		U		A		V	A	G	I	L	E
M		A	M	U				L	E	T		R
U	N	W	E	L	L		B		N		U	
N		E		N		V	I	C	T	O	R	Y
G	A	S	B	A	G		S		R		A	
O	B	O	L		O	U	T	L	Y	I	N	G
	E	M	U		L		R				I	
O	D	E	R		F	O	O	F	A	R	A	W

46

M			W	E	A	T	H	E	R	M	A	N
U	S	E	R		H			U		I		O
Z			Y		E		T	R	U	S	T	S
Z	A	P		P	A	T	I	O		H	U	T
L			T		D	A	L		U	M	B	O
E	X	E	R	T		P		I	S	A	A	C
		N	A	R	C	I	S	S	U	S		
W	O	O	D	Y		O		M	A	H	D	I
R	A	R	E		A	C	E		L			N
A	R	M		G	I	A	N	T		E	L	F
I	S	O	B	A	R		D		H			A
T		U		R			O		A	N	O	N
H	A	S	H	B	R	O	W	N	S			T

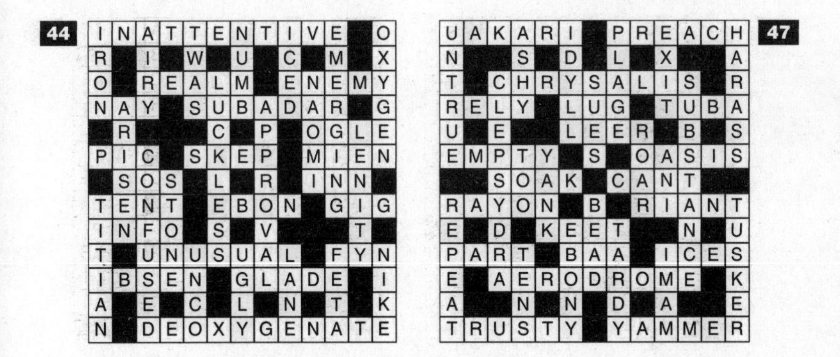

44

I	N	A	T	T	E	N	T	I	V	E		O
R		I		W		U		C		M		X
O		R	E	A	L	M		E	N	E	M	Y
N	A	Y		S	U	B	A	D	A	R		G
	R				C		P		O	G	L	E
P	I	C		S	K	E	P		M	I	E	N
	S	O	S		L		R		I	N	N	
T	E	N	T		E	B	O	N		G	I	G
I	N	F	O		S		V				T	
T		U	N	U	S	U	A	L		F	Y	N
I	B	S	E	N		G	L	A	D	E		I
A		E		C		L		N		T		K
N		D	E	O	X	Y	G	E	N	A	T	E

47

U	A	K	A	R	I		P	R	E	A	C	H
N			S		D		L		X			A
T		C	H	R	Y	S	A	L	I	S		R
R	E	L	Y		L	U	G		T	U	B	A
U		E			L	E	E	R		B		S
E	M	P	T	Y		S		O	A	S	I	S
		S	O	A	K		C	A	N	T		
R	A	Y	O	N		B		R	I	A	N	T
E		D		K	E	E	T			N		U
P	A	R	T		B	A	A		I	C	E	S
E		A	E	R	O	D	R	O	M	E		K
A			N		N		D		A			E
T	R	U	S	T	Y		Y	A	M	M	E	R

45

C	R	U	S		D	E	N	D	R	O	I	D
E			E		O			A			C	
D	O	U	C	E	U	R		I	N	F	E	R
E		N			B	O	E	R		O	D	E
D	Y	S	E	N	T	E	R	Y		R		R
		K		E			I	M	A	M		U
S	K	I		S	A	U	N	A		U	R	N
E		L	A	C	E			I		L		
R		L		I	R	R	A	D	I	A	T	E
A	R	E		E	Y	E	D			I		C
I	O	D	I	N		D	O	M	I	C	I	L
	T			C			P		O			A
B	A	N	N	E	R	E	T		N	E	S	T

48

		I	R	R	E	V	E	R	E	N	C	E
E				O		E			R			
S	T	I	L	T	E	D		S	O	D		S
O		N		T	R	A	C	K	S	U	I	T
P	U	G	R	E	E		R	E	E	D		E
H		E		D		R	A	P		E		P
A	N	N	A		G	E	M		E	R	A	S
G		U		C	O	D		D		A		I
E		O	S	L	O		U	R	A	N	U	S
A	L	U	M	I	N	I	Z	E		C		T
L		S	A	P		W	I	D	T	H		E
			C			I		G				R
C	O	C	K	L	E	S	H	E	L	L		

49

B	U	S	H	F	I	R	E		F	U	E	L
	B				R		A		E	N	D	
B	A	C	C	A	R	A	T		E	M	I	T
	N		A		E		S	E	D	A	T	E
E	G	G	H	E	A	D		X		N		N
	I		I		L		B	A	I	L	I	E
N		E	E	K				M	A	Y		T
E	N	T	R	A	P		B		T		A	
I		E		L		E	A	R	R	I	N	G
G	A	R	D	E	N		F		I		N	
H	O	N	E		O	F	F	I	C	I	A	L
	N	A	B		O		L				L	
F	E	L	T		N	E	E	D	L	E	S	S

52

S			C	O	N	T	R	O	V	E	R	T
U	P	D	O		A			N		S		I
N			N		B		A	C	T	U	A	L
D	U	G		C	O	M	B	E		R	U	T
R			U		B	O	Y		S	I	R	E
Y	A	R	N	S		N		A	H	E	A	D
		E	A	L	D	O	R	M	A	N		
W	E	E	P	Y		C		U	L	T	R	A
R	A	F	T		E	L	D		E			M
A	R	K		P	R	E	E	N		C	R	U
I	N	N	A	T	E		A		A			S
T		O		A			L		S	A	G	E
H	O	T	C	H	P	O	T	C	H			D

50

N	I	G	H	T	S	C	H	O	O	L		E
A		O		H		H		A		E		C
P		E	X	U	D	E		H	U	T	C	H
E	M	S		D	E	F	A	U	L	T		O
	I				S		B		C	E	D	E
I	T	S		I	S	I	S		E	R	A	S
	R	H	O		E		T		R	E	T	
N	A	R	C		R	A	R	E		D	I	N
A	L	E	E		T		A				N	
P		W	A	E	S	U	C	K		E	G	G
P	A	I	N	T		S	T	A	C	K		A
E		S		U		E		L		E		U
R		H	A	I	R	D	R	E	S	S	E	R

53

L	O	N	G	E	R		B	E	L	I	K	E
E			L		E		E		I			S
A		B	A	W	D	I	N	E	S	S		S
D	E	E	D		I	O	N		P	U	M	A
E		D			A	N	E	W		B		Y
D	E	S	E	X		S		A	T	L	A	S
		P	O	R	E		K	N	E	E		
V	A	R	N	A		S		D	A	T	E	D
E		E		Y	I	P	E			H		R
R	E	A	D		S	I	B		K	A	K	A
M		D	I	S	A	V	O	W	A	L		M
I			E		A		N		N			A
N	O	E	T	I	C		Y	E	A	R	N	S

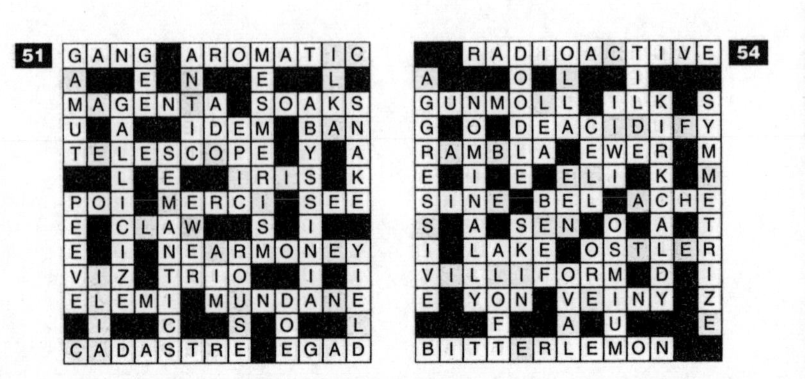

51

G	A	N	G		A	R	O	M	A	T	I	C
A			E		N			E			L	
M	A	G	E	N	T	A		S	O	A	K	S
U		A			I	D	E	M		B	A	N
T	E	L	E	S	C	O	P	E		Y		A
		L		E			I	R	I	S		K
P	O	I		M	E	R	C	I		S	E	E
E		C	L	A	W			S		I		
E		I		N	E	A	R	M	O	N	E	Y
V	I	Z		T	R	I	O			I		I
E	L	E	M	I		M	U	N	D	A	N	E
	I			C			S		O			L
C	A	D	A	S	T	R	E		E	G	A	D

54

		R	A	D	I	O	A	C	T	I	V	E
A				O		L			I			
G	U	N	M	O	L	L		I	L	K		S
G		O		D	E	A	C	I	D	I	F	Y
R	A	M	B	L	A		E	W	E	R		M
E		I		E		E	L	I		K		M
S	I	N	E		B	E	L		A	C	H	E
S		A		S	E	N		O		A		T
I		L	A	K	E		O	S	T	L	E	R
V	I	L	L	I	F	O	R	M		D		I
E		Y	O	N		V	E	I	N	Y		Z
			F			A		U				E
B	I	T	T	E	R	L	E	M	O	N		

55

L	O	C	A	L	I	T	E		K	A	K	A
	B				N		A		I	C	E	
O	V	I	P	O	S	I	T		N	I	C	E
	E		O		A		S	P	E	C	K	S
O	R	E	G	A	N	O		E		U		K
	T		R		E		B	A	I	L	I	E
E		E	O	N				K	O	A		R
X	I	A	M	E	N		S		D		L	
E		R		V		D	I	G	I	T	A	L
R	U	M	M	E	R		S		N		M	
T	R	U	E		I	N	T	R	E	P	I	D
	E	F	T		L		E				N	
C	A	F	E		E	U	R	O	P	E	A	N

56

57

58

59

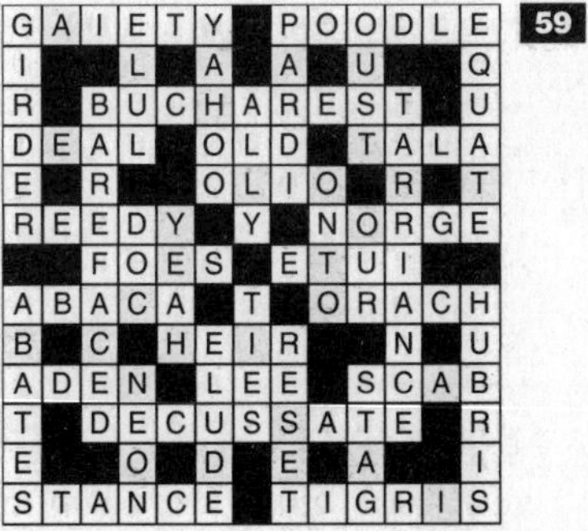

60

61

H	O	R	R	I	F	I	C		S	T	A	G
	N				L		R		O	R	E	
C	A	M	I	S	O	L	E		C	A	R	E
	G		N		A		W	E	A	P	O	N
H	E	I	G	H	T	S		X		P		D
	R		E		S		G	A	Z	E	B	O
P		U	S	A				M	O	D		W
L	E	T	T	E	R		H		N		C	
U		E		O		J	A	C	K	D	A	W
S	O	N	A	N	T		P		E		C	
H	I	S	S		U	P	T	O	D	A	T	E
	L	I	E		B		E				U	
H	Y	L	A		A	N	N	A	L	I	S	T

64

R			U	N	B	L	I	N	K	I	N	G
E	V	E	S		U			I		M		U
D			E		T		A	D	E	P	T	S
E	N	D		C	U	R	S	E		A	A	H
E			C		T	U	P		A	C	R	E
M	O	R	A	L		B		E	N	T	E	R
		O	B	E	D	I	E	N	C	E		
D	U	B	A	I		O		D	O	D	G	E
I	D	O	L		J	U	S		N			X
S	A	T		G	U	S	T	O		L	A	C
P	L	I	A	N	T		O		A			E
E		Z		A			M		N	E	A	P
L	I	E	U	T	E	N	A	N	T			T

62

A	N	A	C	H	R	O	N	I	S	M		G
N		V		O		T		N		U		O
N		E	G	R	E	T		T	E	S	L	A
A	I	R		A	G	O	N	I	S	T		T
	S				G		U		B	A	B	E
P	O	D		S	P	A	M		A	C	R	E
	G	Y	P		L		M		T	H	E	
A	O	N	E		A	Q	U	A		E	A	R
G	N	A	T		N		L				C	
L		M	A	R	T	I	A	L		P	H	I
E	X	I	L	E		T	R	A	C	E		L
A		S		D		C		V		S		L
M		M	I	S	C	H	I	E	V	O	U	S

65

A	R	C	A	D	E		D	E	B	O	N	E
N			K		X		A		E			N
G		M	I	N	I	A	T	U	R	E		D
L	E	A	N		L	I	E		G	A	M	E
E		P			E	D	D	O		S		A
R	U	L	E	D		E		I	N	T	E	R
		E	Y	E	D		P	L	E	B		
M	E	L	E	E		A		S	T	O	A	T
A		E		D	I	S	C			U		I
N	O	A	H		S	E	A		S	N	A	G
U		F	A	N	T	A	S	I	E	D		L
A			N		L		E		A			O
L	E	A	G	U	E		S	U	L	L	E	N

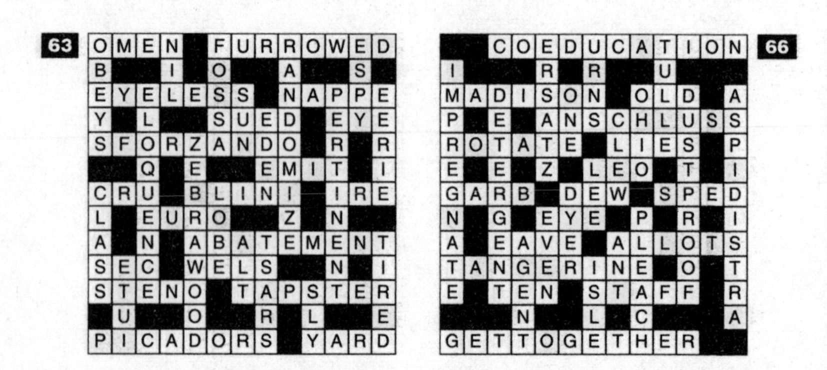

63

O	M	E	N		F	U	R	R	O	W	E	D
B			I		O			A		S		
E	Y	E	L	E	S	S		N	A	P	P	E
Y		L			S	U	E	D		E	Y	E
S	F	O	R	Z	A	N	D	O		R		R
		Q		E			E	M	I	T		I
C	R	U		B	L	I	N	I		I	R	E
L		E	U	R	O			Z		N		
A		N		A	B	A	T	E	M	E	N	T
S	E	C		W	E	L	S			N		I
S	T	E	N	O		T	A	P	S	T	E	R
	U			O			R		L			E
P	I	C	A	D	O	R	S		Y	A	R	D

66

		C	O	E	D	U	C	A	T	I	O	N
I				R		R			U			
M	A	D	I	S	O	N		O	L	D		A
P		E		A	N	S	C	H	L	U	S	S
R	O	T	A	T	E		L	I	E	S		P
E		E		Z		L	E	O		T		I
G	A	R	B		D	E	W		S	P	E	D
N		G		E	Y	E		P		R		I
A		E	A	V	E		A	L	L	O	T	S
T	A	N	G	E	R	I	N	E		O		T
E		T	E	N		S	T	A	F	F		R
			N			L		C				A
G	E	T	T	O	G	E	T	H	E	R		

67

I	N	F	I	N	I	T	E		E	P	O	S
	O				R		D		C	R	U	
S	T	A	B	B	I	N	G		R	A	S	H
	A		O		T		E	Q	U	I	T	Y
T	R	E	L	L	I	S		U		R		D
	Y		E		S		C	A	H	I	E	R
S		I	R	E				D	E	E		A
C	H	R	O	M	A		P		R		F	
O		A		U		J	A	C	O	B	U	S
P	U	N	I	S	H		L		E		R	
E	R	I	N		E	M	I	S	S	A	R	Y
	D	A	L		B		N				O	
P	U	N	Y		E	A	G	L	E	O	W	L

68

S	U	P	E	R	J	A	C	E	N	T		A
W		L		E		C		P		O		S
A		O	R	C	I	N		I	T	E	M	S
P	U	T		K	N	E	E	C	A	P		E
	T				C		X		Z	I	P	S
F	E	W		T	H	E	E		Z	E	U	S
	R	E	P		M		G		A	C	E	
P	U	L	I		E	V	E	N		E	B	B
I	S	L	E		A		S				L	
E		T	R	E	L	L	I	S		F	O	G
R	O	O	S	T		U	S	A	G	E		O
C		D		O		M		T		R		U
E		O	M	N	I	P	R	E	S	E	N	T

69

G	R	U	B		B	I	G	A	M	O	U	S
E			E		E			B			N	
N	E	O	L	I	S	H		Y	A	R	D	S
I		V			E	A	T	S		E	O	N
C	R	E	D	U	L	O	U	S		F		A
		R		N			T	I	L	E		K
O	B	S		B	E	G	U	N		R	U	E
A		P	E	L	T			I		E		
S		E		I	N	G	R	A	I	N	E	D
I	N	N		N	A	N	A			C		O
S	I	D	E	D		U	G	L	I	E	S	T
	G			E			E		D			T
S	H	R	E	D	D	E	D		E	N	V	Y

70

A			S	U	P	E	R	F	E	C	T	A
N	I	C	K		L			O		O		T
O			A		A		P	R	O	N	T	O
I	L	L		A	Z	U	R	E		V	I	N
N			T		A	N	Y		L	U	R	E
T	U	L	I	P		S		H	I	L	L	S
		E	D	E	L	W	E	I	S	S		
W	A	G	E	R		E		E	L	E	C	T
E	V	E	S		F	A	R		E			U
D	O	N		A	U	R	A	L		A	I	R
E	N	D	I	N	G		B		S			B
L		R		A			B		O	R	C	A
N	E	E	D	L	E	F	I	S	H			N

71

C	R	E	D	I	T		Q	I	N	D	A	R
A			U		H		U		I			E
D		I	N	A	U	D	I	B	L	E		B
D	A	R	K		M	A	T		E	S	A	U
I		R			P	R	E	P		C		K
S	P	I	N	S		N		U	K	A	S	E
		T	I	C	S		A	N	I	L		
E	R	A	T	O		F		K	N	A	C	K
I		B		T	S	A	R			T		I
T	A	L	A		P	R	O		W	O	E	S
H		E	M	B	R	O	I	D	E	R		S
E			M		A		L		E			E
R	A	G	O	U	T		Y	O	N	D	E	R

72

		C	O	N	T	A	M	I	N	A	T	E
S				U		N			A			
C	O	L	O	M	B	O		R	O	B		S
A		O		B	E	N	C	H	M	A	R	K
R	A	G	T	A	G		H	E	I	R		E
L		O		T		Q	U	A		R		P
A	L	P	S		C	O	G		D	A	F	T
T		H		A	R	M		I		C		I
I		I	A	G	O		E	C	H	O	I	C
N	U	L	L	I	P	A	R	A		O		I
A		E	O	N		B	A	R	O	N		S
			U			B		I				M
G	R	I	D	D	L	E	C	A	K	E		

73

T	R	I	P	E	D	A	L		S	C	A	M
	O				O		O		K	I	D	
V	O	L	C	A	N	I	C		I	R	A	N
	K		A		A		O	U	T	C	R	Y
H	I	R	S	U	T	E		T		L		L
	E		E		E		M	A	K	E	D	O
W		O	R	B				H	A	T		N
O	P	E	N	E	D		A		O		A	
R		D		A		A	D	U	L	A	T	E
S	T	I	C	K	Y		Y		I		T	
T	Y	P	O		A	S	T	O	N	I	E	D
	P	A	L		W		U				N	
M	E	L	D		N	E	M	A	T	O	D	E

76

S			B	L	A	N	D	I	S	H	E	D
E	L	B	E		U			N		A		A
P			D		D		E	C	T	Y	P	E
T	A	G		T	I	A	R	A		M	A	D
U			O		O	N	E		R	A	G	A
M	E	R	R	Y		N		Y	O	K	E	L
		A	C	I	D	U	L	A	T	E		
A	M	M	A	N		L		G	O	R	E	S
Z	I	P	S		P	E	T		R			E
O	C	A		G	A	T	E	S		S	E	C
N	A	R	R	O	W		M		A			T
A		T		B			P		I	N	T	O
L	A	S	C	I	V	I	O	U	S			R

74

D	E	T	E	R	I	O	R	A	T	E		F
U		O		U		U		N		X		A
L		N	E	G	U	S		T	A	C	E	T
Y	A	G		A	S	T	A	I	R	E		H
	R				U		R		G	E	N	E
B	A	T		A	F	A	R		O	D	E	R
	B	A	H		R		A		N	E	G	
I	L	I	A		U	R	N	S		D	A	G
S	E	L	L		C		G				T	
O		B	L	A	T	H	E	R		R	E	D
B	R	O	O	D		E	D	E	M	A		O
A		N		Z		F		N		K		Z
R		E	L	E	C	T	R	O	C	U	T	E

77

A	P	O	D	A	L		B	E	L	L	O	W
P			U		O		L		A			A
P		E	N	D	U	R	A	N	C	E		S
A	O	N	E		P	I	N		K	A	P	H
L		G			E	N	D	S		L		E
L	U	R	I	D		D		E	I	D	E	R
		A	C	I	D		H	E	R	O		
L	E	V	E	R		T		N	E	R	V	E
I		I		E	X	I	T			M		S
L	I	N	E		Y	E	A		V	A	M	P
I		G	U	I	L	D	S	M	A	N		I
T			R		A		T		S			A
H	E	R	O	I	N		E	Y	E	F	U	L

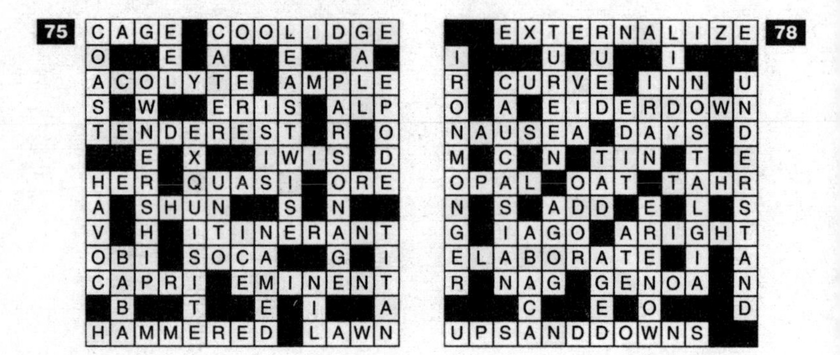

79

C	A	N	A	D	I	A	N	■	F	I	S	C
■	T	■	■	■	N	■	I	■	E	K	E	■
D	A	N	D	R	U	F	F	■	T	E	R	M
■	X	■	U	■	R	■	F	L	A	B	B	Y
C	I	R	C	L	E	T	■	E	■	A	■	E
■	A	■	K	■	S	■	V	E	R	N	A	L
I	■	K	E	Y	■	■	■	S	E	A	■	O
V	A	N	D	A	L	■	B	■	F	■	C	■
I	■	O	■	M	■	A	R	R	I	V	A	L
E	C	T	Y	P	E	■	I	■	N	■	S	■
D	A	T	A	■	D	E	G	R	E	A	S	E
■	P	E	W	■	I	■	H	■	■	■	I	■
R	E	D	S	■	T	U	T	O	R	I	A	L

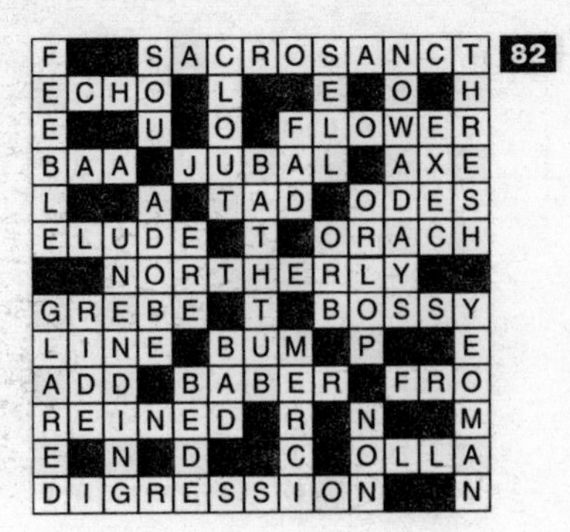

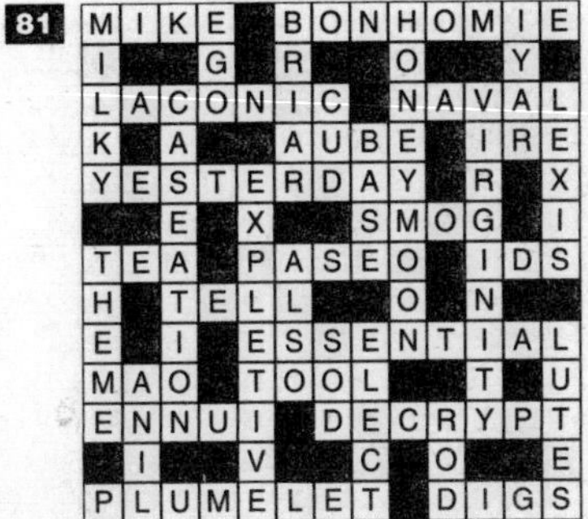

85

W	I	T	C	H	I	N	G		C	H	A	T
	S				R		I		H	O	G	
C	A	T	A	C	O	M	B		A	M	O	K
	I		D		N		E	N	R	A	G	E
V	A	C	A	T	E	D		E		G		E
	H		G		D		R	E	P	E	A	L
A		M	E	L				D	O	R		S
B	I	A	S	E	D		N		M		L	
A		R		F		B	A	R	M	A	I	D
T	O	A	S	T	Y		U		E		Q	
E	L	S	E		O	R	G	U	L	O	U	S
	I	C	E		Y		H				O	
W	O	A	D		O	C	T	O	N	A	R	Y

88

T			M	O	N	O	P	L	E	G	I	A
O	B	I	E		O			A		R		R
T			T		M		I	M	P	A	L	E
T	I	L		P	A	D	R	E		Z	O	O
E			H		D	O	E		G	I	R	L
R	O	B	O	T		L		A	R	E	N	A
		A	I	R	L	E	T	T	E	R		
M	E	S	S	Y		F		E	A	S	E	D
E	M	I	T		D	U	B		T			E
N	I	L		D	O	L	O	R		E	L	F
I	R	I	D	I	C		F		G			A
A		S		A			F		A	D	A	M
L	I	K	E	L	I	H	O	O	D			E

86

F	L	O	O	R	L	E	N	G	T	H		A
L		V		A		E		R		O		S
O		I	M	P	E	L		O	G	L	E	S
G	A	D		E	N	S	I	G	N	S		U
	V				E		M		A	T	O	M
L	A	C		T	R	A	P		R	E	D	E
	L	A	D		V		O		L	I	D	
T	O	F	U		A	P	S	E		N	I	T
I	N	F	O		T		T				T	
P		E	M	P	E	R	O	R		L	Y	E
P	R	I	O	R		I	R	A	Q	I		D
E		N		O		C		I		D		I
T		E	A	S	T	E	R	N	M	O	S	T

89

S	I	T	T	E	R		P	I	R	A	C	Y
H			E		O		U		O			E
I		T	R	O	U	B	L	O	U	S		A
M	E	A	N		G	A	S		E	W	E	R
M		X			H	U	E	S		A		L
Y	I	E	L	D		M		T	I	Z	Z	Y
		X	E	R	O		L	O	C	I		
T	H	E	T	A		S		P	Y	L	O	N
O		M		W	H	Y	S			A		E
P	A	P	A		A	N	T		A	N	T	E
E		T	R	U	N	C	A	T	E	D		D
K			M		D		C		O			E
A	B	U	S	E	S		K	I	N	D	E	R

87

		C	A	R	D	I	N	A	L	A	T	E
S				E		M			A			
K	N	E	E	C	A	P		O	P	S		M
I		A		I	N	S	E	N	S	A	T	E
L	E	V	I	T	Y		D	Y	E	D		D
L		E		E		M	I	X		D		D
F	A	S	T		J	O	T		E	L	U	L
U		D		T	A	P		T		E		E
L		R	U	S	E		E	R	E	B	U	S
L	O	O	K	A	L	I	K	E		A		O
Y		P	A	R		D	E	B	U	G		M
			S			E		L				E
S	U	P	E	R	J	A	C	E	N	T		

90

		C	I	T	Y	C	O	U	N	C	I	L
E				O		U			A			
V	I	S	I	T	O	R		P	I	P		A
I		O		T	A	B	U	L	A	T	O	R
S	H	R	I	E	K		S	O	D	A		M
C		R		R		G	E	T		R		A
E	R	O	S		M	A	D		S	M	U	G
R		W		E	E	L		B		I		E
A		F	A	C	E		T	U	R	G	I	D
T	O	U	C	H	D	O	W	N		A		D
E		L	O	O		H	O	G	A	N		O
			C			I		E				N
N	I	C	K	E	L	O	D	E	O	N		

91

M	E	M	O	R	I	Z	E		B	U	C	K
	L				S		P		E	R	A	
S	A	N	N	Y	A	S	I		E	A	S	E
	N		A		I		C	A	N	N	E	D
A	D	M	I	R	A	L		L		I		G
	S		L		H		P	U	P	A	T	E
O		E	E	L				M	A	N		D
D	I	A	D	E	M		A		R		K	
E		R		A		U	N	A	S	K	E	D
U	P	L	A	N	D		T		O		A	
M	I	D	I		E	C	H	I	N	A	T	E
	C	O	D		M		E				O	
K	A	M	E		I	M	M	A	N	E	N	T

94

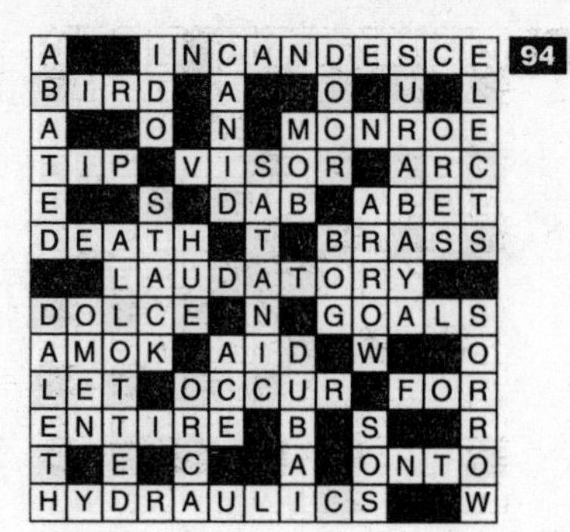

92 **95**

93

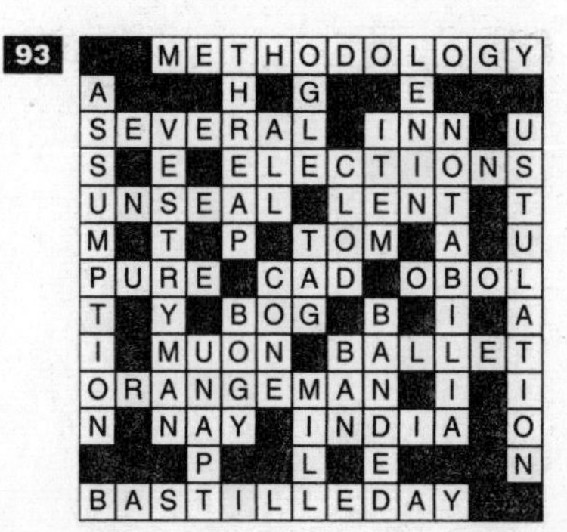

96

97

S	Y	M	P	H	O	N	Y		C	H	O	P
	O				P		O		O	A	R	
K	N	I	T	T	I	N	G		S	N	A	G
	D		E		A		I	N	H	A	L	E
D	E	C	A	N	T	S		E		P		N
	R		M		E		B	A	T	E	A	U
A		J	E	T				P	A	R		S
M	A	I	D	E	N		F		S		F	
A		M		R		D	O	O	M	F	U	L
S	E	J	A	N	T		R		A		N	
S	W	A	B		A	L	I	E	N	A	G	E
	E	M	U		L		N				A	
E	R	S	T		E	N	T	A	N	G	L	E

100

S			T	U	M	U	L	T	U	O	U	S
C	I	N	E		A			E		U		T
E			A		F		C	E	N	T	R	E
N	O	T		N	I	S	U	S		D	A	W
I			C		A	T	E		D	A	N	E
C	O	M	E	T		A		F	E	T	I	D
		R	A	I	N	G	A	U	G	E		
C	R	I	S	P		G		R	A	D	I	X
L	O	D	E		M	E	M		S			U
O	D	A		B	O	R	E	D		V	I	Z
C	E	N	S	E	R		R		M			H
H		G		A			C		A	U	T	O
E	L	A	S	T	I	C	I	T	Y			U

98

R	E	C	L	A	M	A	T	I	O	N		H
A		A		B		N		O		O		A
K		T	A	U	N	T		T	O	T	A	L
E	M	S		T	U	A	T	A	R	A		L
	I				R		E		A	B	L	E
A	S	S		S	T	A	G		T	E	A	L
	E	T	C		U		U		E	N	D	
U	R	E	A		R	U	M	P		E	D	H
N	Y	E	T		E		E				E	
I		P	E	A	S	A	N	T		E	R	A
S	T	E	R	N		I	T	A	L	Y		D
O		S		N		D		R		R		Z
N		T	R	A	N	S	L	O	C	A	T	E

101

I	N	S	E	C	T		C	O	L	E	U	S
N			B		R		I		Y			O
F		C	O	P	E	S	T	O	N	E		U
U	P	O	N		E	K	E		X	M	A	S
S		M			S	A	S	H		B		E
E	M	P	T	Y		W		O	A	R	E	D
		L	I	E	N		O	R	C	A		
W	H	E	E	L		O		N	E	C	K	S
A		T		L	A	P	S			I		E
N	E	E	D		N	E	T		O	V	A	L
G		D	E	L	I	N	E	A	T	E		D
L			M		O		A		I			O
E	N	J	O	I	N		D	I	C	T	U	M

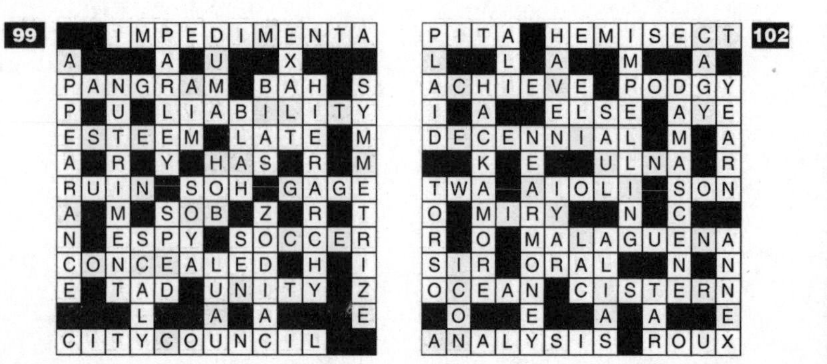

99

		I	M	P	E	D	I	M	E	N	T	A
A				A		U			X			
P	A	N	G	R	A	M		B	A	H		S
P		U		L	I	A	B	I	L	I	T	Y
E	S	T	E	E	M		L	A	T	E		M
A		R		Y		H	A	S		R		M
R	U	I	N		S	O	H		G	A	G	E
A		M		S	O	B		Z		R		T
N		E	S	P	Y		S	O	C	C	E	R
C	O	N	C	E	A	L	E	D		H		I
E		T	A	D		U	N	I	T	Y		Z
			L			A		A				E
C	I	T	Y	C	O	U	N	C	I	L		

102

P	I	T	A		H	E	M	I	S	E	C	T
L			L		A			M			A	
A	C	H	I	E	V	E		P	O	D	G	Y
I		A			E	L	S	E		A	Y	E
D	E	C	E	N	N	I	A	L		M		A
		K		E			U	L	N	A		R
T	W	A		A	I	O	L	I		S	O	N
O		M	I	R	Y			N		C		
R		O		M	A	L	A	G	U	E	N	A
S	I	R		O	R	A	L			N		N
O	C	E	A	N		C	I	S	T	E	R	N
	O			E			A		A			E
A	N	A	L	Y	S	I	S		R	O	U	X

103

P	A	R	A	D	R	O	P		D	O	R	P
	V				A		O		E	R	E	
H	I	J	A	C	K	E	R		L	E	A	F
	A		S		I		E	N	I	G	M	A
P	R	E	C	E	S	S		I		A		C
	Y		E		H		P	L	U	N	G	E
A		I	N	K				E	G	O		T
P	O	N	D	E	R		E		A		L	
I		H		E		P	I	O	N	E	E	R
S	Q	U	I	N	T		T		D		S	
H	A	M	S		R	E	H	E	A	R	S	E
	D	A	L		E		E				E	
T	I	N	E		Y	A	R	D	B	I	R	D

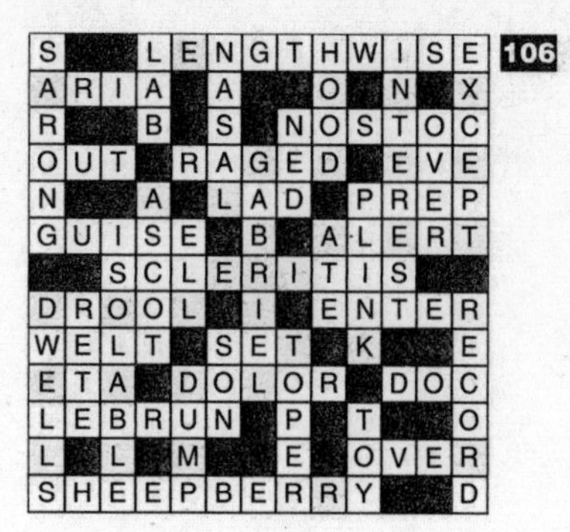

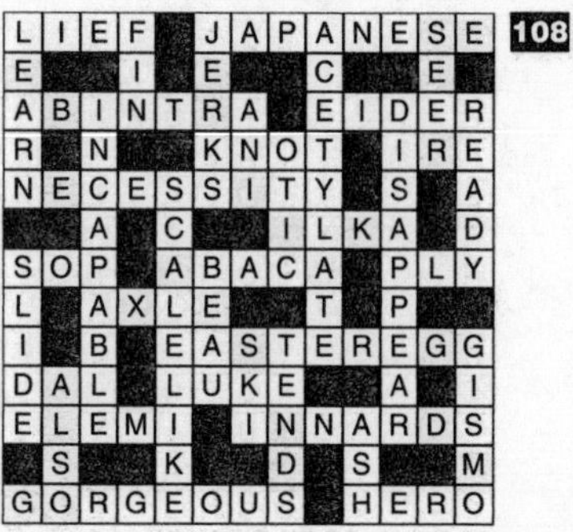

109

D	I	V	I	S	I	O	N	■	S	C	A	D
■	N	■	■	■	R	■	O	■	P	A	Y	■
F	L	A	M	B	E	A	U	■	I	B	I	S
■	A	■	O	■	N	■	N	A	T	A	N	T
E	N	C	H	A	I	N	■	L	■	R	■	A
■	D	■	A	■	C	■	U	P	R	E	A	R
S	■	O	I	L	■	■	■	S	I	T	■	K
M	I	R	R	O	R	■	M	■	D	■	A	■
A	■	B	■	N	■	L	I	N	G	A	L	A
S	T	I	N	G	Y	■	N	■	E	■	L	■
H	A	T	E	■	A	M	U	N	D	S	E	N
■	B	A	N	■	K	■	E	■	■	■	G	■
I	S	L	E	■	S	I	T	U	A	T	E	D

112

R	■	■	C	O	N	G	E	N	I	T	A	L
E	W	E	R	■	A	■	■	E	■	R	■	I
T	■	■	Y	■	I	■	D	A	M	A	S	K
A	C	E	■	C	A	V	E	R	■	P	I	E
I	■	■	H	■	D	O	N	■	M	U	L	L
N	O	D	A	L	■	L	■	S	A	N	D	Y
■	■	E	N	A	C	T	M	E	N	T	■	■
C	O	C	K	Y	■	A	■	A	E	O	N	S
O	B	E	Y	■	R	I	D	■	S	■	■	K
B	O	A	■	J	A	C	O	B	■	O	B	I
W	E	S	K	I	T	■	I	■	B	■	■	D
E	■	E	■	B	■	■	N	■	A	M	I	D
B	U	D	G	E	R	I	G	A	R	■	■	Y

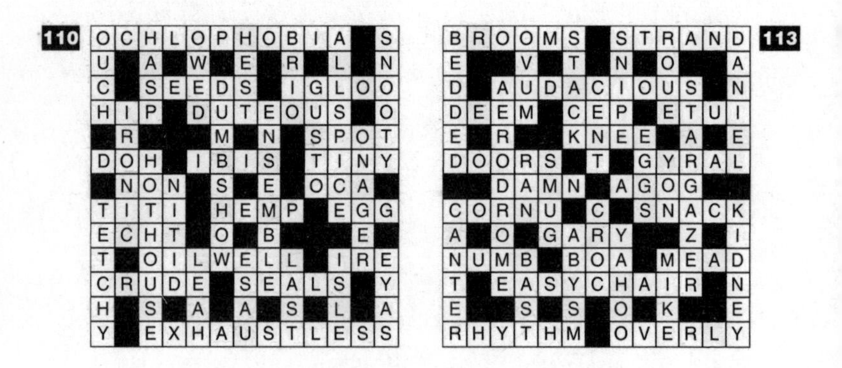

110

O	C	H	L	O	P	H	O	B	I	A	■	S
U	■	A	■	W	■	E	■	R	■	L	■	N
C	■	S	E	E	D	S	■	I	G	L	O	O
H	I	P	■	D	U	T	E	O	U	S	■	O
■	R	■	■	■	M	■	N	■	S	P	O	T
D	O	H	■	I	B	I	S	■	T	I	N	Y
■	N	O	N	■	S	■	E	■	O	C	A	■
T	I	T	I	■	H	E	M	P	■	E	G	G
E	C	H	T	■	O	■	B	■	■	■	E	■
T	■	O	I	L	W	E	L	L	■	I	R	E
C	R	U	D	E	■	S	E	A	L	S	■	Y
H	■	S	■	A	■	A	■	S	■	L	■	A
Y	■	E	X	H	A	U	S	T	L	E	S	S

113

B	R	O	O	M	S	■	S	T	R	A	N	D
E	■	■	V	■	T	■	N	■	O	■	■	A
D	■	A	U	D	A	C	I	O	U	S	■	N
D	E	E	M	■	C	E	P	■	E	T	U	I
E	■	R	■	■	K	N	E	E	■	A	■	E
D	O	O	R	S	■	T	■	G	Y	R	A	L
■	■	D	A	M	N	■	A	G	O	G	■	■
C	O	R	N	U	■	C	■	S	N	A	C	K
A	■	O	■	G	A	R	Y	■	■	Z	■	I
N	U	M	B	■	B	O	A	■	M	E	A	D
T	■	E	A	S	Y	C	H	A	I	R	■	N
E	■	■	S	■	S	■	O	■	K	■	■	E
R	H	Y	T	H	M	■	O	V	E	R	L	Y

111

■	■	C	A	M	A	R	A	D	E	R	I	E
A	■	■	■	I	■	E	■	■	Q	■	■	■
S	N	O	O	Z	E	D	■	P	U	S	■	H
T	■	E	■	Z	O	O	G	R	A	P	H	Y
R	A	N	T	E	D	■	R	I	L	L	■	D
O	■	O	■	N	■	J	I	G	■	E	■	R
N	M	P	S	■	C	A	P	■	S	E	R	A
A	■	H	■	M	O	B	■	O	■	N	■	U
U	■	I	M	A	M	■	A	R	T	F	U	L
T	O	L	E	R	A	B	L	E	■	U	■	I
S	■	E	A	T	■	L	E	G	A	L	■	C
■	■	■	L	■	■	O	■	O	■	■	■	S
S	U	B	S	I	S	T	E	N	C	E	■	■

114

F	O	L	K	■	J	U	N	C	T	I	O	N
R	■	■	E	■	E	■	■	A	■	■	G	■
I	M	A	G	E	R	Y	■	M	E	A	L	S
E	■	M	■	■	K	E	L	P	■	N	E	T
D	I	S	M	I	S	S	E	S	■	O	■	A
■	■	T	■	N	■	■	S	H	I	V	■	G
F	E	E	■	C	O	A	T	I	■	U	S	E
L	■	R	E	A	D	■	■	R	■	L	■	■
O	■	D	■	P	E	N	E	T	R	A	N	T
O	C	A	■	A	R	A	B	■	■	N	■	O
D	E	M	O	B	■	B	O	O	S	T	E	D
■	R	■	■	L	■	■	N	■	U	■	■	A
R	O	C	K	E	T	R	Y	■	B	E	V	Y

115

SMOCKING CAPE
I R R ALE
HARAKIRI LIRA
S D D TAMMUZ
EMBROIL W E O
A I C GANNET
T AFT YET H
UNITED J A A
B R E WAFTAGE
BECOME I L N
YARD ALLEYCAT
SEE R E I
MEWS SCRABBLE

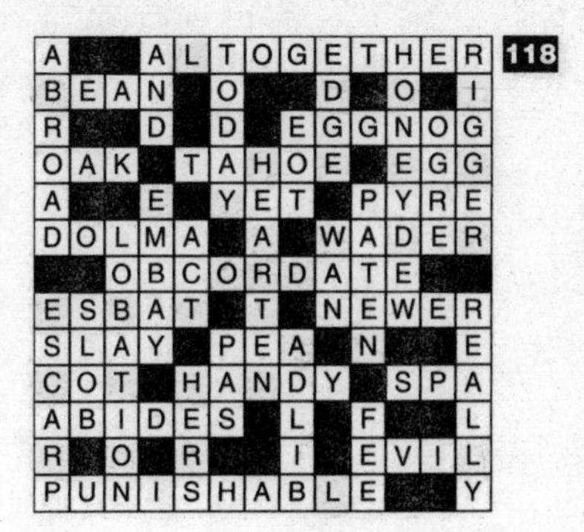

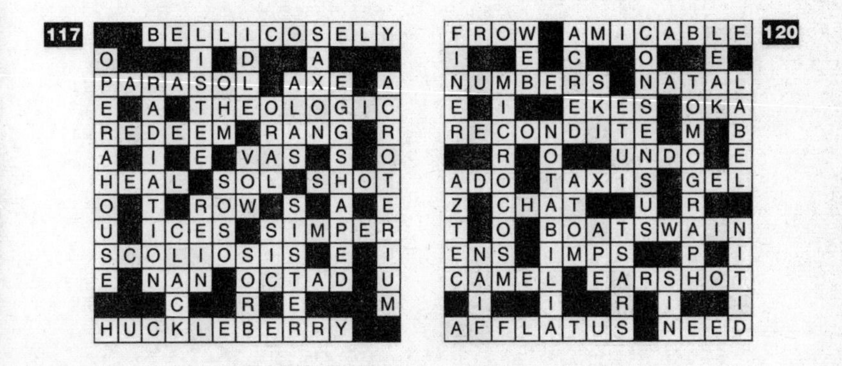

121

G	R	E	E	N	I	S	H		P	R	O	D
	E				N		U		L	A	G	
O	B	S	T	A	C	L	E		E	Y	E	S
	A		U		U		S	U	B	L	E	T
S	T	A	B	I	L	E		T		E		O
	E		A		T		C	A	U	S	A	L
E		S	T	Y				H	A	S		E
J	U	N	E	A	U		O		K		D	
E		E		N		U	N	C	A	G	E	D
C	H	A	N	G	E		W		R		L	
T	A	K	E		R	E	A	L	I	S	E	S
	K	E	A		I		R				T	
H	E	R	R		E	N	D	A	N	G	E	R

124

B			I	M	P	A	T	I	E	N	C	E
A	V	O	N		A			Y		O		C
N			K		S		Y	A	H	W	E	H
Y	E	S		C	H	A	I	R		A	G	O
A			D		A	S	P		E	D	G	E
N	A	D	I	R		T		B	R	A	S	S
		I	C	O	N	O	L	O	G	Y		
L	O	V	E	D		U		D	O	S	E	D
A	R	I	D		A	N	T		T			E
P	A	S		A	R	D	O	R		T	A	B
P	L	I	A	N	T		R		H			R
E		O		O			I		I	N	T	I
T	U	N	I	N	G	P	I	P	E			S

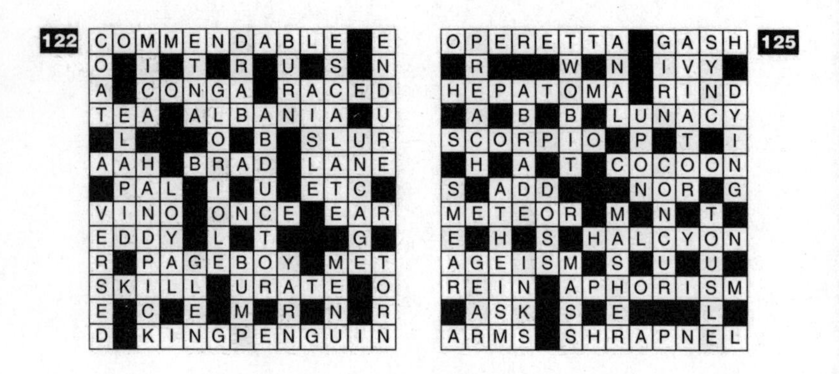

122

C	O	M	M	E	N	D	A	B	L	E		E
O		I		T		R		U		S		N
A		C	O	N	G	A		R	A	C	E	D
T	E	A		A	L	B	A	N	I	A		U
	L				O		B		S	L	U	R
A	A	H		B	R	A	D		L	A	N	E
	P	A	L		I		U		E	T	C	
V	I	N	O		O	N	C	E		E	A	R
E	D	D	Y		L		T				G	
R		P	A	G	E	B	O	Y		M	E	T
S	K	I	L	L		U	R	A	T	E		O
E		C		E		M		R		N		R
D		K	I	N	G	P	E	N	G	U	I	N

125

O	P	E	R	E	T	T	A		G	A	S	H
	R				W		N		I	V	Y	
H	E	P	A	T	O	M	A		R	I	N	D
	A		B		B		L	U	N	A	C	Y
S	C	O	R	P	I	O		P		T		I
	H		A		T		C	O	C	O	O	N
S		A	D	D				N	O	R		G
M	E	T	E	O	R		M		N		T	
E		H		S		H	A	L	C	Y	O	N
A	G	E	I	S	M		S		U		U	
R	E	I	N		A	P	H	O	R	I	S	M
	A	S	K		S		E				L	
A	R	M	S		S	H	R	A	P	N	E	L

123

		A	R	C	H	A	E	O	L	O	G	Y
S				O		I			O			
K	N	E	E	P	A	D		H	A	P		G
E		A		P	I	S	C	A	T	O	R	Y
P	A	L	M	E	R		O	A	H	U		M
T		D		R		B	A	G		L		N
I	D	O	L		S	A	X		S	T	O	A
C		R		M	I	D		H		E		S
I		M	A	I	N		G	A	R	R	E	T
S	E	A	R	C	H	I	N	G		E		I
M		N	E	E		A	U	G	E	R		C
			A			G		A				S
Q	U	E	S	T	I	O	N	I	N	G		

126

N	A	R	C		S	N	O	B	B	E	R	Y
E			O		T			A			U	
I	M	M	O	R	A	L		T	H	O	L	E
G		O			G	I	S	H		R	E	D
H	U	N	D	R	E	D	T	H		I		I
		A		E			A	O	N	E		C
P	U	S		N	E	H	R	U		N	E	T
O		T	W	E	E			S		T		
U		E		G	L	O	M	E	R	A	T	E
N	O	R		A	S	H	Y			T		N
D	R	Y	A	D		M	O	P	P	E	T	S
	Z			E			M		U			K
M	O	U	S	S	A	K	A		T	H	E	Y

127

S	A	L	E	S	M	A	N		S	E	M	E
	V				O		O		H	A	O	
W	E	A	R	A	B	L	E		O	R	L	E
	N		E		I		L	E	T	T	E	R
I	G	N	O	B	L	E		B		H		A
	E		P		E		A	B	J	E	C	T
N		H	E	T				S	O	N		O
E	R	E	N	O	W		S		Y		B	
P		A		U		R	U	F	F	I	A	N
A	D	D	E	R	S		L		U		D	
L	O	I	N		A	C	C	O	L	A	D	E
	E	N	D		G		U				I	
E	R	G	S		O	B	S	C	U	R	E	D

130

128 **131**

129 **132**

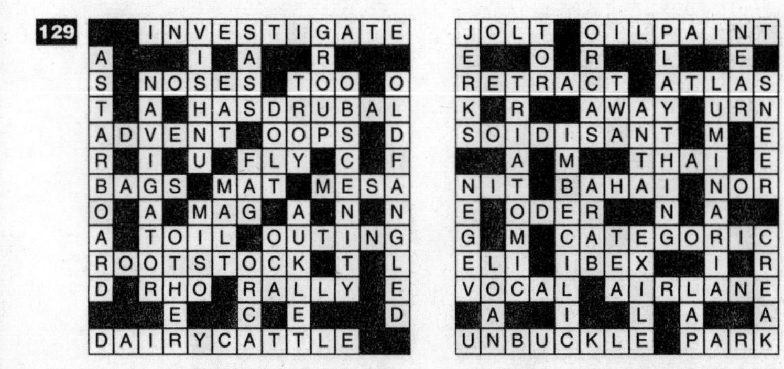

133

T	R	O	M	B	O	N	E		T	I	M	E
	E				N		B		A	M	U	
H	I	T	H	E	R	T	O		H	I	L	T
	N		U		U		N	E	A	T	L	Y
H	E	I	R	E	S	S		R		A		C
	D		L		H		S	N	A	T	C	H
R		J	E	T				E	V	E		E
A	L	I	Y	A	H		A		E		P	
B		M		X		O	P	E	N	A	I	R
A	D	J	O	I	N		A		U		T	
T	R	A	P		A	S	T	H	E	N	I	A
	E	M	U		O		H				E	
L	E	S	S		S	A	Y	O	N	A	R	A

136

M			T	H	U	M	B	S	C	R	E	W
U	L	N	A		S			O		O		A
T			P		N		A	B	R	U	P	T
A	F	T		P	E	S	T	S		N	E	E
T			K		A	W	E		A	D	A	R
E	L	A	N	D		E		S	U	L	K	Y
		C	E	A	S	E	F	I	R	E		
A	L	I	E	N		P		B	A	T	I	K
C	O	D	S		Y	E	P		L			E
T	A	R		X	E	R	I	C		W	A	R
I	M	A	G	E	S		A		G			N
O		I		N			N		Y	I	P	E
N	I	N	C	O	M	P	O	O	P			L

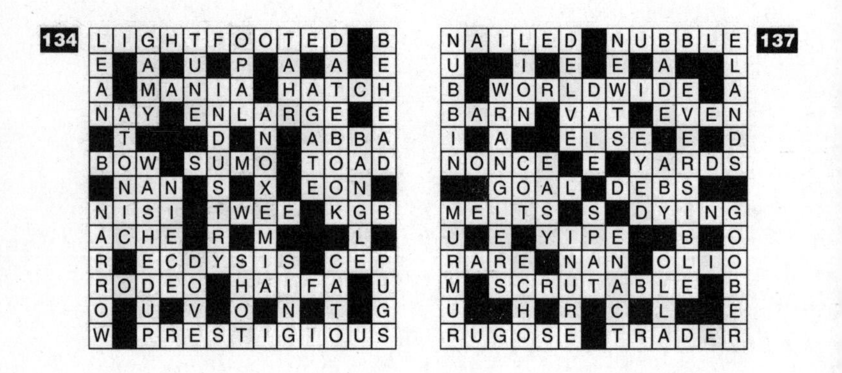

134

L	I	G	H	T	F	O	O	T	E	D		B
E		A		U		P		A		A		E
A		M	A	N	I	A		H	A	T	C	H
N	A	Y		E	N	L	A	R	G	E		E
	T				D		N		A	B	B	A
B	O	W		S	U	M	O		T	O	A	D
	N	A	N		S		X		E	O	N	
N	I	S	I		T	W	E	E		K	G	B
A	C	H	E		R		M				L	
R		E	C	D	Y	S	I	S		C	E	P
R	O	D	E	O		H	A	I	F	A		U
O		U		V		O		N		T		G
W		P	R	E	S	T	I	G	I	O	U	S

137

N	A	I	L	E	D		N	U	B	B	L	E
U			I		E		E		A			L
B		W	O	R	L	D	W	I	D	E		A
B	A	R	N		V	A	T		E	V	E	N
I		A			E	L	S	E		E		D
N	O	N	C	E		E		Y	A	R	D	S
		G	O	A	L		D	E	B	S		
M	E	L	T	S		S		D	Y	I	N	G
U		E		Y	I	P	E			B		O
R	A	R	E		N	A	N		O	L	I	O
M		S	C	R	U	T	A	B	L	E		B
U			H		R		C		L			E
R	U	G	O	S	E		T	R	A	D	E	R

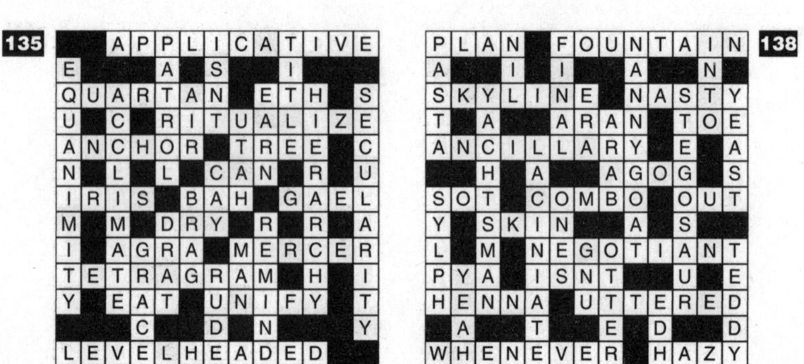

135

		A	P	P	L	I	C	A	T	I	V	E
E				A		S			I			
Q	U	A	R	T	A	N		E	T	H		S
U		C		R	I	T	U	A	L	I	Z	E
A	N	C	H	O	R		T	R	E	E		C
N		L		L		C	A	N		R		U
I	R	I	S		B	A	H		G	A	E	L
M		M		D	R	Y		R		R		A
I		A	G	R	A		M	E	R	C	E	R
T	E	T	R	A	G	R	A	M		H		I
Y		E	A	T		U	N	I	F	Y		T
			C			D		N				Y
L	E	V	E	L	H	E	A	D	E	D		

138

P	L	A	N		F	O	U	N	T	A	I	N
A			I		I			A			N	
S	K	Y	L	I	N	E		N	A	S	T	Y
T		A			A	R	A	N		T	O	E
A	N	C	I	L	L	A	R	Y		E		A
		H		A			A	G	O	G		S
S	O	T		C	O	M	B	O		O	U	T
Y		S	K	I	N			A		S		
L		M		N	E	G	O	T	I	A	N	T
P	Y	A		I	S	N	T			U		E
H	E	N	N	A		U	T	T	E	R	E	D
	A			T			E		D			D
W	H	E	N	E	V	E	R		H	A	Z	Y

139

O	R	G	U	L	O	U	S		C	A	N	E
	A				N		L		U	S	E	
W	R	E	C	K	A	G	E		R	H	E	A
	E		R		G		D	R	E	A	M	S
O	F	F	E	R	E	D		U		M		P
	Y		A		R		T	E	R	E	T	E
B		S	K	A				D	I	D		N
L	A	W	Y	E	R		S		B		B	
E		A		O		S	T	A	B	I	L	E
E	R	R	A	N	D		A		O		A	
D	U	T	Y		A	L	P	I	N	I	S	T
	S	H	E		M		E				T	
K	E	Y	S		E	S	S	A	Y	I	S	T

142

B			Y	E	L	L	O	W	J	A	C	K
U	N	D	O		I			H		C		A
R			B		B		C	O	N	C	U	R
L	A	P		P	R	I	A	M		U	R	N
A			O		A	C	T		A	R	I	A
P	E	P	P	Y		E		C	R	A	C	K
		H	E	A	D	F	I	R	S	T		
S	L	A	N	G		A		Y	I	E	L	D
W	I	N	S		F	L	U		S			E
E	F	T		D	U	L	S	E		R	E	V
D	E	A	D	E	N		A		V			I
E		S		N			G		A	W	E	S
N	U	M	B	E	R	L	E	S	S			E

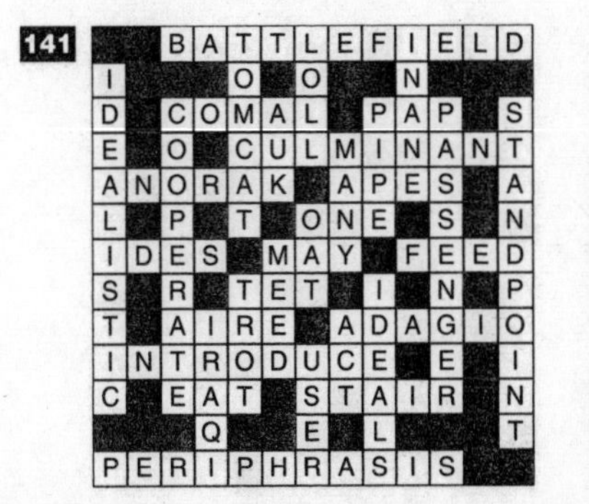

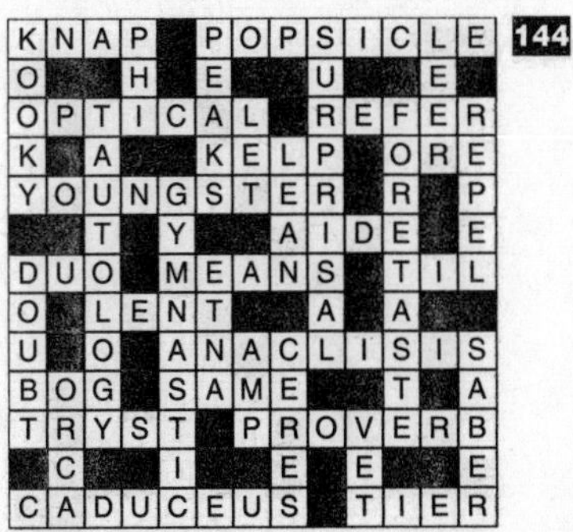

145

T	H	R	E	N	O	D	Y		H	I	L	L
	I				H		A		O	N	E	
P	E	R	F	U	M	E	R		O	G	E	E
	M		O		A		D	E	F	O	R	M
F	A	R	R	A	G	O		X		I		O
	L		E		E		G	A	N	N	E	T
G		A	G	E				M	U	G		E
R	U	G	O	S	E		D		D		A	
O		E		A		B	E	G	G	A	R	Y
U	M	L	A	U	T		P		E		C	
P	E	O	N		O	V	E	R	S	E	A	S
	A	N	T		S		N				D	
E	D	G	E		H	Y	D	R	O	G	E	N

148

A			A	B	S	T	E	M	I	O	U	S
S	K	E	P		C			E		U		M
L			E		R		B	L	O	T	T	O
E	A	T		B	I	P	E	D		H	A	O
E			A		M	A	Y		B	O	L	T
P	A	N	G	S		G		V	O	U	C	H
		U	L	I	G	I	N	O	U	S		
V	O	T	E	S		N		W	R	E	A	K
A	W	A	Y		J	A	M		G			E
R	E	T		S	O	L	A	N		D	R	Y
I	D	I	O	C	Y		C		D			P
E		O		A			A		A	R	I	A
D	E	N	D	R	I	F	O	R	M			D

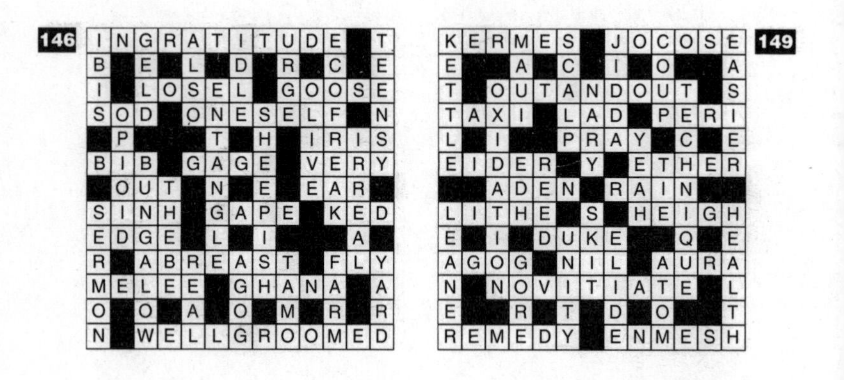

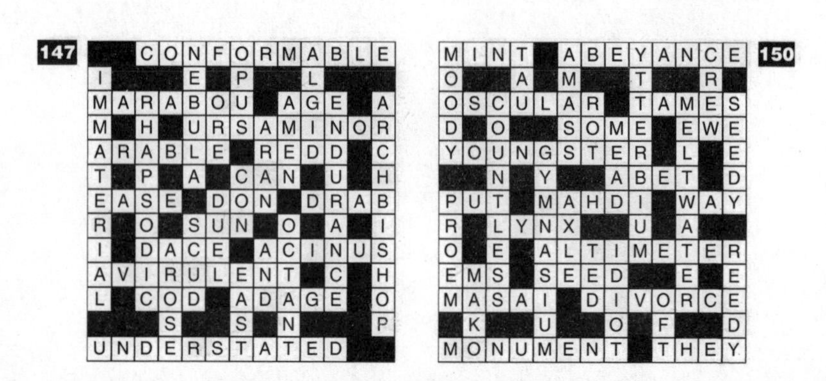

151

M	U	C	H	N	E	S	S		S	O	S	O
	R				N		T		O	P	T	
R	A	N	C	H	E	R	O		U	S	E	D
	N		O		R		B	A	R	O	N	Y
P	I	L	L	A	G	E		W		N		I
	A		D		Y		N	A	T	I	O	N
T		A	L	B				Y	O	N		G
A	L	I	Y	A	H		E		M		A	
B		R		L		E	Y	E	B	A	L	L
B	E	C	O	M	E		E		O		W	
Y	A	R	D		A	L	L	E	Y	C	A	T
	S	E	E		S		E				Y	
Y	E	W	S		T	O	T	A	L	I	S	M

154

S			A	C	C	O	R	D	A	N	C	E
E	G	O	S		O			U		A		G
R			H		B		A	D	A	G	I	O
M	O	T		C	R	E	P	E		A	N	I
O			T		A	X	E		A	S	K	S
N	I	C	H	E		C		B	O	A	S	T
		H	A	N	D	I	W	O	R	K		
E	L	A	N	D		T		A	T	I	L	T
G	O	N	E		Y	E	N		A			A
O	R	C		G	E	R	A	H		Y	O	U
I	D	E	A	L	S		O		H			T
S		R		E			M		I	S	L	E
M	A	Y	O	N	N	A	I	S	E			N

152

R	E	A	D	Y	T	O	W	E	A	R		S
A		C		A		B		A		E		P
I		R	O	N	D	O		R	E	N	A	L
N	E	E		G	R	E	A	S	E	D		A
	U				A		L		R	E	L	Y
A	R	C		U	M	B	O		I	R	I	S
	O	H	O		S		E		E	E	N	
E	P	I	C		H	I	V	E		D	E	E
M	A	L	T		O		E				A	
E		D	A	M	P	D	R	Y		E	R	E
R	U	B	L	E		D	A	I	L	Y		L
G		E		M		A		P		R		B
E		D	E	O	X	Y	G	E	N	A	T	E

155

O	A	K	L	E	Y		C	U	R	L	E	D
P			O		E		L		O			U
E		F	A	N	A	T	I	C	A	L		N
N	A	R	D		R	A	M		M	I	L	L
E		I			N	I	B	S		N		I
D	I	C	E	R		L		A	R	G	O	N
		A	V	E	R		A	G	U	E		
E	A	T	E	N		I		A	E	R	I	E
V		I		T	A	S	K			I		N
E	N	V	Y		F	L	U		A	N	A	L
N		E	A	S	T	E	R	E	G	G		A
T			R		E		U		O			C
S	P	I	D	E	R		S	I	G	N	E	E

153

		K	I	N	G	O	F	K	I	N	G	S
O				I		D			R			
P	O	L	Y	P	O	D		D	O	E		B
E		A		P	A	S	S	E	N	G	E	R
R	A	N	C	O	R		P	E	S	O		I
A		D		N		Y	O	D		T		D
H	I	S	S		P	O	T		B	I	D	E
O		C		S	U	B		A		S		S
U		A	T	O	M		A	C	E	T	U	M
S	U	P	E	R	A	B	L	E		I		A
E		E	A	T		A	T	T	I	C		I
			C			L		I				D
M	A	C	H	U	P	I	C	C	H	U		

156

L	I	M	P		M	E	D	I	C	A	T	E
O			A		U			N			I	
Y	A	R	D	A	G	E		G	E	C	K	O
A		E			G	L	E	E		A	I	D
L	I	V	E	R	Y	M	A	N		R		O
		O		E			T	I	E	R		U
B	E	L		L	A	S	S	O		E	A	R
E		T	H	A	N			U		F		
G		I		T	O	A	D	S	T	O	O	L
U	R	N		I	N	L	Y			U		E
N	E	G	E	V		L	I	G	U	R	I	A
	A			E			N		G			C
E	L	A	P	S	I	N	G		H	E	T	H

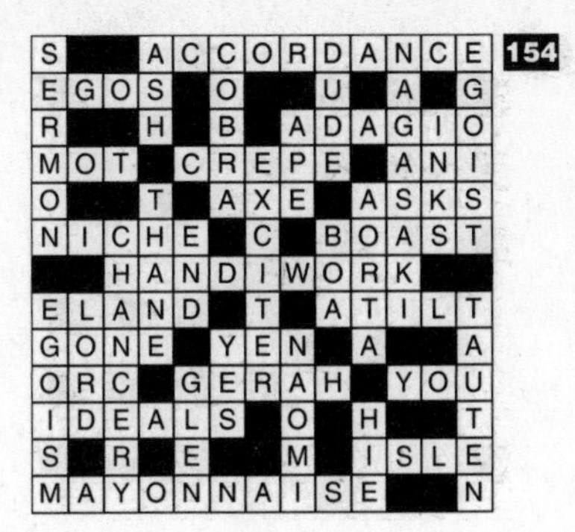

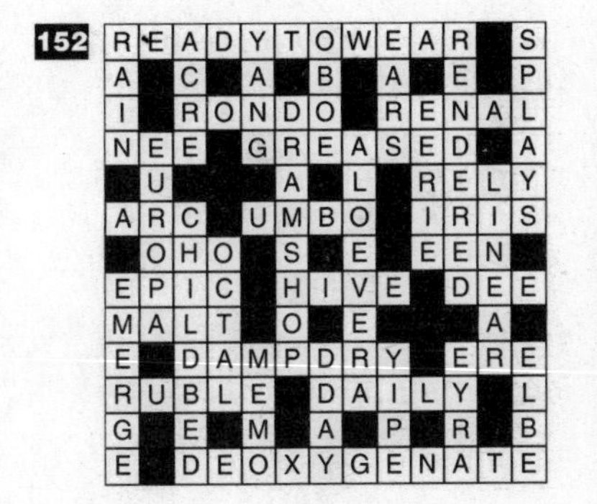

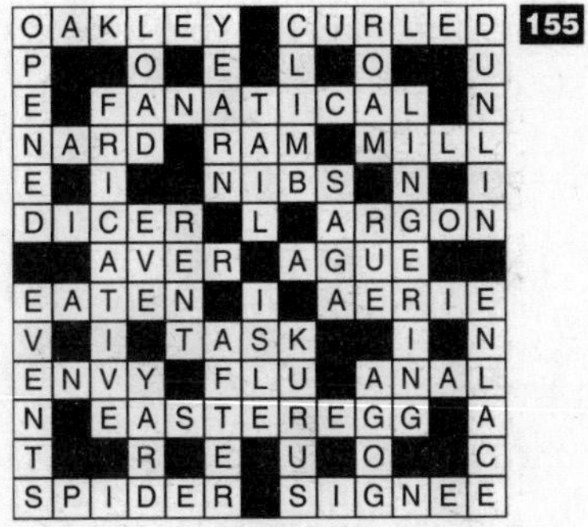

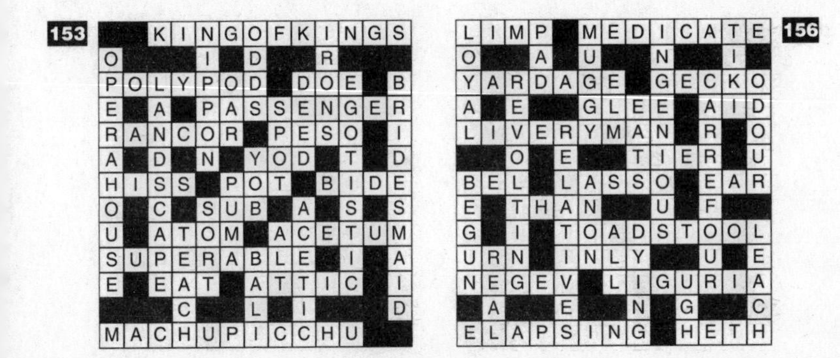

157

E	X	E	R	C	I	S	E		M	I	C	A
	Y				N		D		I	L	L	
S	L	I	P	S	H	O	D		N	E	A	P
	E		I		A		Y	O	G	I	N	I
O	N	E	S	E	L	F		B		T		A
	E		C		E		S	I	M	I	A	N
S		F	E	U				E	O	S		O
T	O	U	S	L	E		D		U		G	
A		R		N		C	E	A	S	I	N	G
K	I	T	B	A	G		P		S		E	
E	C	H	O		O	L	I	V	E	O	I	L
	K	E	D		O		C				S	
G	Y	R	E		F	A	T	A	L	I	S	M

163

F	L	A	G	P	O	L	E		S	E	E	R
	A				D		D		E	A	R	
T	W	I	N	N	I	N	G		E	R	I	N
	F		A		O		Y	I	P	P	E	E
T	U	M	U	L	U	S		D		L		V
	L		G		S		I	L	L	U	M	E
A		O	H	M				Y	A	G		R
B	I	T	T	E	R		J		T		L	
Y		A		R		H	E	S	H	V	A	N
S	O	L	E	L	Y		S		E		R	
S	A	G	S		O	U	T	B	R	A	V	E
	H	I	P		G		E				A	
Q	U	A	Y		A	R	R	A	N	G	E	D

166

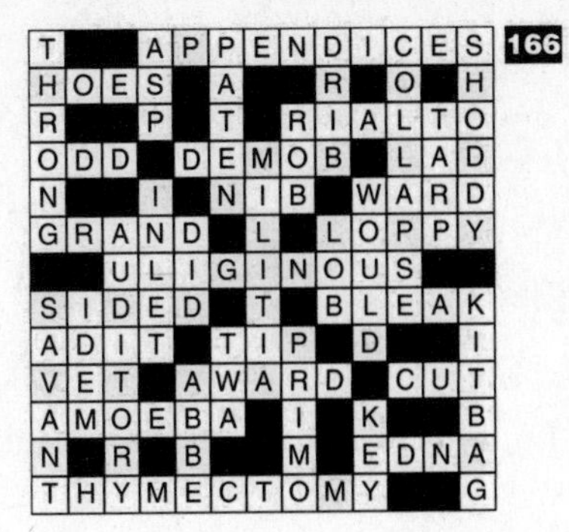

164

167

165

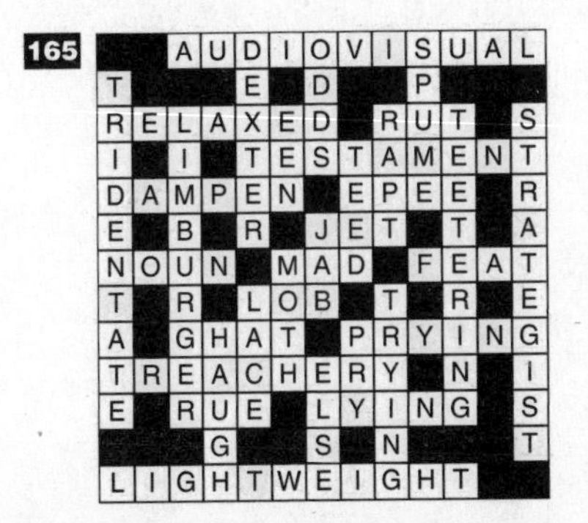

168

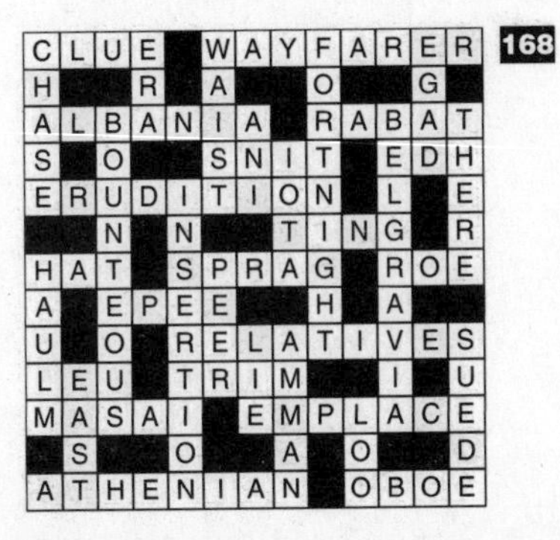

169

P	O	L	T	R	O	O	N		M	I	F	F
	V				N		U		O	N	E	
K	E	E	L	H	A	U	L		P	I	T	A
	R		O		G		L	U	S	T	E	R
O	D	Y	S	S	E	Y		R		I		R
	O		E		R		L	E	G	A	T	O
G		O	R	B				A	L	L		W
A	M	U	S	E	D		W		I		E	
N		T		L		W	A	F	T	A	G	E
E	X	C	I	T	E		L		C		G	
F	R	O	M		X	A	N	T	H	E	N	E
	A	M	P		I		U				O	
A	Y	E	S		T	U	T	E	L	A	G	E

172

T			L	I	N	S	E	E	D	O	I	L
H	O	L	Y		A			X		V		I
R			E		S		M	A	K	E	D	O
O	A	F		H	A	K	I	M		R	A	N
N			F		L	A	X		B	R	I	E
E	X	I	L	E		S		M	O	I	S	T
		N	O	R	T	H	L	A	N	D		
A	R	D	O	R		R		D	U	E	T	S
L	O	U	D		F	U	G		S			T
M	A	R		D	A	T	E	D		F	A	Y
O	N	A	G	E	R		E		D			L
S		T		N			S		A	X	L	E
T	E	E	N	Y	W	E	E	N	Y			T

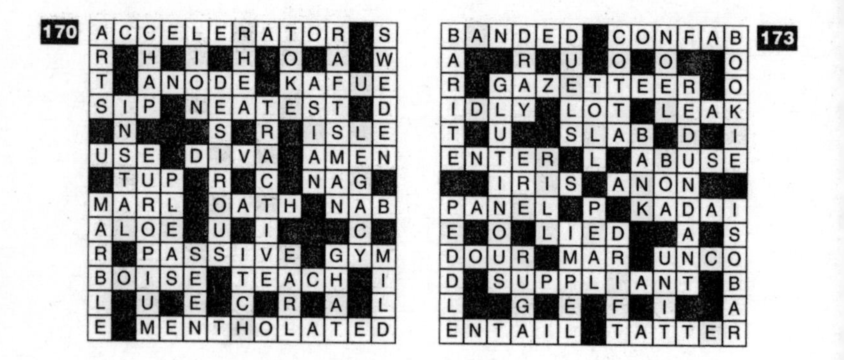

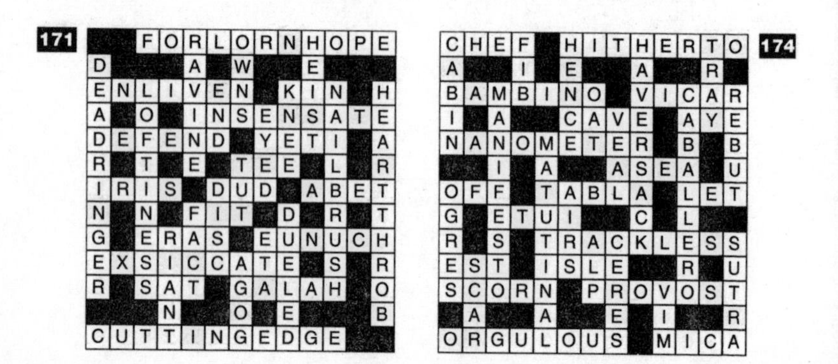

175

S	C	R	A	G	G	L	Y	■	R	U	I	N
■	H	■	■	■	U	■	O	■	A	N	D	■
F	U	R	B	E	L	O	W	■	C	L	O	D
■	B	■	I	■	L	■	L	I	K	E	L	Y
A	B	D	O	M	E	N	■	T	■	A	■	I
■	Y	■	N	■	T	■	R	E	A	S	O	N
A	■	V	I	A	■	■	■	M	P	H	■	G
B	R	A	C	E	R	■	S	■	P	■	T	■
A	■	G	■	R	■	F	U	N	E	R	A	L
S	P	R	A	Y	S	■	R	■	A	■	E	■
H	E	A	R	■	C	O	V	E	R	I	N	G
■	O	N	E	■	U	■	E	■	■	■	I	■
A	N	T	A	■	D	A	Y	B	R	E	A	K

178

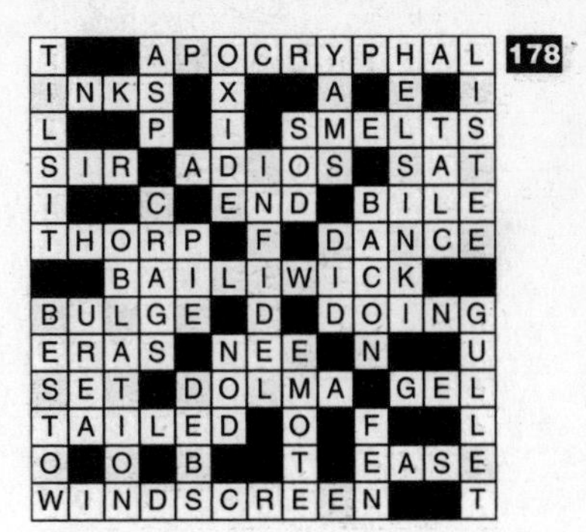

176

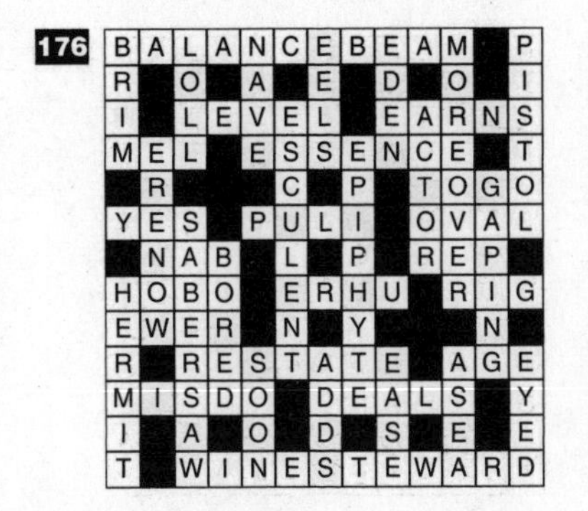

179

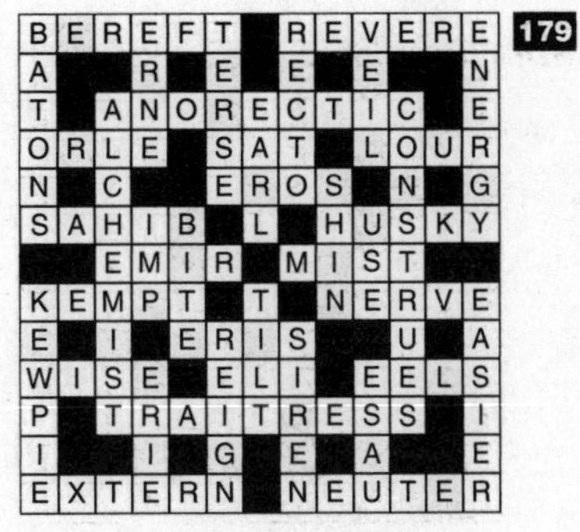

177 **180**

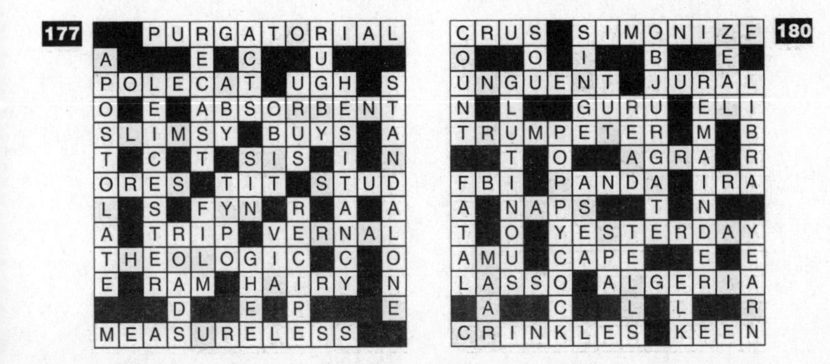

181

B	E	D	L	I	N	E	N		G	N	A	R
	C				A		I		R	E	X	
C	L	O	T	H	I	N	G		A	B	E	D
	A		I		L		H	U	M	B	L	E
T	I	D	D	L	E	R		P		I		M
	R		B		D		B	O	N	S	A	I
S		D	I	D				N	O	H		T
W	R	I	T	E	R		B		R		H	
I		M		B		O	U	T	W	E	A	R
S	E	N	A	T	E		R		A		Z	
S	T	E	P		A	L	L	E	Y	C	A	T
	U	S	E		V		A				R	
D	I	S	S		E	M	P	A	N	A	D	A

184

U			W	O	R	K	P	E	O	P	L	E
P	I	C	A		I			C		A		L
C			S		F		W	H	E	N	C	E
A	D	O		F	L	E	E	T		O	R	C
S			H		E	N	D		B	R	A	T
T	U	N	E	D		L		D	R	A	G	S
		A	L	U	M	I	N	I	U	M		
A	M	P	L	E		V		G	I	A	N	T
C	O	H	O		G	E	T		N			H
C	A	T		J	A	N	U	S		C	U	E
E	N	A	M	E	L		B		B			I
P		L		A			A		A	V	E	R
T	R	I	A	N	G	U	L	A	R			S

187

J	A	M	B	O	R	E	E	■	U	N	I	T
■	M	■	■	■	E	■	L	■	R	E	D	■
C	A	P	Y	B	A	R	A	■	I	C	E	D
■	Z	■	A	■	D	■	N	E	C	T	A	R
B	O	A	R	D	E	R	■	X	■	A	■	O
■	N	■	R	■	R	■	F	A	R	R	O	W
M	■	B	O	A	■	■	■	M	A	Y	■	N
B	L	E	W	I	T	■	B	■	D	■	P	■
I	■	A	■	D	■	S	O	L	I	C	I	T
R	U	D	E	S	T	■	W	■	A	■	S	■
A	R	I	A	■	I	M	M	O	L	A	T	E
■	E	N	S	■	R	■	A	■	■	■	I	■
R	A	G	E	■	E	X	N	I	H	I	L	O

190

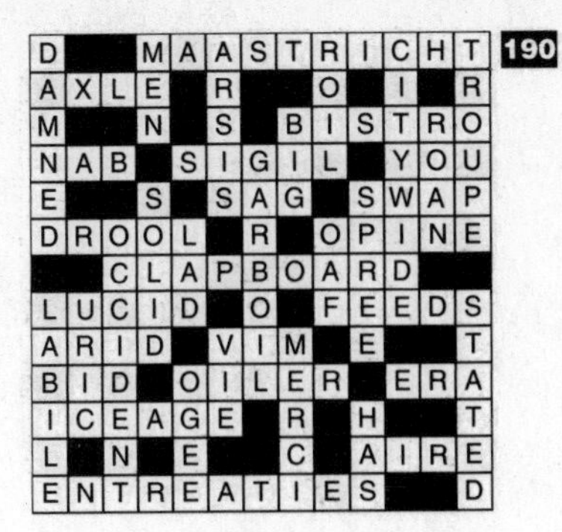

188

191

189

192

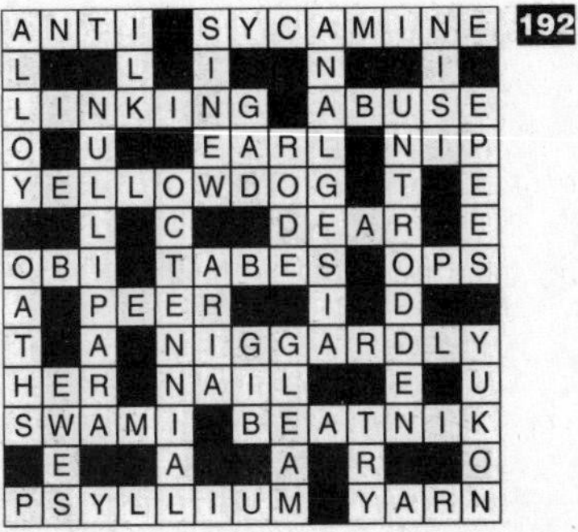

193

P	U	L	L	O	V	E	R		T	W	A	S
	R					E	O		Y	E	N	
H	A	C	H	U	R	E	S		P	A	T	E
	N		A		B		E	X	O	T	I	C
V	I	C	I	N	A	L		I		H		L
	C		N		L		G	A	L	E	N	A
B		O	A	F				N	O	R		T
R	A	I	N	E	D		C		A		B	
A		L		T		G	A	I	N	F	U	L
S	Y	S	T	E	M		N		E		C	
S	A	K	E		A	C	C	U	R	A	C	Y
	W	I	N		T		E				A	
I	S	N	T		S	C	R	A	B	B	L	E

196

L			B	L	A	C	K	M	A	G	I	C
I	D	L	Y		R			O		R		L
N			E		I		V	I	R	A	G	O
G	E	L		U	S	U	A	L		P	O	W
E			A		E	N	S		S	P	A	N
R	O	N	D	O		R		H	I	L	L	S
		E	D	U	C	A	T	I	V	E		
P	O	U	L	T		V		S	A	D	H	U
O	G	R	E		B	E	E		N			N
E	L	I		H	A	L	L	S		T	O	W
T	E	T	H	E	R		F		L			I
I		I		R			I		E	B	O	N
C	A	S	A	B	L	A	N	C	A			D

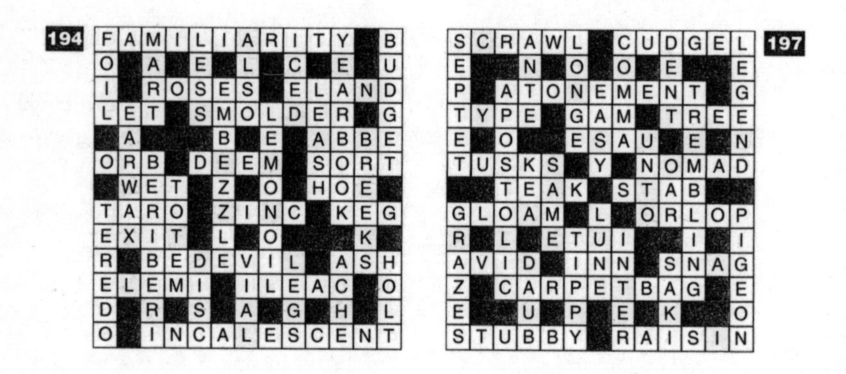

199

P	U	N	C	T	U	R	E		C	O	K	E
	S				P		X		L	E	U	
P	A	W	N	S	H	O	P		A	D	D	S
	B		U		I		O	S	M	I	U	M
P	L	I	A	B	L	E		I		P		I
	E		N		L		P	L	I	A	N	T
U		A	C	E				D	A	L		H
S	A	F	E	T	Y		T		T		A	
U		F		C		Q	U	A	R	R	E	L
A	L	I	G	H	T		B		I		O	
L	I	R	A		O	P	U	S	C	U	L	E
	E	M	S		R		L				U	
B	U	S	H		N	E	E	D	L	E	S	S

202

G			P	A	R	M	I	G	I	A	N	A
R	E	D	E		E			L		N		N
O			G		A		K	A	K	A	P	O
O	F	F		A	P	H	I	D		B	A	R
V			D		S	A	P		G	A	G	A
E	N	S	U	E		N		S	L	E	E	K
		E	N	L	I	G	H	T	E	N		
F	L	A	C	K		D		Y	E	A	S	T
L	U	B	E		D	O	C		D			R
A	G	O		L	O	G	O	S		C	H	I
K	E	A	T	O	N		A		H			N
E		R		F			T		A	Q	U	A
S	U	D	A	T	O	R	I	U	M			L

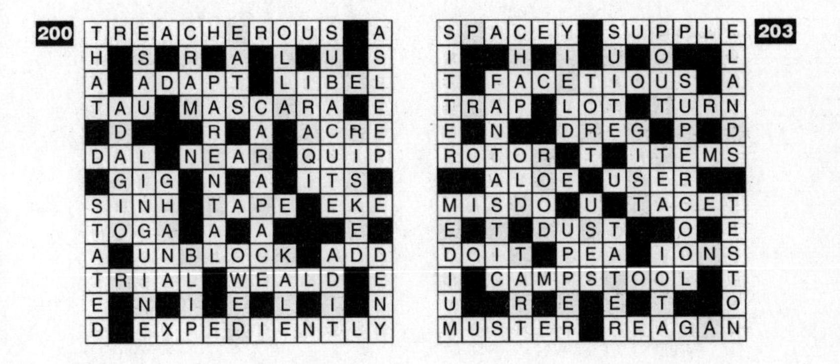

200

T	R	E	A	C	H	E	R	O	U	S		A
H		S		R		A		L		U		S
A		A	D	A	P	T		L	I	B	E	L
T	A	U		M	A	S	C	A	R	A		E
	D				R		A		A	C	R	E
D	A	L		N	E	A	R		Q	U	I	P
	G	I	G		N		A		I	T	S	
S	I	N	H		T	A	P	E		E	K	E
T	O	G	A		A		A				E	
A		U	N	B	L	O	C	K		A	D	D
T	R	I	A	L		W	E	A	L	D		E
E		N		I		E		L		I		N
D		E	X	P	E	D	I	E	N	T	L	Y

203

S	P	A	C	E	Y		S	U	P	P	L	E
I			H		I		U		O			L
T		F	A	C	E	T	I	O	U	S		A
T	R	A	P		L	O	T		T	U	R	N
E		N			D	R	E	G		P		D
R	O	T	O	R		T		I	T	E	M	S
		A	L	O	E		U	S	E	R		
M	I	S	D	O		U		T	A	C	E	T
E		T		D	U	S	T			O		E
D	O	I	T		P	E	A		I	O	N	S
I		C	A	M	P	S	T	O	O	L		T
U			R		E		E		T			O
M	U	S	T	E	R		R	E	A	G	A	N

201

		P	E	S	S	I	M	I	S	T	I	C
O				L		T			T			
V	E	N	T	U	R	E		S	A	P		S
A		E		M	O	M	E	N	T	A	R	Y
L	E	G	U	M	E		M	I	E	N		M
O		O		Y		T	U	G		E		M
F	U	T	Z		V	A	S		O	G	E	E
F		I		S	I	N		R		Y		T
I		A	S	K	S		T	E	R	R	O	R
C	O	N	C	E	A	L	E	D		I		I
E		T	A	G		A	D	H	O	C		Z
			L			M		A				E
C	A	R	D	I	O	P	A	T	H	Y		

204

S	P	A	T		A	C	R	I	M	O	N	Y
P			O		C			M			I	
A	R	M	O	U	R	Y		M	O	O	C	H
N		E			E	A	V	E		F	E	E
G	U	A	R	D	S	M	A	N		F		T
		N		E			I	S	L	E		U
S	O	S		P	E	N	N	I		N	A	P
I		T	H	A	W			T		B		
G		E		R	E	A	D	Y	M	A	D	E
H	A	S		T	R	U	E			C		L
T	U	T	T	I		K	R	I	S	H	N	A
	R			N			B		O			N
M	A	H	O	G	A	N	Y		Y	A	R	D

205

C	I	T	Y	W	I	D	E		E	D	G	E
	N				T		D		T	E	A	
S	U	K	I	Y	A	K	I		U	S	E	S
	R		N		L		T	A	I	P	A	N
R	E	C	L	A	I	M		C		A		E
	S		A		C		M	E	D	I	A	L
A		O	N	E				S	I	R		L
M	I	D	D	A	Y		C		A		B	
A		O		S		C	O	M	P	E	E	R
S	P	R	A	Y	S		D		E		R	
S	O	O	N		I	N	D	U	R	A	T	E
	G	U	T		P		L				H	
D	O	S	A		S	K	E	L	E	T	A	L

206

C	H	O	C	K	A	B	L	O	C	K		A
U		L		H		I		V		E		S
R		I	N	A	P	T		E	G	E	S	T
T	O	O		N	O	S	T	R	I	L		U
	R				S		E		A	B	U	T
L	A	D		K	I	T	S		N	O	N	E
	T	A	G		T		T		T	A	P	
S	O	Y	A		R	E	A	D		T	A	N
A	R	D	S		O		T				I	
D		R	E	U	N	I	O	N		O	D	D
D	R	E	S	S		T	R	A	C	K		O
E		A		E		C		T		I		N
N		M	A	R	C	H	I	O	N	E	S	S

207

		E	X	P	R	O	P	R	I	A	T	E
R				E		D			D			
H	A	S	T	A	T	E		S	E	A		Y
E		O		R	E	S	A	L	A	B	L	E
U	N	B	O	L	T		L	I	L	Y		S
M		R		Y		P	U	P		S		T
A	K	I	N		G	E	M		I	S	L	E
T		Q		K	O	A		U		I		R
I		U	L	N	A		A	G	E	N	C	Y
S	K	E	L	E	T	O	N	S		I		E
M		T	A	W		K	I	O	W	A		A
			M			I		M				R
E	N	J	A	M	B	E	M	E	N	T		

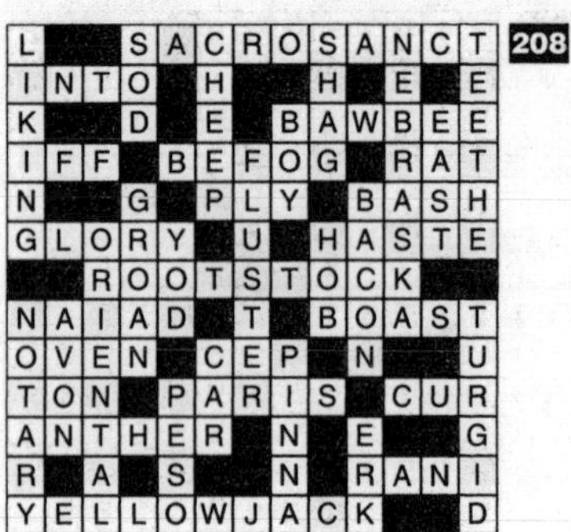

208

L			S	A	C	R	O	S	A	N	C	T
I	N	T	O		H			H		E		E
K			D		E		B	A	W	B	E	E
I	F	F		B	E	F	O	G		R	A	T
N			G		P	L	Y		B	A	S	H
G	L	O	R	Y		U		H	A	S	T	E
		R	O	O	T	S	T	O	C	K		
N	A	I	A	D		T		B	O	A	S	T
O	V	E	N		C	E	P		N			U
T	O	N		P	A	R	I	S		C	U	R
A	N	T	H	E	R		N		E			G
R		A		S			N		R	A	N	I
Y	E	L	L	O	W	J	A	C	K			D

209

K	E	L	O	I	D		J	A	L	O	P	Y
R			B		E		A		O			I
E		C	O	R	R	E	C	T	L	Y		P
T	I	L	E		B	R	A		L	E	A	P
E		A			Y	U	L	E		A		E
K	A	Y	A	K		V		D	I	R	G	E
		S	L	A	B		P	A	R	R		
H	O	T	E	L		F		M	A	O	R	I
I		O		E	X	A	M			U		M
N	U	N	S		E	R	A		S	N	A	P
D		E	N	G	R	O	S	S	E	D		A
E			O		I		A		C			L
R	U	S	T	I	C		I	N	T	O	N	E

210

S	U	V	A		S	Y	N	C	L	I	N	E
N			N		U			A		O		
A	F	F	I	A	N	T		M	A	U	V	E
K		A			N	U	M	B		N	A	N
E	X	C	A	V	A	T	O	R		D		V
		E		E			D	I	V	E		O
S	O	T		H	A	T	E	D		R	A	Y
H		I	B	E	X			G		H		
E		O		M	I	S	B	E	H	A	V	E
E	M	U		E	S	A	U			N		R
R	E	S	I	N		T	R	U	N	D	L	E
	M			C			E		O			C
C	O	N	T	E	M	P	T		H	O	L	T

211

M	I	R	T	H	F	U	L		W	A	V	E
	R				E		I		A	L	E	
H	E	B	E	T	A	T	E		R	A	I	D
	N		G		L		N	I	M	B	L	E
R	I	C	O	T	T	A		D		A		I
	C		I		Y		C	O	M	M	I	T
A		U	S	E				L	E	A		Y
S	U	M	M	E	D		R		D		R	
C		P		L		H	E	A	D	M	A	N
O	T	I	O	S	E		D		L		C	
T	U	R	N		B	A	C	T	E	R	I	A
	N	E	E		O		A				A	
M	A	S	S		N	A	P	H	T	A	L	I

212

213

214

215

216

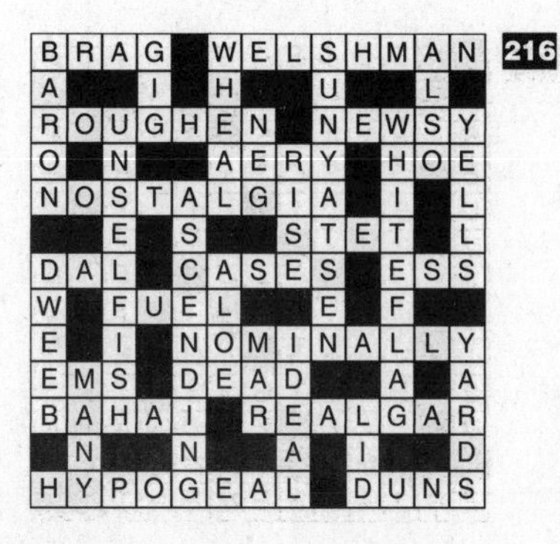

217

B	E	C	O	M	I	N	G		T	E	E	D
	L				N		O		H	E	W	
C	A	U	S	E	R	I	E		O	R	E	S
	N		E		O		S	Q	U	I	R	T
A	D	A	X	I	A	L		U		E		E
	S		I		D		H	A	W	S	E	R
S		U	S	E				Y	E	T		N
P	E	L	T	R	Y		E		S		D	
R		U		N		C	L	A	T	T	E	R
A	L	L	I	E	D		U		E		C	
T	E	A	T		U	N	D	E	R	P	I	N
	A	T	E		A		E				D	
T	H	E	M		D	O	D	D	E	R	E	D

220

S			A	R	R	H	Y	T	H	M	I	A
A	L	M	S		O			H		A		L
U			K		A		F	I	S	C	A	L
G	A	P		A	S	H	E	N		A	T	E
E			H		T	O	W		P	R	O	G
R	I	G	O	R		G		E	L	O	P	E
		O	R	A	N	G	E	M	A	N		
B	L	O	A	T		I		S	C	I	O	N
A	I	D	E		E	S	T		E			A
R	A	W		O	T	H	E	R		L	I	P
I	R	I	D	I	C		A		B			I
T		L		L			S		U	R	G	E
E	N	L	I	S	T	M	E	N	T			R

223

V	I	P	E	R	O	U	S		E	B	O	N
	T				N		E		Y	O	N	
P	A	G	I	N	A	T	E		R	O	C	K
	L		N		G		K	R	A	K	E	N
F	I	D	D	L	E	R		I		I		O
	C		I		R		H	O	B	N	O	B
T		J	U	G				T	E	G		S
E	N	A	M	E	L		P		T		B	
A		W		S		O	R	C	H	A	R	D
R	A	B	A	T	O		O		E		E	
S	H	O	P		U	N	B	E	L	I	E	F
	E	N	E		R		E				K	
A	M	E	X		S	U	D	A	N	E	S	E

226

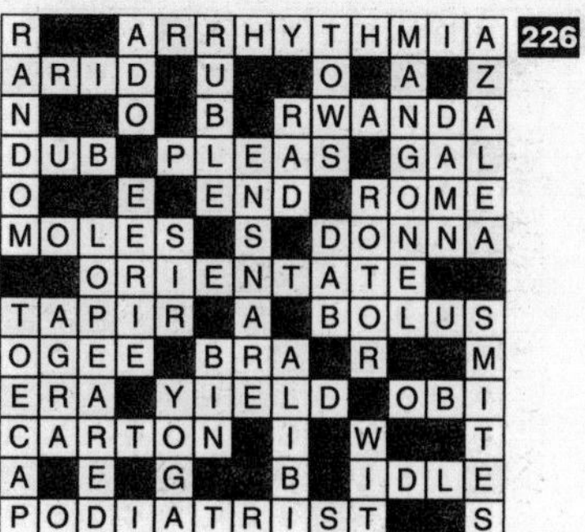

224

227

225

228

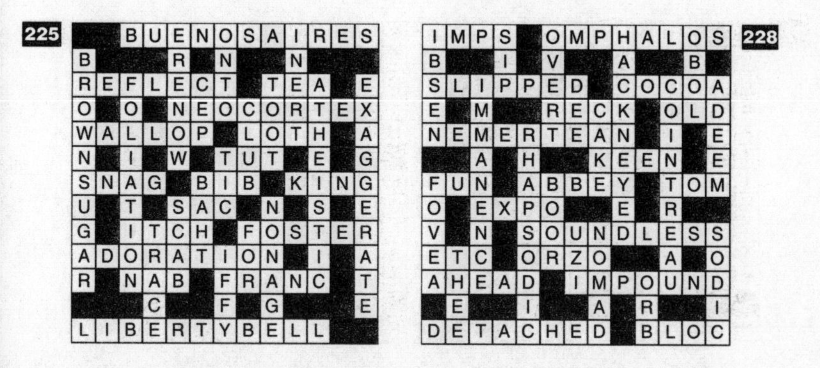

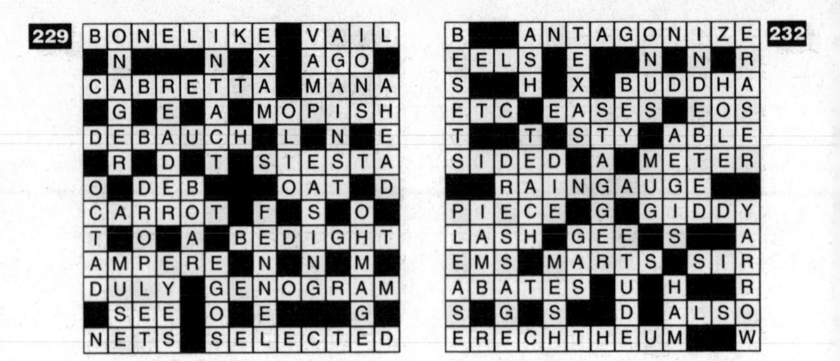
229
BONELIKE VAIL
N N X AGO
CABRETTA MANA
G E A MOPISH
DEBAUCH L N E
R D T SIESTA
O DEB OAT D
CARROT F S O
T O A BEDIGHT
AMPERE N N M
DULY GENOGRAM
SEE O E G
NETS SELECTED
232
B ANTAGONIZE
EELS E N N R
S H X BUDDHA
ETC EASES EOS
T T STY ABLE
SIDED A METER
RAINGAUGE
PIECE G GIDDY
LASH GEE S A
EMS MARTS SIR
ABATES U H R
S G S D ALSO
ERECHTHEUM W

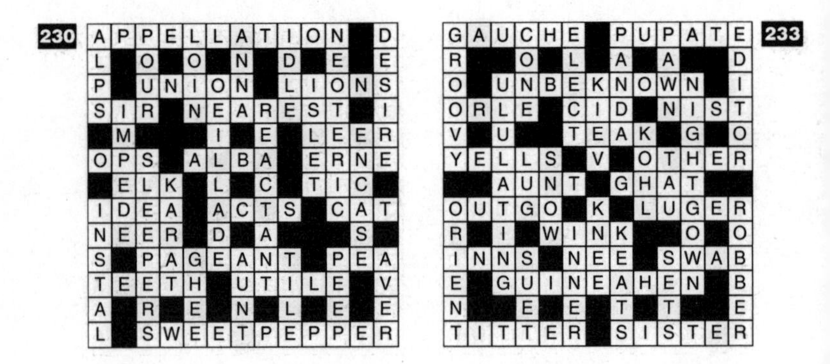
230
APPELLATION D
L O O N D E E
P UNION LIONS
SIR NEAREST I
M I E LEER
OPS ALBA ERNE
ELK L C TIC
IDEA ACTS CAT
NEER D A S
S PAGEANT PEA
TEETH UTILE V
A R E N L E E
L SWEETPEPPER
233
GAUCHE PUPATE
R O L A A D
O UNBEKNOWN I
ORLE CID NIST
V U TEAK G O
YELLS V OTHER
AUNT GHAT
OUTGO K LUGER
R I WINK O O
INNS NEE SWAB
E GUINEAHEN B
N E E T T E
TITTER SISTER

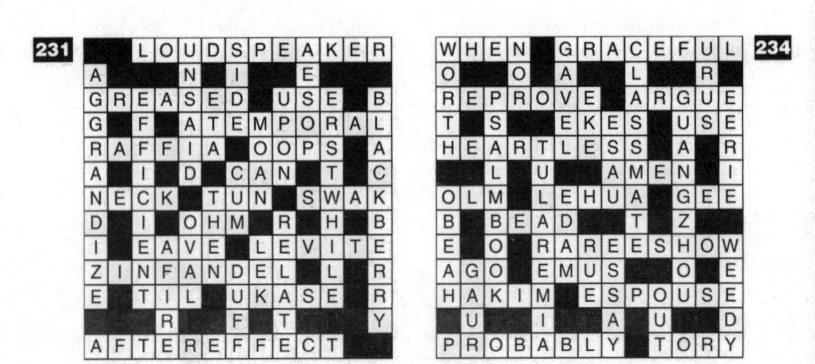
231
LOUDSPEAKER
A N I E
GREASED USE B
G F ATEMPORAL
RAFFIA OOPS A
A I D CAN T C
NECK TUN SWAK
D I OHM R H B
I EAVE LEVITE
ZINFANDEL L R
E TIL UKASE R
R F T Y
AFTEREFFECT
234
WHEN GRACEFUL
O O A L R
REPROVE ARGUE
T S EKES USE
HEARTLESS A R
L U AMEN I
OLM LEHUA GEE
B BEAD T Z
E O RAREESHOW
AGO EMUS O E
HAKIM ESPOUSE
U I A U D
PROBABLY TORY

235

F	I	G	H	T	E	R	S		D	H	O	W
	R				V		O		Y	A	G	
R	E	D	D	W	A	R	F		E	W	E	S
	N		E		D		T	U	R	K	E	Y
P	I	L	S	N	E	R		R		I		N
	C		A		D		G	A	R	N	E	T
S		O	L	D				S	A	G		H
P	I	S	T	I	L		F		V		T	
A		C		E		B	O	T	A	N	I	C
S	Q	U	A	S	H		R		G		S	
M	A	L	L		I	N	C	R	E	A	S	E
	D	A	L		C		E				U	
M	I	R	Y		K	E	D	G	E	R	E	E

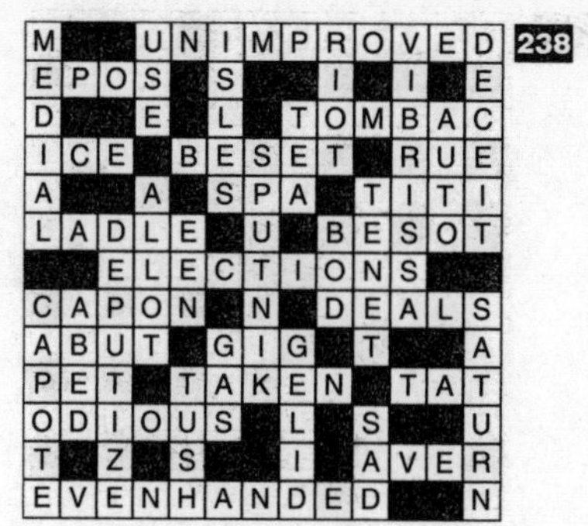

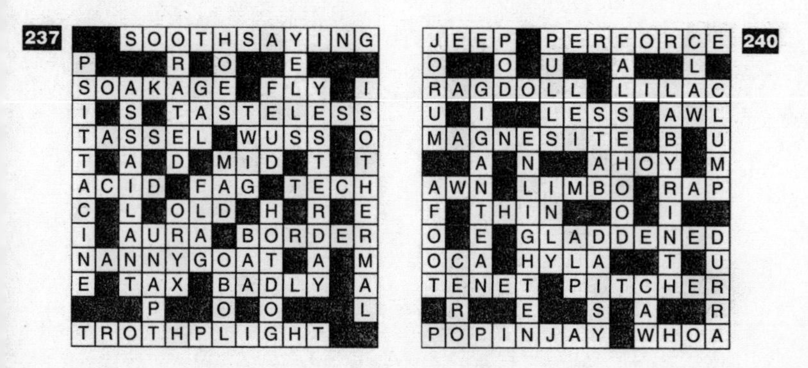

241

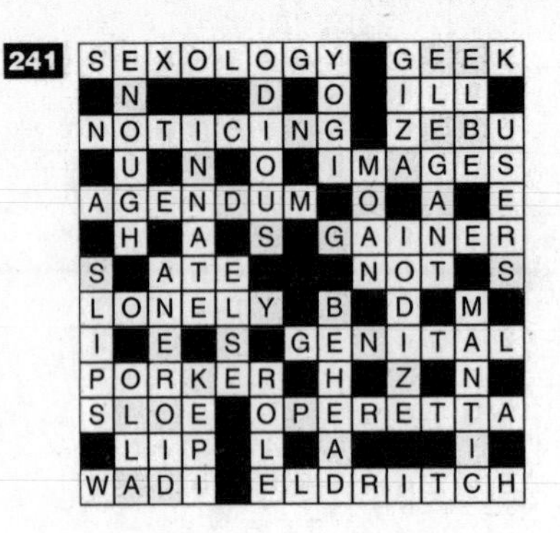

244

Z SUPERFECTA
ORLE E A O D
N E N CLOCHE
KEN ENSUE KOP
E S ACE CENT
DUMPS A DARES
ORIENTATE
TONES D BELIE
ALOE SAC R U
NIP FELON JAR
DOODLE A A O
E L A T TRAP
MAYONNAISE A

242

245

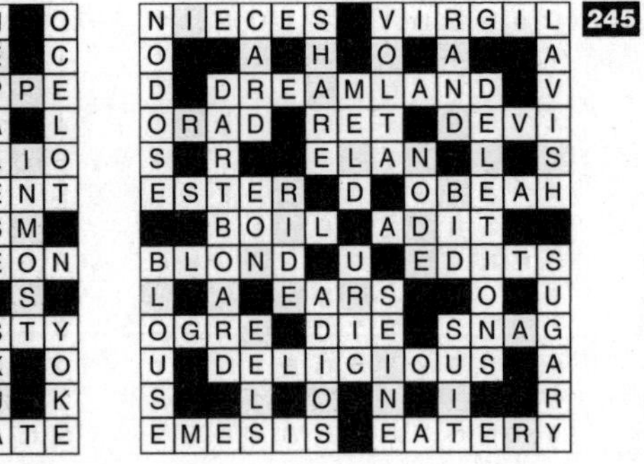

243

246

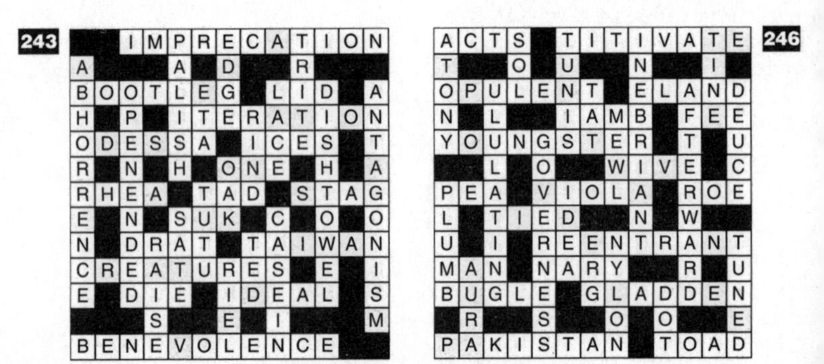

247

UPRISING SEJM
U R A HUE
FLAMBEAU IDES
P A N DIVERT
DISDAIN C M U
T C C SHROFF
A RAP TEN F
STAPES V M R
K P A CITADEL
EDIBLE R N P
DADO GRANDEUR
SLY O G G
WHYS SWOOPING

253

B	E	W	I	L	D	E	R		S	C	O	T
	M				O		A		K	O	P	
A	B	A	T	T	O	I	R		I	D	E	S
	O		U		M		E	X	T	E	N	T
O	D	Y	S	S	E	Y		I		I		A
	Y		C		D		K	A	R	N	A	K
S		B	A	A				N	A	E		E
T	E	E	N	S	Y		T		I		I	
O		A		I		S	W	E	D	I	S	H
M	I	S	H	A	P		I		E		S	
A	N	T	A		A	P	T	E	R	O	U	S
	K	I	N		I		C				E	
D	Y	E	D		R	E	H	E	A	R	S	E

256

R			U	N	C	A	R	E	D	F	O	R
O	D	D	S		A			Y		E		A
B			E		N		N	E	R	V	E	S
O	I	L		F	E	T	I	D		E	D	H
T			A		A	S	P		U	R	G	E
S	T	O	L	E		U		O	S	I	E	R
		A	I	L	A	N	T	H	U	S		
A	S	K	E	D		A		M	A	H	D	I
B	O	R	N		A	M	U		L			M
A	N	I		T	W	I	S	T		H	A	M
C	E	D	A	R	N		N		N			U
U		G		A			E		E	V	E	R
S	W	E	E	P	S	T	A	K	E			E

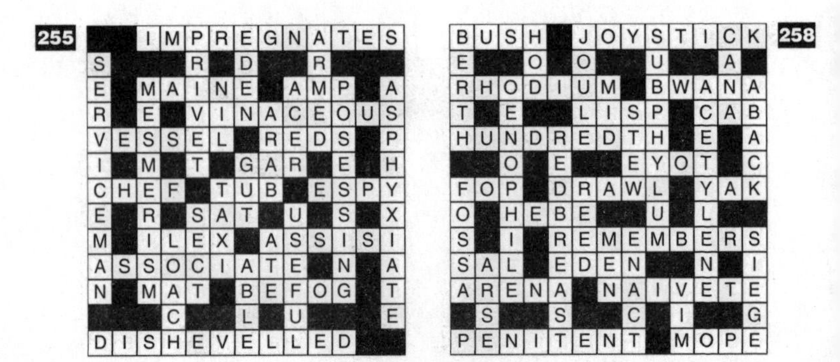

259

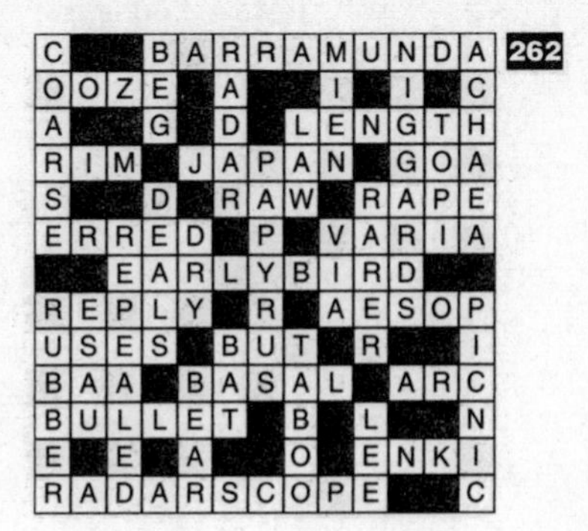

262

260

263

261

264

265

R	E	I	N	S	U	R	E		S	N	A	G
	V				P		Y		Y	E	N	
F	A	S	C	I	C	L	E		N	E	T	S
	D		E		A		D	I	C	D	I	C
C	E	L	L	I	S	T		L		F		A
	D		L		T		L	I	Q	U	O	R
A		P	A	D				A	I	L		P
B	E	I	R	U	T		B		N		U	
Y		T		N		W	A	F	T	A	G	E
S	L	E	I	G	H		N		A		A	
M	U	O	N		I	G	N	O	R	A	N	T
	T	U	N		V		E				D	
L	E	S	S		E	U	R	A	S	I	A	N

268

F			H	O	C	U	S	P	O	C	U	S
E	C	H	O		E			O		A		T
C			B		C		S	K	I	M	P	Y
U	D	O		B	U	M	P	Y		P	U	L
N			W		M	O	A		M	A	L	E
D	E	C	O	R		N		A	E	G	I	S
		O	R	A	N	G	E	M	A	N		
M	I	N	T	Y		R		P	L	A	N	T
A	R	C	H		S	E	T		S			A
R	O	E		S	O	L	U	S		W	A	S
A	N	I	M	A	L		T		S			M
C		V		I			T		A	B	B	A
A	N	E	C	D	O	T	I	S	T			N

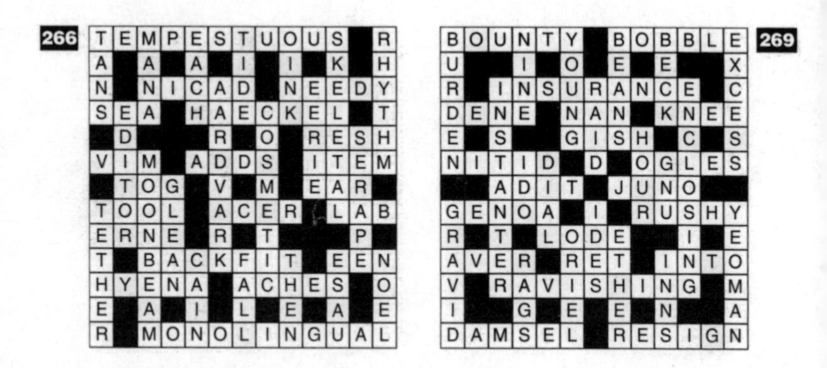

266

T	E	M	P	E	S	T	U	O	U	S		R
A		A		A		I		I		K		H
N		N	I	C	A	D		N	E	E	D	Y
S	E	A		H	A	E	C	K	E	L		T
	D				R		O		R	E	S	H
V	I	M		A	D	D	S		I	T	E	M
	T	O	G		V		M		E	A	R	
T	O	O	L		A	C	E	R		L	A	B
E	R	N	E		R		T				P	
T		B	A	C	K	F	I	T		E	E	N
H	Y	E	N	A		A	C	H	E	S		O
E		A		I		L		E		A		E
R		M	O	N	O	L	I	N	G	U	A	L

269

B	O	U	N	T	Y		B	O	B	B	L	E
U			I		O		E		E			X
R		I	N	S	U	R	A	N	C	E		C
D	E	N	E		N	A	N		K	N	E	E
E		S			G	I	S	H		C		S
N	I	T	I	D		D		O	G	L	E	S
		A	D	I	T		J	U	N	O		
G	E	N	O	A		I		R	U	S	H	Y
R		T		L	O	D	E			I		E
A	V	E	R		R	E	T		I	N	T	O
V		R	A	V	I	S	H	I	N	G		M
I			G		E		E		N			A
D	A	M	S	E	L		R	E	S	I	G	N

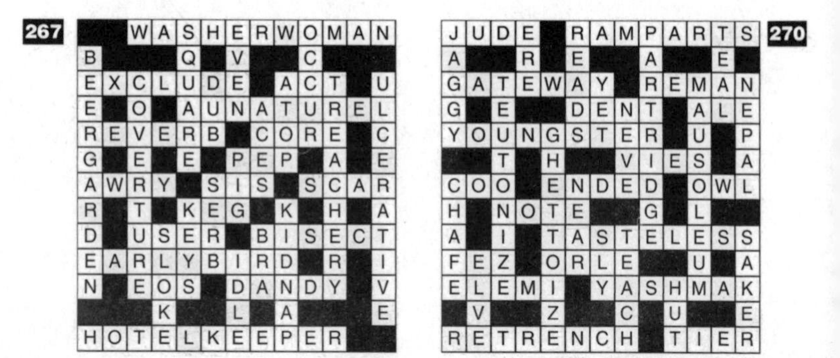

267

		W	A	S	H	E	R	W	O	M	A	N
B				Q		V			C			
E	X	C	L	U	D	E		A	C	T		U
E		O		A	U	N	A	T	U	R	E	L
R	E	V	E	R	B		C	O	R	E		C
G		E		E		P	E	P		A		E
A	W	R	Y		S	I	S		S	C	A	R
R		T		K	E	G		K		H		A
D		U	S	E	R		B	I	S	E	C	T
E	A	R	L	Y	B	I	R	D		R		I
N		E	O	S		D	A	N	D	Y		V
			K			L		A				E
H	O	T	E	L	K	E	E	P	E	R		

270

J	U	D	E		R	A	M	P	A	R	T	S
A			R		E			A			E	
G	A	T	E	W	A	Y		R	E	M	A	N
G		E			D	E	N	T		A	L	E
Y	O	U	N	G	S	T	E	R		U		P
		T		H			V	I	E	S		A
C	O	O		E	N	D	E	D		O	W	L
H		N	O	T	E			G		L		
A		I		T	A	S	T	E	L	E	S	S
F	E	Z		O	R	L	E			U		A
E	L	E	M	I		Y	A	S	H	M	A	K
	V			Z			C		U			E
R	E	T	R	E	N	C	H		T	I	E	R

271

C	O	A	N	C	H	O	R		C	I	N	E
	S				E		E		O	N	E	
A	M	B	U	L	A	N	T		O	N	T	O
	I		N		V		E	R	S	A	T	Z
S	U	B	D	U	E	D		O		R		O
	M		O		D		S	U	D	D	E	N
O		A	C	T				E	O	S		E
B	A	C	K	E	D		N		U		A	
E		C		W		Q	U	I	B	B	L	E
S	T	R	E	S	S		T		T		L	
E	W	E	R		W	A	R	D	S	H	I	P
	E	T	A		O		I				E	
F	E	E	S		T	E	A	C	A	D	D	Y

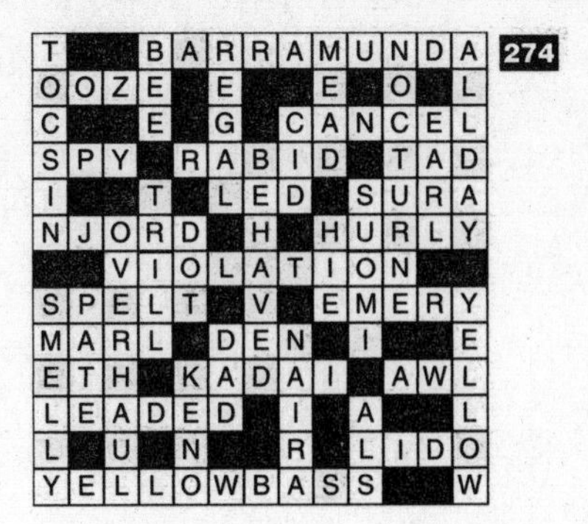

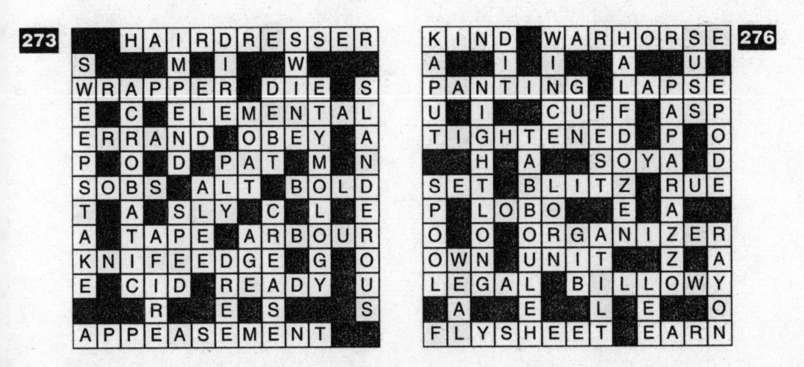

277

E	S	T	R	A	N	G	E		S	C	A	N
	P				O		V		L	A	C	
C	U	B	A	T	U	R	E		U	L	N	A
	N		T		G		N	E	R	V	E	S
S	K	E	T	C	H	Y		P		A		H
	Y		I		T		H	O	A	R	S	E
C		A	L	E				S	H	Y		S
R	E	L	A	T	E		U		O		M	
A		L		E		E	N	T	R	E	A	T
C	L	O	C	H	E		I		S		L	
K	I	W	I		W	E	S	T	E	R	L	Y
	N	E	T		E		O				E	
C	E	D	E		R	E	N	D	E	R	E	D

280

S			I	N	E	Q	U	A	L	I	T	Y
I	C	O	N		M			C		S		I
C			N		B		I	M	P	O	N	E
K	E	Y		C	A	D	R	E		M	E	L
L			C		Y	E	A		P	E	N	D
E	L	B	O	W		R		S	I	T	E	S
		R	A	I	N	M	A	K	E	R		
E	J	E	C	T		O		A	R	Y	A	N
L	O	T	H		O	I	L		S			E
A	S	H		U	D	D	E	R		B	Y	E
P	H	R	A	S	E		N		A			D
I		E		E			T		I	D	O	L
D	E	N	D	R	I	F	O	R	M			E

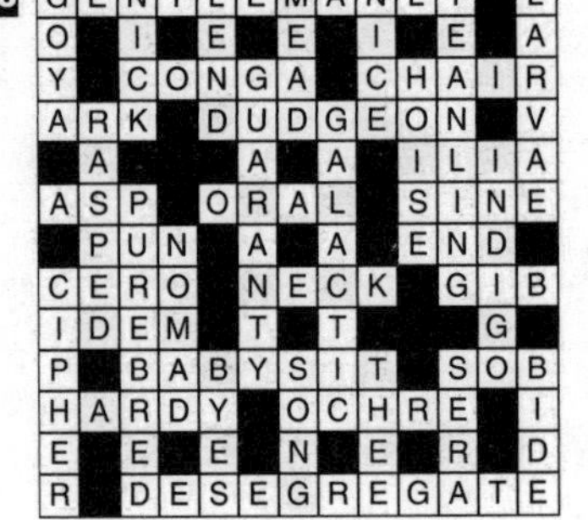

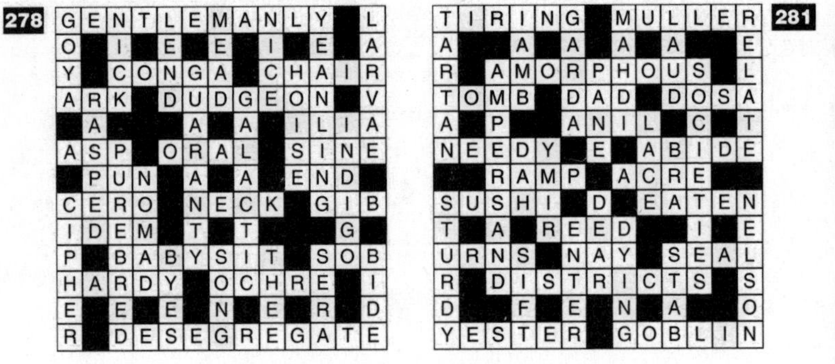

278

G	E	N	T	L	E	M	A	N	L	Y		L
O		I		E		E		I		E		A
Y		C	O	N	G	A		C	H	A	I	R
A	R	K		D	U	D	G	E	O	N		V
	A				A		A		I	L	I	A
A	S	P		O	R	A	L		S	I	N	E
	P	U	N		A		A		E	N	D	
C	E	R	O		N	E	C	K		G	I	B
I	D	E	M		T		T				G	
P		B	A	B	Y	S	I	T		S	O	B
H	A	R	D	Y		O	C	H	R	E		I
E		E		E		N		E		R		D
R		D	E	S	E	G	R	E	G	A	T	E

281

T	I	R	I	N	G		M	U	L	L	E	R
A			A		A		A		A			E
R		A	M	O	R	P	H	O	U	S		L
T	O	M	B		D	A	D		D	O	S	A
A		P			A	N	I	L		C		T
N	E	E	D	Y		E		A	B	I	D	E
		R	A	M	P		A	C	R	E		
S	U	S	H	I		D		E	A	T	E	N
T		A		R	E	E	D			I		E
U	R	N	S		N	A	Y		S	E	A	L
R		D	I	S	T	R	I	C	T	S		S
D			F		E		N		A			O
Y	E	S	T	E	R		G	O	B	L	I	N

279

		A	N	D	R	O	G	E	N	O	U	S
L				E		A			O			
I	N	H	A	B	I	T		F	B	I		D
N		A		U	N	H	E	A	L	T	H	Y
S	H	R	I	N	K		G	L	E	E		S
E		B		K		P	A	L		R		A
E	X	I	T		Z	E	D		F	A	I	R
D		N		P	O	W		T		T		T
O		G	E	A	R		O	A	F	I	S	H
I	N	E	B	R	I	A	N	T		O		R
L		R	O	E		L	E	A	R	N		I
			N			K		M				A
K	A	R	Y	O	T	Y	P	I	N	G		

282

S	E	E	R		S	U	C	C	I	N	C	T
U			Y		T			O			O	
N	I	N	E	V	E	H		V	E	S	T	A
N		U			E	A	S	E		T	E	D
Y	O	M	K	I	P	P	U	R		E		A
		E		M			E	T	N	A		P
B	A	R		P	E	R	D	U		M	E	T
I		A	L	A	S			R		S		
N		B		C	A	C	O	E	T	H	E	S
G	A	L		T	U	R	F			I		M
E	L	E	M	I		U	T	S	U	P	R	A
	S			O			E		G			C
R	O	M	A	N	I	A	N		H	A	I	K

283

D	Y	N	A	M	I	C	S		D	I	P	S
	E				R		I		E	R	A	
M	O	U	R	N	I	N	G		A	I	R	E
	M		H		D		H	O	L	D	E	R
B	A	B	Y	S	I	T		U		I		G
	N		T		C		E	S	C	U	D	O
A		O	H	M				T	O	M		T
F	A	R	M	E	R		D		M		B	
O		A		O		T	E	L	A	M	O	N
O	T	T	A	W	A		L		T		D	
T	R	O	Y		U	K	U	L	E	L	E	S
	I	R	E		T		D				G	
T	O	Y	S		O	V	E	R	B	E	A	R

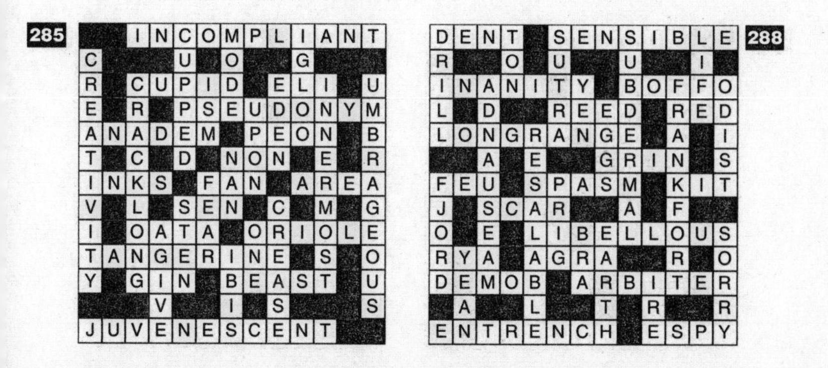

289

L	U	S	T	R	O	U	S		D	U	S	K
	P				X		E		U	G	H	
B	L	I	S	S	F	U	L		C	L	O	G
	A		P		O		L	O	T	I	O	N
O	N	S	H	O	R	E		T		E		A
	D		E		D		R	I	P	S	A	W
S		O	R	B				C	A	T		S
C	O	L	E	U	S		B		V		T	
U		D		N		B	E	T	A	R	A	Y
B	E	S	E	T	S		L		N		R	
A	C	H	Y		U	N	F	R	E	E	Z	E
	H	O	E		R		R				A	
C	O	E	D		A	N	Y	T	H	I	N	G

292

P			E	S	P	E	C	I	A	L	L	Y
A	R	I	D		A			R		I		E
R			H		T		D	O	U	B	T	S
U	R	N		A	S	H	E	N		A	I	M
R			U		Y	A	W		E	T	N	A
E	X	I	S	T		Y		A	L	I	E	N
		T	A	E	K	W	O	N	D	O		
S	T	A	G	E		I		T	E	N	E	T
H	A	L	E		O	R	E		R			H
E	L	I		S	U	E	D	E		Q	U	A
E	L	A	P	I	D		U		A			M
N		N		D			C		I	D	L	E
Y	E	S	T	E	R	Y	E	A	R			S

290

S	E	R	V	I	C	E	A	B	L	E		S
P		O		C		D		L		X		N
E		D	R	E	A	D		A	N	O	D	E
D	E	E		D	E	O	R	B	I	T		E
	N				R		I		V	E	E	R
A	R	D		M	O	B	S		A	R	M	S
	O	R	E		B		S		L	I	P	
C	O	A	X		I	R	O	N		C	E	P
E	T	U	I		C		L				R	
D		G	L	I	S	T	E	N		B	Y	E
A	S	H	E	N		O	S	I	E	R		A
R		T		T		R		G		A		S
N		S	H	O	R	T	C	H	A	N	G	E

293

S	I	M	I	L	E		A	W	A	K	E	N
T			T		B		R		L			A
A		R	E	D	B	R	E	A	S	T		U
T	E	A	M		E	O	N		O	O	P	S
U		P			D	I	A	L		R		E
E	N	T	E	R		L		O	M	E	G	A
		U	R	A	L		A	R	E	A		
H	A	R	E	M		P		E	N	D	E	D
E		O		P	L	A	Y			O		O
R	O	U	E		I	R	E		B	R	A	D
D		S	A	L	E	R	A	T	U	S		D
E			S		G		R		S			E
R	E	V	E	R	E		N	E	T	H	E	R

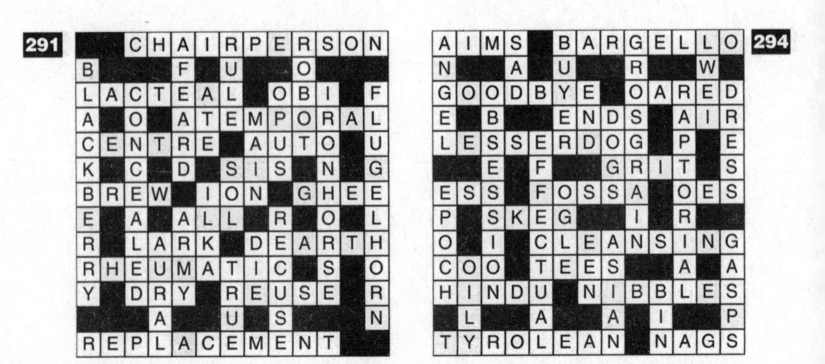

291

		C	H	A	I	R	P	E	R	S	O	N
B				F		U		O				
L	A	C	T	E	A	L		O	B	I		F
A		O		A	T	E	M	P	O	R	A	L
C	E	N	T	R	E		A	U	T	O		U
K		C		D		S	I	S		N		G
B	R	E	W		I	O	N		G	H	E	E
E		A		A	L	L		R		O		L
R		L	A	R	K		D	E	A	R	T	H
R	H	E	U	M	A	T	I	C		S		O
Y		D	R	Y		R	E	U	S	E		R
			A			U		S				N
R	E	P	L	A	C	E	M	E	N	T		

294

A	I	M	S		B	A	R	G	E	L	L	O
N			A		U			R			W	
G	O	O	D	B	Y	E		O	A	R	E	D
E		B			E	N	D	S		A	I	R
L	E	S	S	E	R	D	O	G		P		E
		E		F			G	R	I	T		S
E	S	S		F	O	S	S	A		O	E	S
P		S	K	E	G			I		R		
O		I		C	L	E	A	N	S	I	N	G
C	O	O		T	E	E	S			A		A
H	I	N	D	U		N	I	B	B	L	E	S
	L			A				A		I		P
T	Y	R	O	L	E	A	N		N	A	G	S

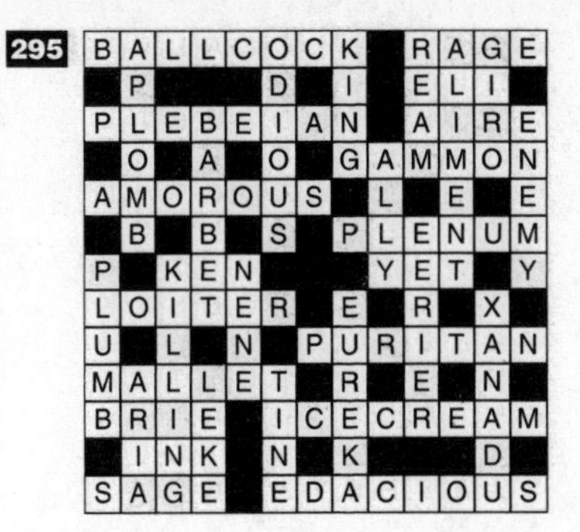
295
BALLCOCK RAGE
P D I ELI
PLEBEIAN AIRE
O A O GAMMON
AMOROUS L E E
B B S PLENUM
P KEN YET Y
LOITER E R X
U L N PURITAN
MALLET R E N
BRIE ICECREAM
INK N K D
SAGE EDACIOUS

298
F PENMANSHIP
LOPE A E I A
O G I NEIGHS
WAR DREAD HUT
E I AIM LWEI
RIANT D CEASE
NEUROLOGY
SWORN L BASIL
WART SOP L I
EKE FINER BUS
DEXTER T A B
E I R T INRO
NUCLEONICS N

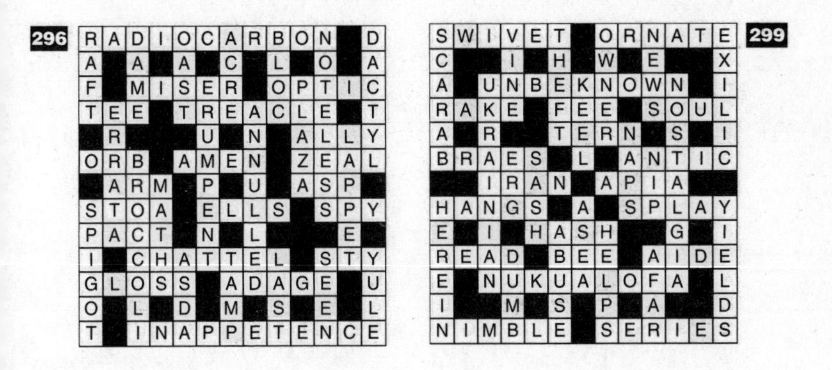
296
RADIOCARBON D
A A A C L O A
F MISER OPTIC
TEE TREACLE T
R U N ALLY
ORB AMEN ZEAL
ARM P U ASP
STOA ELLS SPY
PACT N L E
I CHATTEL STY
GLOSS ADAGE U
O L D M S E L
T INAPPETENCE
299
SWIVET ORNATE
C I H W E X
A UNBEKNOWN I
RAKE FEE SOUL
A R TERN S I
BRAES L ANTIC
IRAN APIA
HANGS A SPLAY
E I HASH G I
READ BEE AIDE
E NUKUALOFA L
I M S P A D
NIMBLE SERIES

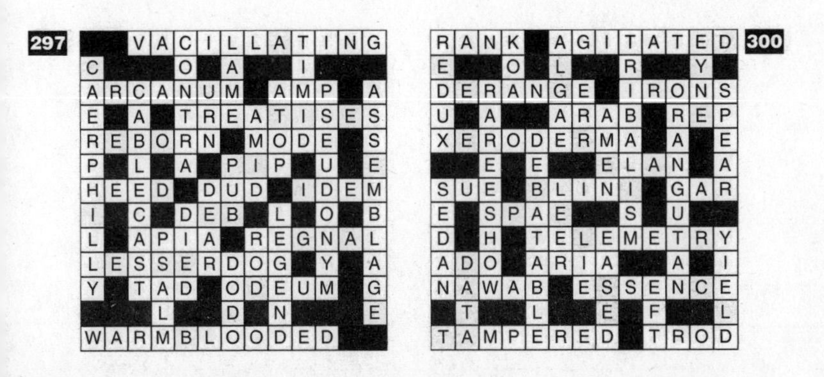
297
VACILLATING
C O A I
ARCANUM AMP A
E A TREATISES
REBORN MODE S
P L A PIP U E
HEED DUD IDEM
I C DEB L O B
L APIA REGNAL
LESSERDOG Y A
Y TAD ODEUM G
L D N E
WARMBLOODED
300
RANK AGITATED
E O L R Y
DERANGE IRONS
U A ARAB REP
XERODERMA A E
E E ELAN A
SUE BLINI GAR
E SPAE S U
D H TELEMETRY
ADO ARIA A I
NAWAB ESSENCE
T L E F L
TAMPERED TROD

301

B	U	R	G	L	A	R	Y		B	E	R	M
	P				C		A		E	R	A	
A	S	T	E	R	I	S	K		N	O	T	E
	H		X		D		S	O	D	D	E	N
S	O	L	I	C	I	T		N		I		D
	T		L		C		N	U	A	N	C	E
A		J	E	T				S	O	G		D
F	O	O	D	I	E		F		U		S	
I		I		L		D	E	A	D	E	N	D
R	A	N	T	E	D		N		A		I	
E	P	E	E		R	I	N	G	D	O	V	E
	I	R	E		A		E				E	
L	A	Y	S		G	U	L	L	I	B	L	E

304

A			W	E	L	L	F	O	R	M	E	D
D	O	Z	E		O			M		I		E
J			D		O		R	E	G	N	A	L
U	S	E		A	S	H	E	N		A	X	E
S			A		E	A	T		G	R	I	T
T	R	I	C	E		L		G	E	E	S	E
		N	U	T	R	I	M	E	N	T		
W	I	D	T	H		D		E	O	S	I	N
E	R	I	E		D	O	P		A			I
D	O	C		F	A	M	E	D		T	I	C
G	N	A	R	L	Y		N		H			K
E		T		A			N		I	D	L	E
S	W	E	E	P	S	T	A	K	E			

302

F	R	A	C	T	I	O	N	A	T	E		C
L		T		I		G		X		N		A
A		O	C	C	U	R		E	N	T	E	R
T	A	M		K	N	E	E	L	E	R		V
	R				I		Q		R	A	G	E
E	R	N		E	C	R	U		V	I	E	S
	E	A	R		Y		A		E	L	L	
P	A	G	E		C	U	L	L		S	A	P
A	R	A	B		L		I				D	
R		S	E	L	E	C	T	S		W	A	G
A	B	A	C	A		H	Y	E	N	A		L
D		K		S		E		A		I		U
E		I	N	H	E	R	I	T	A	N	C	E

305

C	A	J	O	L	E		C	O	N	O	I	D
R			M		R		H		E			Y
A		B	I	C	A	M	E	R	A	L		A
T	W	I	T		S	E	E		P	I	E	D
E		A			E	A	R	L		N		I
R	O	T	O	R		D		I	L	E	A	C
		H	U	E	S		P	L	E	A		
H	O	L	D	S		E		T	U	T	O	R
O		E		H	I	C	K			I		O
D	O	T	S		O	H	O		H	O	B	O
M		E	A	L	D	O	R	M	A	N		T
A			L		I		A		I			E
N	O	E	T	I	C		N	U	L	L	E	D

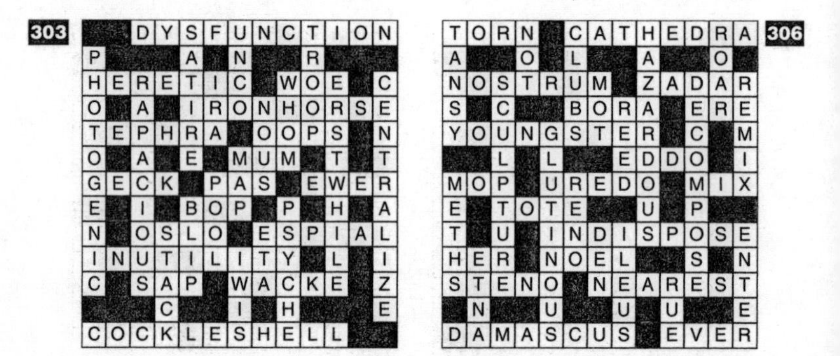

303

		D	Y	S	F	U	N	C	T	I	O	N
P				A		N			R			
H	E	R	E	T	I	C		W	O	E		C
O		A		I	R	O	N	H	O	R	S	E
T	E	P	H	R	A		O	O	P	S		N
O		A		E		M	U	M		T		T
G	E	C	K		P	A	S		E	W	E	R
E		I		B	O	P		P		H		A
N		O	S	L	O		E	S	P	I	A	L
I	N	U	T	I	L	I	T	Y		L		I
C		S	A	P		W	A	C	K	E		Z
			C			I		H				E
C	O	C	K	L	E	S	H	E	L	L		

306

T	O	R	N		C	A	T	H	E	D	R	A
A			O		L			A			O	
N	O	S	T	R	U	M		Z	A	D	A	R
S		C			B	O	R	A		E	R	E
Y	O	U	N	G	S	T	E	R		C		M
		L		L			E	D	D	O		I
M	O	P		U	R	E	D	O		M	I	X
E		T	O	T	E			U		P		
T		U		I	N	D	I	S	P	O	S	E
H	E	R		N	O	E	L			S		N
S	T	E	N	O		N	E	A	R	E	S	T
	N			U			U		U			E
D	A	M	A	S	C	U	S		E	V	E	R

307

C	O	M	A	T	O	S	E	■	W	H	E	N
■	V	■	■	■	H	■	A	■	O	A	R	■
D	U	L	C	I	M	E	R	■	A	N	N	A
■	L	■	I	■	A	■	N	O	D	D	E	D
V	E	R	T	I	G	O	■	B	■	B	■	O
■	S	■	I	■	E	■	D	E	C	A	M	P
S	■	R	E	D	■	■	■	Y	A	G	■	T
C	R	E	D	I	T	■	F	■	N	■	R	■
A	■	M	■	C	■	B	U	B	O	N	I	C
R	E	N	D	E	R	■	T	■	P	■	A	■
F	R	A	Y	■	U	N	I	C	Y	C	L	E
■	I	N	K	■	N	■	L	■	■	■	T	■
M	E	T	E	■	E	R	E	C	T	I	O	N

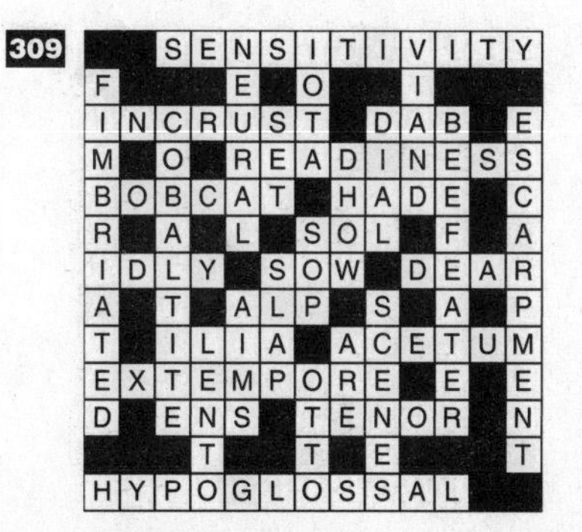

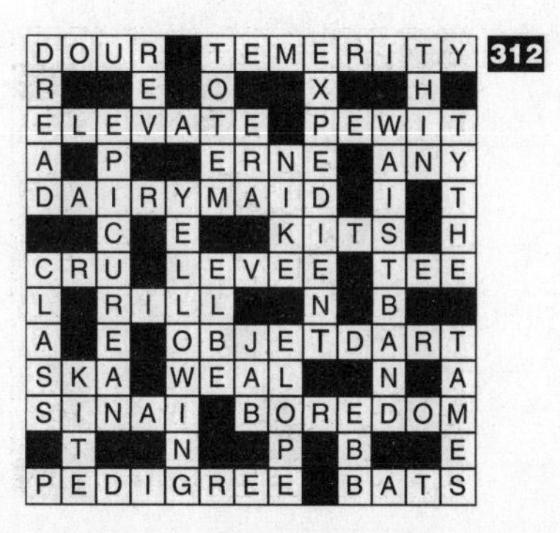

313

T	R	A	N	S	E	C	T		L	I	K	E
	E				L		A		O	N	E	
V	A	C	A	T	I	O	N		U	S	E	S
	D		N		C		S	U	R	E	T	Y
S	E	I	S	M	I	C		R		C		L
	R		A		T		P	E	N	T	U	P
D		E	T	A				A	I	S		H
E	N	S	E	R	F		T		C		J	
B		T		E		J	A	V	E	L	I	N
I	N	R	O	A	D		G		N		T	
T	I	E	D		E	L	E	M	E	N	T	S
	D	A	D		F		N				E	
G	E	T	S		T	I	D	E	M	A	R	K

316

B			A	R	T	H	R	A	L	G	I	A
O	R	A	L		R			G		A		S
N			B		I		P	E	A	N	U	T
N	U	N		L	A	D	L	E		G	N	U
E			C		L	E	Y		F	L	I	T
T	U	N	I	C		T		S	L	A	T	E
		A	D	O	R	A	T	I	O	N		
W	A	G	E	S		I		R	A	D	A	R
A	L	A	R		E	L	M		T			A
S	O	S		L	O	S	E	L		C	H	I
H	E	A	D	O	N		T		D			D
U		K		G			R		U	R	G	E
P	R	I	E	S	T	H	O	O	D			R

314 **317**

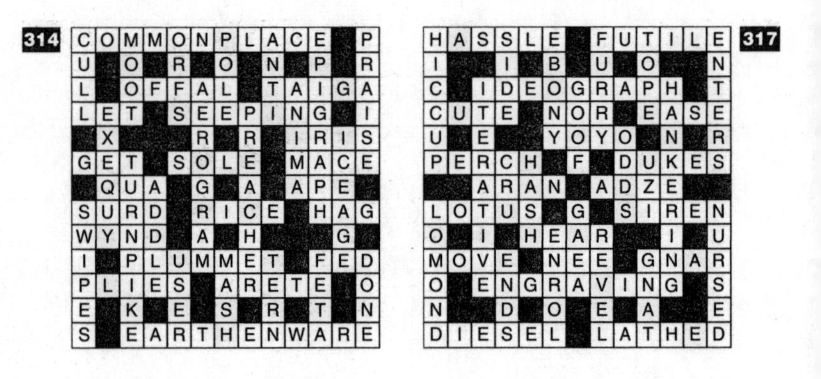

315 **318**

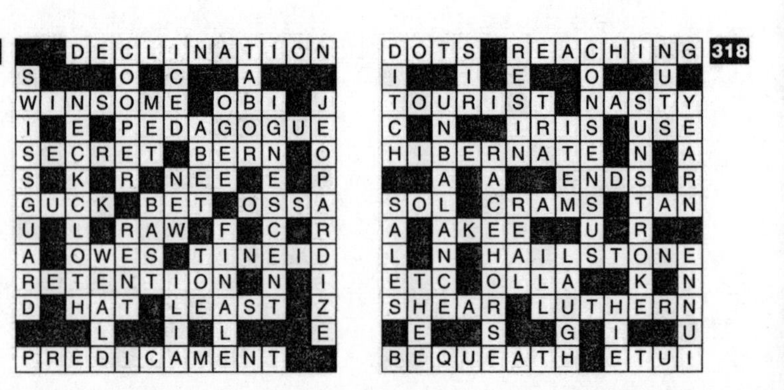

319

UNTANGLE■ABBE
■O■■■R■X■MOA■
SUKIYAKI■ILKA
■G■L■B■TEDIUM
EARLOBE■D■V■O
■T■U■Y■XANADU
U■IMP■■■MAR■R
SCREAK■N■T■B■
U■I■G■HABITAT
REDEEM■U■O■R■
PAIR■ENGENDER
■RUG■T■H■■■G■
ALMS■EXTENDED

322

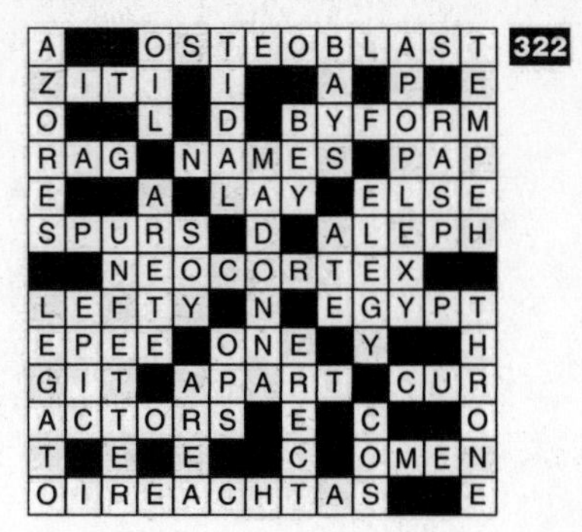

320

323

321

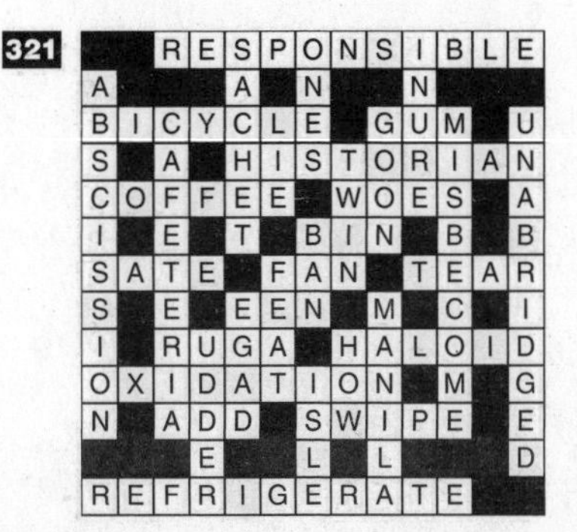

324

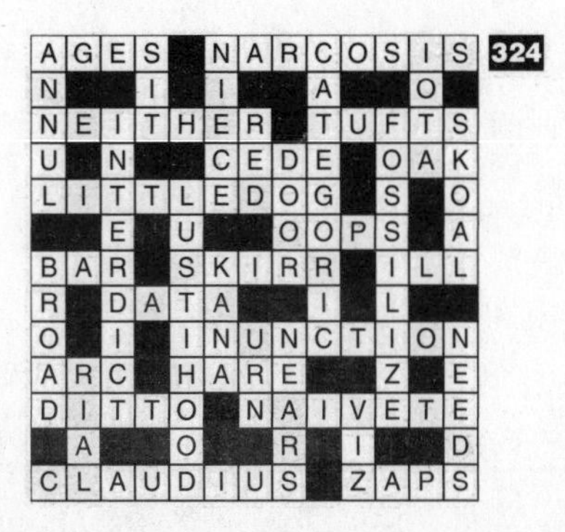

325

S	T	R	A	N	G	E	R		O	G	R	E
	E				L		I		V	I	A	
F	A	T	A	L	I	S	M		E	R	N	S
	M		C		D		E	N	R	A	G	E
D	E	S	I	R	E	D		O		F		A
	D		D		R		B	U	F	F	E	T
H		C	I	D				N	E	E		S
A	P	I	C	A	L		I		I		H	
T		T		U		S	M	A	S	H	E	D
C	R	A	B	B	Y		B		T		R	
H	I	D	E		E	D	I	F	Y	I	N	G
	P	E	T		A		B				I	
W	E	L	S		R	H	E	O	S	T	A	T

328

S			C	R	I	T	I	C	I	Z	E	D
Y	I	P	E		D			H		A		E
S			E		E		V	E	S	I	C	A
T	U	X		L	A	S	E	R		B	A	D
E			D		L	U	X		M	A	R	L
M	A	G	I	C		B		K	I	T	T	Y
		A	C	O	U	S	T	I	C	S		
R	O	M	E	O		U		D	R	U	I	D
A	V	E	R		E	M	S		O			U
B	U	S		E	R	E	C	T		H	E	R
A	M	O	E	B	A		A		P			B
T		M		B			L		A	Q	U	A
O	V	E	R	S	H	A	D	O	W			N

326

W	E	A	T	H	E	R	W	O	R	N		J
A		C		I		U		P		A		A
V		I	N	G	L	E		E	N	R	O	L
E	N	D		H	E	D	O	N	I	C		O
	I				G		P		G	O	O	P
A	C	T		R	A	F	T		E	S	P	Y
	E	W	E		L		I		L	I	P	
S	T	O	A		E	M	M	Y		S	O	B
A	Y	E	S		S		I				S	
F		D	E	C	E	A	S	E		F	E	W
A	N	G	L	E		E	M	A	I	L		I
R		E		R		R		S		E		D
I		D	E	O	X	Y	G	E	N	A	T	E

329

M	A	G	P	I	E		C	E	M	E	N	T
O			E		B		O		O			E
I		D	E	C	O	C	T	I	O	N		N
E	V	I	L		N	U	T		D	U	M	A
T		S			Y	E	A	H		M		N
Y	I	E	L	D		D		E	L	E	C	T
		N	E	A	P		S	C	A	R		
L	A	G	E	R		K		K	H	A	K	I
I		A		T	A	N	G			B		C
N	I	G	H		P	E	A		A	L	O	E
N		E	U	P	H	E	M	I	Z	E		A
E			M		I		A		A			G
T	R	E	P	I	D		Y	A	N	K	E	E

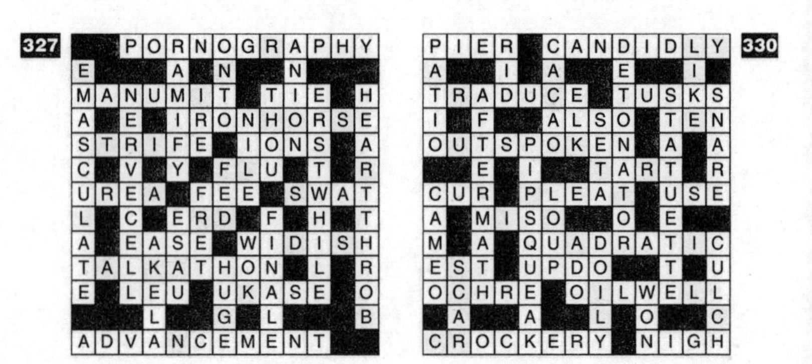

331

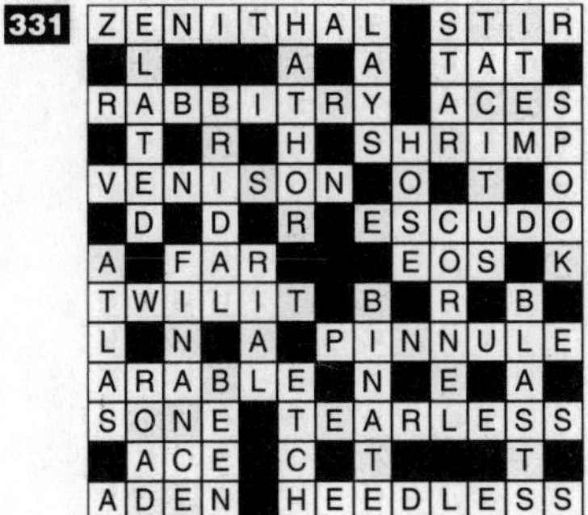

334

332

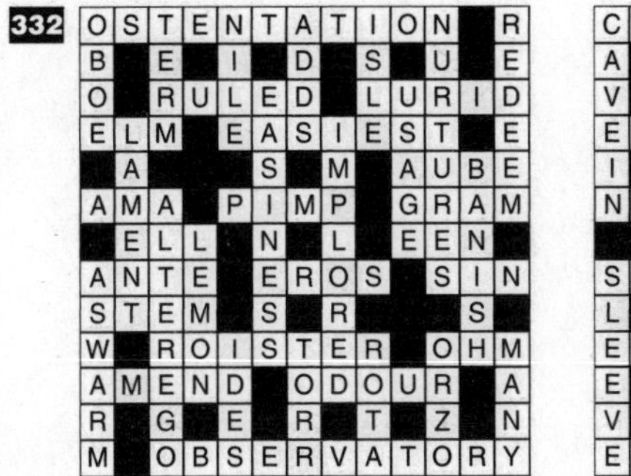

335

333

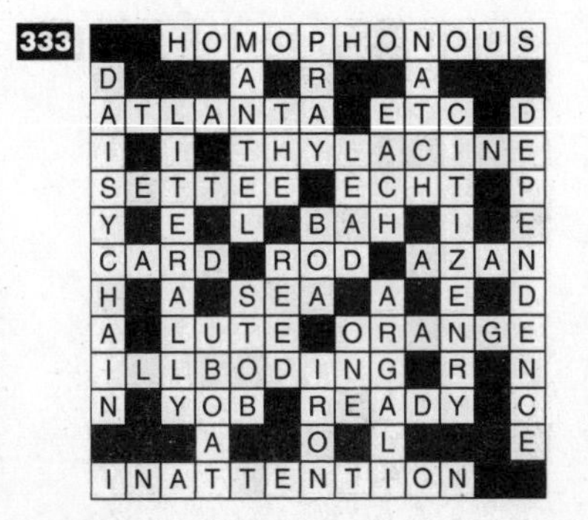

336

337

A	M	E	N	D	I	N	G		L	E	V	I
	A				T		O		I	C	E	
M	E	S	S	H	A	L	L		F	O	I	N
	N		P		L		D	U	E	N	N	A
J	A	C	O	B	I	N		P		O		N
	D		I		C		C	O	S	M	I	C
U		I	L	L				N	A	Y		E
R	I	N	S	E	D		E		U		U	
E		C		L		E	L	E	G	I	S	T
D	O	L	L	A	R		A		E		A	
O	B	I	E		U	N	T	I	R	I	N	G
	O	N	E		N		E				C	
J	E	E	R		E	N	D	A	N	G	E	R

340

H			S	T	E	R	E	O	P	S	I	S
A	Q	U	A		R			O		E		P
T			D		I		S	P	A	R	G	E
T	H	E		I	C	T	U	S		P	I	N
E			K		A	R	E		B	E	N	D
R	U	S	H	Y		O		M	O	N	K	S
		E	M	O	L	U	M	E	N	T		
F	A	M	E	D		P		T	U	S	K	S
E	V	E	R		K	E	N		S			K
C	O	S		S	E	R	A	C		U	Z	I
U	N	T	O	L	D		O		G			D
N		E		O			M		I	C	E	D
D	A	R	J	E	E	L	I	N	G			Y

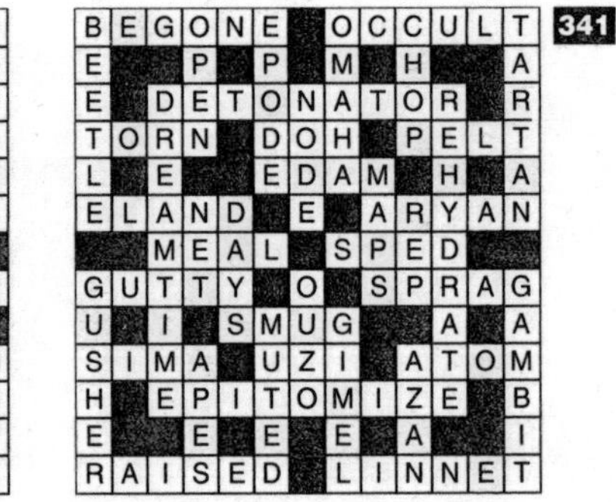

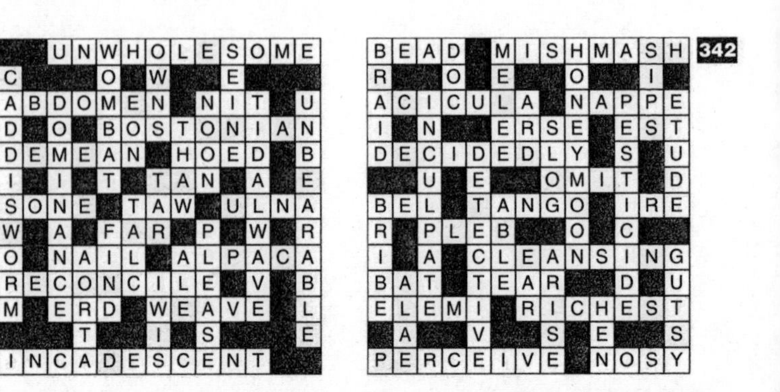

343

P	A	R	A	G	U	A	Y		D	I	M	E
	R				S		O		A	D	O	
F	R	O	I	D	E	U	R		S	I	L	O
	A		M		F		E	C	H	O	E	D
E	N	V	I	O	U	S		H		T		I
	T		D		L		J	A	B	I	R	U
A		D	I	N				R	O	C		M
B	R	A	C	E	D		F		I		V	
A		Y		S		P	U	R	L	I	E	U
S	P	L	A	S	H		D		E		S	
E	R	O	S		U	N	D	E	R	B	I	D
	I	N	K		T		L				C	
E	G	G	S		S	K	E	L	E	T	A	L

346

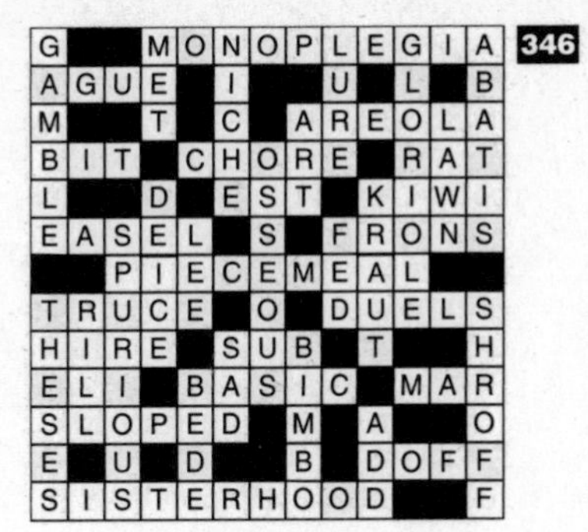

344 **347**

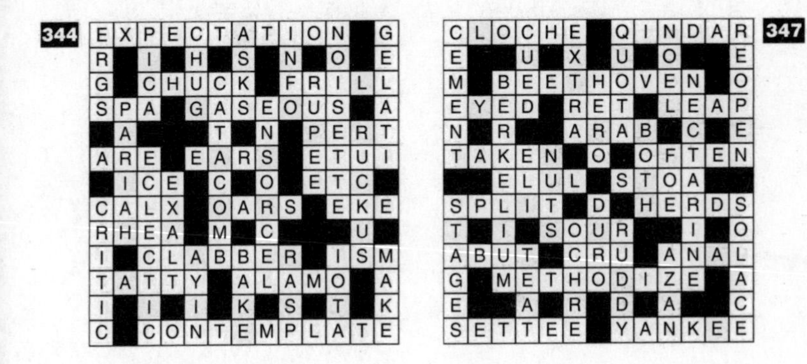

345

348

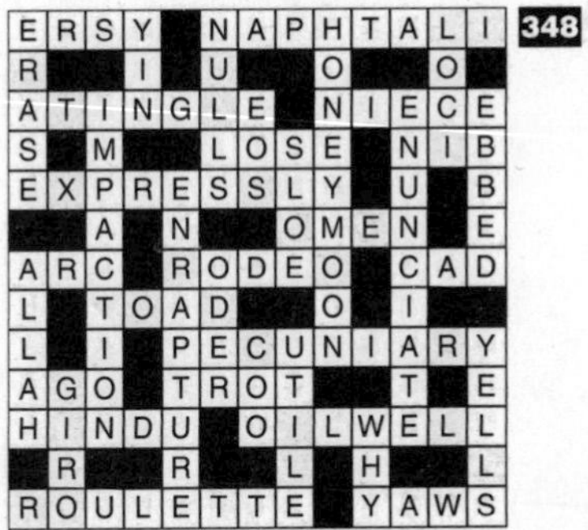

349

A	L	T	E	R	I	N	G	■	G	U	F	F
■	E	■	■	■	M	■	L	■	A	N	E	■
U	N	C	O	U	P	L	E	■	F	L	E	A
■	I	■	U	■	U	■	E	N	F	O	L	D
S	T	A	T	U	R	E	■	E	■	V	■	L
■	Y	■	I	■	E	■	Y	E	M	E	N	I
O	■	A	N	D	■	■	■	D	I	D	■	B
F	I	D	G	E	T	■	G	■	F	■	T	■
F	■	J	■	E	■	A	R	A	F	U	R	A
A	B	O	A	R	D	■	E	■	E	■	E	■
L	O	U	D	■	U	N	E	N	D	I	N	G
■	A	R	D	■	L	■	D	■	■	■	D	■
U	R	N	S	■	L	O	Y	A	L	I	S	T

352

Y	■	■	O	P	H	T	H	A	L	M	I	C
A	L	A	R	■	A	■	■	S	■	A	■	O
N	■	■	B	■	D	■	S	P	E	C	K	S
K	I	T	■	T	E	S	T	S	■	A	N	T
E	■	■	W	■	S	O	Y	■	O	R	A	L
E	R	R	O	R	■	N	■	I	V	O	R	Y
■	■	O	R	A	N	G	E	M	A	N	■	■
A	N	T	S	Y	■	F	■	P	R	I	N	K
M	O	A	T	■	P	U	B	■	Y	■	■	E
O	U	T	■	Y	E	L	L	S	■	T	O	Y
E	N	I	G	M	A	■	I	■	R	■	■	P
B	■	V	■	I	■	■	N	■	U	L	N	A
A	B	E	R	R	A	T	I	O	N	■	■	D

350

B	I	M	O	L	E	C	U	L	A	R	■	E
E	■	O	■	I	■	A	■	O	■	I	■	G
E	■	A	C	R	E	S	■	C	A	C	A	O
P	E	T	■	A	C	E	H	I	G	H	■	I
■	N	■	■	■	L	■	E	■	I	M	P	S
V	I	Z	■	M	E	A	L	■	L	O	O	M
■	G	A	S	■	C	■	S	■	E	N	S	■
O	M	I	T	■	T	H	I	S	■	D	A	B
B	A	B	A	■	I	■	N	■	■	■	D	■
E	■	A	S	H	C	A	K	E	■	C	A	B
L	I	T	H	E	■	N	I	C	E	R	■	I
I	■	S	■	L	■	A	■	H	■	A	■	T
A	■	U	N	P	A	L	A	T	A	B	L	E

353

J	A	E	G	E	R	■	C	L	O	S	E	R
U	■	■	R	■	I	■	O	■	I	■	■	E
N	■	T	A	N	G	E	R	I	N	E	■	H
I	T	E	M	■	I	M	P	■	K	A	L	E
O	■	R	■	■	D	U	S	K	■	L	■	A
R	A	R	E	R	■	S	■	N	A	D	I	R
■	■	I	R	I	S	■	G	I	R	O	■	■
O	F	F	A	L	■	O	■	T	E	R	R	A
B	■	I	■	E	B	B	S	■	■	M	■	L
E	V	E	N	■	W	O	K	■	V	A	I	L
L	■	D	U	R	A	L	U	M	I	N	■	I
U	■	■	D	■	N	■	L	■	N	■	■	E
S	C	H	E	M	A	■	K	E	Y	P	A	D

351

■	■	R	E	C	E	S	S	I	O	N	A	L
H	■	■	■	I	■	U	■	■	B	■	■	■
E	F	F	O	R	T	S	■	R	E	D	■	E
L	■	A	■	R	E	A	L	I	S	I	N	G
L	E	B	R	U	N	■	O	N	E	S	■	O
A	■	R	■	S	■	Y	O	D	■	A	■	C
C	O	I	F	■	D	A	P	■	E	P	E	E
I	■	C	■	P	O	P	■	O	■	P	■	N
O	■	A	G	E	S	■	A	R	R	E	S	T
U	N	T	E	N	A	B	L	E	■	A	■	R
S	■	E	A	T	■	E	A	G	E	R	■	I
■	■	■	R	■	■	A	■	O	■	■	■	C
S	U	B	S	E	Q	U	E	N	C	E	■	■

354

L	E	E	T	■	P	T	Y	A	L	I	S	M
U	■	■	O	■	R	■	■	R	■	■	I	■
M	A	R	R	I	E	D	■	T	I	A	R	A
P	■	O	■	■	S	I	K	H	■	G	E	E
Y	O	U	N	G	S	T	E	R	■	R	■	G
■	■	N	■	A	■	■	N	I	S	I	■	I
A	N	D	■	L	E	A	S	T	■	P	U	S
Z	■	W	E	L	T	■	■	I	■	P	■	■
T	■	O	■	A	N	A	R	C	H	I	S	T
E	R	R	■	N	A	M	E	■	■	N	■	R
C	O	M	E	T	■	P	L	I	C	A	T	E
■	I	■	■	R	■	■	A	■	O	■	■	A
A	L	L	E	Y	W	A	Y	■	G	O	L	D

355

O	L	Y	M	P	I	A	D		H	E	S	T
	O				R		I		O	P	T	
W	I	S	T	E	R	I	A		R	I	E	L
	T		O		E		L	E	N	G	T	H
S	E	C	U	L	A	R		K		R		A
	R		C		L		M	E	D	A	L	S
O		B	A	A				S	U	M		A
R	W	A	N	D	A		A		E		A	
E		B		E		O	D	D	N	E	S	S
A	L	B	I	N	O		J		D		S	
D	O	L	T		N	E	O	T	E	R	I	C
	P	E	E		U		I				G	
T	E	R	M		S	Y	N	C	L	I	N	E

356

357

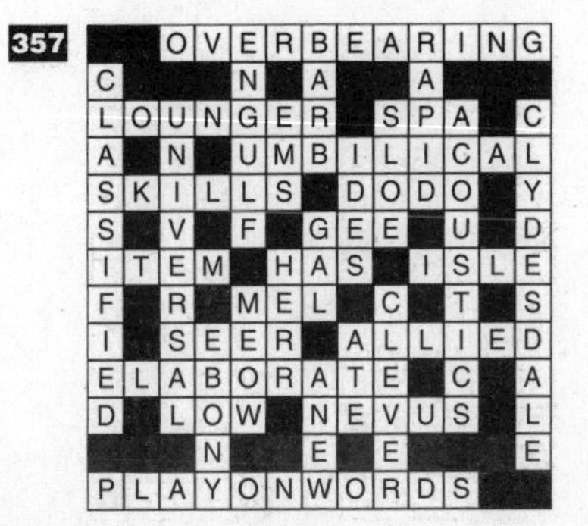

358

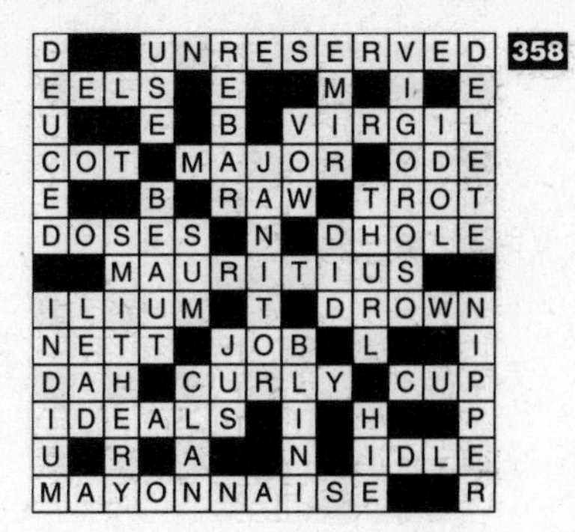

359

360

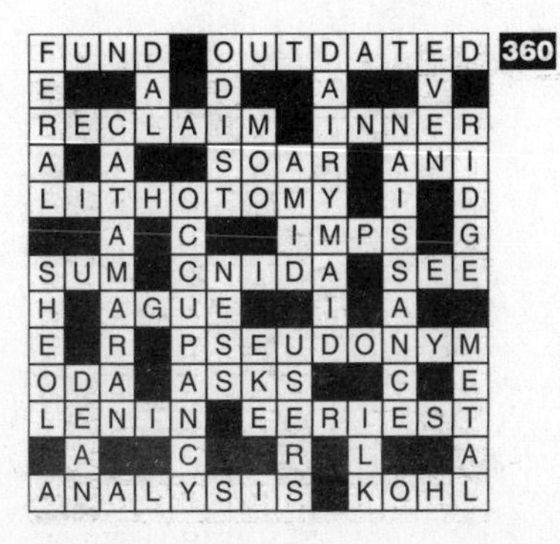

361

O	R	N	I	T	H	I	C		L	I	M	E
	U				I		A		O	D	E	
R	E	C	K	L	E	S	S		C	I	T	E
	F		E		M		E	C	H	O	E	S
A	U	S	T	R	A	L		E		T		B
	L		O		L		T	R	O	I	K	A
P		I	S	M				E	T	C		T
H	E	R	E	A	T		A		H		A	
I		A		N		O	B	J	E	C	T	S
A	N	N	E	X	E		L		R		O	
L	O	I	N		T	H	O	U	S	A	N	D
	T	A	D		C		O				I	
D	E	N	S		H	E	M	I	S	E	C	T

362

M			A	L	T	O	G	E	T	H	E	R
U	R	U	S		W			M		A		H
R			H		E		Q	U	I	N	S	Y
M	O	P		R	A	M	U	S		D	O	T
U			N		K	E	A		A	M	A	H
R	A	T	I	O		M		A	L	A	R	M
		A	C	U	L	E	A	T	E	D		
I	L	I	A	D		N		E	R	E	C	T
G	O	L	D		E	T	A		T			U
N	O	R		M	O	O	C	H		T	O	M
I	M	A	G	E	S		R		P			U
T		C		S			I		O	P	A	L
E	V	E	N	H	A	N	D	E	D			T